KV-610-916

THE PAN BOOK OF ANIMAL STORIES

CONDITIONS OF SALE

This book shall not be lent, re-sold, hired out or otherwise disposed of by way of trade in any form of binding or cover other than that in which it is published.

THE PAN BOOK OF
ANIMAL STORIES

Selected by

JOHN MONTGOMERY

PAN BOOKS LTD: LONDON

This collection first published 1964 by

PAN BOOKS LTD.

8 Headfort Place, London S.W.1

© Pan Books Ltd., 1964

Printed in Great Britain by
Cox and Wyman Ltd., London, Fakenham and Reading

CONTENTS

ACKNOWLEDGEMENTS

Mazo de la Roche: APRIL DAY, from *The Sacred Bullock*: Macmillan & Co. Ltd.

G. B. Stern: SUNSTROKE, from *Long Story Short*: Cassell & Co. Ltd. and A. D. Peters.

Sir Hugh Walpole: HAVING NO HEARTS, from *Head in Green Bronze*: Macmillan & Co. Ltd.

Ernest Thompson Seton: THE BOY AND THE BADGER, from *Wild Animals at Home*: Hodder & Stoughton Ltd.

James Fenimore Cooper: A FIGHT WITH A MOTHER PANTHER from *The Pioneers*.

Sir Percy Fitzpatrick: AN AFRICAN TIGER HUNT, from *Jock of the Bushveld*: Longmans, Green & Co. Ltd.

Kenneth Anderson: THE SANGAM PANTHER, from *Man-Eaters and Jungle Killers*: George Allen & Unwin Ltd.

H. M. Tomlinson: A BROWN OWL, from *Out of Soundings*: A. P. Watt & Son.

Robert Ruark: THE VULGAR ASSASSIN: A. D. Peters and the Harold Matson Company Inc.

Margery Sharp: MR HAMBLE'S BEAR: A. D. Peters.

Liam O'Flaherty: HIS FIRST FLIGHT: Jonathan Cape Ltd.

John Collier: MADEMOISELLE KIKI, from *Pictures in the Fire*: Rupert Hart-Davis Ltd. and A. D. Peters.

V. S. Pritchett: THE APE, from *Collected Short Stories of V. S. Pritchett*: Chatto & Windus Ltd. and A. D. Peters.

Gerald Bullett: THE GOAT, from *Ten Minute Tales*: J. M. Dent and Son Ltd.

John Gloag: BEDROOM SCENE, from *It Makes a Nice Change*: A. D. Peters.

Evelyn Waugh: ON GUARD, from *Mr Loveday's Little Outing*: Chapman & Hall Ltd. and A. D. Peters.

C. T. Stoneham: THE BLIND ELEPHANT: Rupert Crew.

Joy Adamson: THE FINAL TEST, from *Born Free*: Wm. Collins Sons & Co. Ltd. and Harvill Press Ltd.

F. G. Turnbull: GRUMPHIE from *Kallee and Other Stories*: Sampson, Low & Co Ltd and Rupert Crew & Co. Ltd.

Anna Sewell: MY LAST HOME, from *Black Beauty*.

Colin Willock: THE ANIMAL CATCHERS, from *The Animal Catchers*: André Deutsch Ltd.

The Emperor Napoleon: AFTER THE BATTLE

Alec Waugh: GIVEN YOUR HEART TO A DOG TO TEAR: A. D. Peters.

Cherry Kearton: THE INQUISITIVE MONGOOSE, from *My Animal Friends*: Mrs Ada Kearton.

Rupert Croft-Cooke: ONE MAN AND HIS DOG, from *A Football for the Brigadier*: A. D. Peters.

Saki (H. H. Munro:) TOBERMORY, John Lane, the Bodley Head Ltd.

Gavin Maxwell: LIVING WITH MIJBIL, from *Ring of Bright Water*: Longmans, Green & Co Ltd.

James Thurber: THE DOG THAT BIT PEOPLE, from *The Thurber Carnival*: Hamish Hamilton Ltd.

Stuart Cloete: THE BABY BULLET: A. D. Peters.

Konrad Z. Lorenz: THE LANGUAGE OF ANIMALS, from *King Solomon's Ring*: Methuen & Co Ltd.

Grey Owl: THE BEAVERS, from *Pilgrims of the Wild*: Peter Davies Ltd.

APRIL DAY

by

Mazo de la Roche

(from *The Sacred Bullock*, Macmillan & Co.)

It was seven in the morning and the Scottie and the Cairn knew that soon it would be time to get up. They heard stirrings in the house below. They slept on the top floor in a dressing-room between the bedrooms of their mistresses, Zia and Cara. The two round dog baskets, with the cretonne cushions exactly alike, stood side by side. Dan, the Scottie, was able to look straight into Robbie's face.

Out of his almond-shaped eyes that were set high in his hard brindle head, Dan gazed lovingly into Robbie's face, veiled in fine grey hair which stood in tremulous half-curls on his brow, curved into a tiny moustache on his lip, and turned velvet and close on his ears.

Robbie knew that Dan was staring at him and the love did not matter, for, at this moment, he wanted nothing but to be let alone. He was savouring the last delicious doze before the moment when he would spring out of his basket. He kept his eyes shut tight. His head rested against the side of the basket helpless-looking, like a little child's.

Dan stared and stared. A quiver ran down his spine, making the tip of his tail vibrate. He was sixteen months old and Robbie had had his first birthday last week. Dan seemed much older, for he often had a dour look. He poured out his soul in love to Robbie all day long.

Now a felt-slippered step shuffled outside the door and it opened a little way. The cook put in her head. 'Come, boys, come now, time to get up,' she said and held the door open wide enough for them to pass through.

Dan jumped from his basket and reared himself on his hind

legs. He waved his forepaws at the cook, but she had barely a word for him. Robbie was her charmer.

Now, as he coyly descended the stairs behind her, she encouraged him with endearments. At each landing he lay on his back and rolled, talking to himself in a low pleasant growl. 'Come along, darling, do,' urged the cook, half-way down the stairs, but she had to plod back to the landing to persuade him.

Dan had gone down the two flights of stairs like a bullet. Now he stood waiting by the open front door, looking back over his shoulder. When Robbie reached the bottom step, Dan ran out and Robbie after him.

They went to their usual place under the weeping rose tree that was newly in leaf. The sun had just risen above the great shoulder of the nearest hill. The spring morning lay spread before them, to the distant mountains of Wales.

Shoulder to shoulder they trotted round the house and up the slope, pushing aside the faces of daffodils and narcissus, hastening a little as they neared the denseness of trees. Among the trees there was a moist, mossy twilight and across it flitted the brown hump of a young rabbit. Dan saw it first. He gave a cry, as of agony, and hurled himself into the wood. With a little moan of bewilderment Robbie flew after him, not yet knowing what he chased.

Head to tail, they dived into the green twilight. The rabbit whirled beneath the prickly fortress of a holly bush. Out at the other side it flew, skimming the wet grass, its ears flat in stark terror. Dan circled the holly bush, screaming.

Now Robbie was sure that what they were pursuing had escaped, though he had never known what it was. He stood pensive a moment, listening to Dan's screams, then drifted back towards the house. He found the front door shut, as the cook did against their return, so he went to the green knoll outside the kitchen window and sat there under the green-and-white spread of the sycamore tree. He looked imploringly, from under his fine fringe, into the window at the cook bending over the range, at the maid putting on her cap, tucking her curls beneath it.

He heard the clump of a step on the cobbled path and saw the milkman coming with his carrier of milk. It was a shock to find that he had drawn so near without molestation. Robbie hurled himself down the knoll, screaming and champing at the milkman's legs. The cook came out of the kitchen calling:

'Robbie! Robbie! He won't hurt you! He's as gentle as a lamb!'

She said this every morning to the milkman who never believed her but came on grumbling. The cook picked Robbie up and he let his head rest against her bosom. She still held him a moment after the milkman had gone. He was patient but he wanted to go upstairs.

As soon as she put him down he glided along the hall and up the two flights of stairs. He scratched on the door of the dressing-room. Zia opened it and she and Cara told him how good and beautiful he was. He lay on his back looking up at them gently but haughtily, savouring their homage. His pointed grey paws hung quiet.

He saw the gas-fire burning and stretched himself before it.

At first Dan did not miss Robbie, then suddenly realized that he had gone back to the house. What might not Robbie be doing without him? He tore across the grass, found the front door shut and barked insistently till it was opened by the maid.

On his short legs he pulled himself up the stairs and scratched peremptorily on the door of the dressing-room. Inside he reared and walked on his hind legs for a few steps with the sturdy grace of a pony stallion. He rolled his eyes towards the cupboard where the big glass marble lived. Zia went to the cupboard.

'Oh, must he have that?' said Cara. 'It makes such a noise!'

'He says he must,' said Zia. She laid the glass marble, with the silver bear in its middle, on the floor.

With a growl of joy, Dan pounced on it. He struck it with his paw, then bounded after it. Up and down the room he chased it, pushing it swiftly with his nose then panting after it, banging it against the wall and, at last, between Robbie's paws.

Robbie hated the marble with a bitter hatred. The rolling and the noise of it made him feel sick. Now he lay, with half-closed eyes, guarding it between his paws. Dan looked up into Zia's face.

'Robbie's got my ball,' his look said.

'Get it, then,' said Zia.

Dan approached Robbie tremblingly, pretending he was afraid or really being afraid.

Zia gave him back the marble. He struck it with his muzzle, then flew after it growling. After a little he began to gnaw it.

'Enough!' said Zia, taking it from him. 'You'll ruin your teeth.'

The four went down to breakfast. The dogs' plates stood waiting, filled with bits of hard-toasted brown bread. They crunched in delight, Dan's tail waving, Robbie's laid close. The moment they had finished they ran to the table to beg. Dan sat staring up out of glowing eyes. Cara dropped bits of bacon to him which he caught with a snap. Robbie mounted the arm of the settee behind Zia's chair. He put his paws on her shoulder and his cheek close to hers, so that she gave him bits of roll and honey.

At the first whiff of cigarette-smoke Dan clambered into his basket and Robbie established himself on the fender stool, with his back turned to the table. He wore a look of disdain.

The children came in on their way to school. The dogs suffered themselves to be caressed but they wanted to doze.

As the sun shone warmer they went to the drive and stretched themselves at ease, ready for what might happen. Each time an errand boy came through the gate they went after him, exploding in barks as they ran. Cara or Zia or the gardener called to them, apologized for them, petted them for coming when they were called. They felt fearless and proud and obedient, wagging their tails after each sortie.

After a while the cook brought bones to them. She chose the biggest, hardest bone for Dan and the one with the most juicy meat on it for Robbie. But it was Dan who looked up at her in an ecstasy of gratitude; Robbie who took his haughtily, as though it were no more than he had expected. They settled down with the bones, eyeing each other distrustfully before they began to gnaw.

Dan gnawed his bone in long steady grinds, wearing it down with his strong teeth, exposing its granular interior, arching his muscular neck above it. Robbie ripped the red meat from his, gnawed at the end where the marrow was, grew tired and rose with the bone in his mouth, looking about for a place to bury it.

Dan saw this with dismay. To bury so soon! It could not be done! He darted at Robbie and tried to take the bone from him. Robbie lifted his lip in a defensive sneer. He growled in his throat. Dan returned to his own bone.

After a little while Robbie glided into the shrubbery and began to dig in the moist mossy earth. He buried the bone well, drawing the earth over it with paws and delicate nose. He came out of the shrubbery just as Cara came out of the house.

'Too much bone,' she said, 'you're having too much bone.' She went towards Dan.

He wagged his tail at her to take the sting from his ferocious growl. 'Don't touch my bone!' he shouted. 'Don't touch my bone!'

'You'd growl at me!' cried Cara, and she made a dart for the bone.

He caught it up and romped away from her.

Zia came out of the house with collars and leads in one hand and a dog brush in the other.

'Walkee, walkee,' she said as she came. 'Walkee, walkee!'

Dan dropped his bone and ran to her. Robbie danced towards her. Jealously Dan shouldered him away, pulling him gently by the ear. He loved him but he did not want him making up to Zia.

She took Dan in her hands and laid him flat. She began vigorously to brush him. He stretched himself at full length, giving himself to the brush in delight, kicking joyfully where it touched a sensitive spot. He showed his teeth in a grin of love and beamed up at Zia.

When Dan was brushed Zia stretched out her hand for Robbie, but he slid from under it like water. He looked at her coyly from over his shoulder. He kept always just out of reach, as she followed him on her knees across the grass.

'Walkee, walkee,' she cooed. 'Brushee, brushee!'

He bowed politely and touched her hand with his nose but was gone before she could catch him.

'Very well,' said Zia, 'we'll go without you.'

She and Cara went into the house, ignoring Robbie. When they came down with their coats and hats on he was sitting on the pink best chair. Zia caught him up, sat down with him on her lap and began to brush him. He could tolerate this. He sat resigned as she brushed his long delicate hair first up, then down, then in a swirl to follow the streamline of his spine. But when she put the harness and lead on him he stiffened himself and an icy aloofness came into his eyes. He looked as aloof as a carved unicorn on the top of a stone gateway. He was not Robbie at all.

But he was himself again as he and Dan trotted down the drive and through the gate shoulder to shoulder, their mistresses on the other end of the leads. They turned from the main road into a country road past the fields where the new lambs were being suckled and the glossy hunters were nibbling the grass, past the duck-pond. Robbie averted his eyes from the ducks with a bleak look as though he could not bear the sight of them but Dan, now off the lead, looked at them with beaming interest. He beamed up at Zia. 'What about it?' his eyes asked.

'Don't dare!' said Zia.

On and on they walked, the great hills always rising before them, the primrose wreathes palely blooming on the banks. But hills and flowers meant nothing to the dogs. The thousand scents of road and ditch meant much. A rabbit had passed this way. A weasel had passed that. Only an hour ago the Hunt had crossed the road.

Dan never wearied of the pleasures of the road. He jogged

jauntily on and on as though he would go for ever. From a front view, one saw first his pricked ears, with the tail appearing exactly between them, then the strong shoulders, the bent elbows and the round paws that padded one over the other as though he were climbing a ladder.

Now Robbie was bored. He wanted to go home. He drifted along the road like a resigned little old lady with her grey shawl draped about her. He looked neither to right nor left.

They took the short cut home through the lane where the holly berries still shone bright among the prickly leaves. They found the break in the hedge. Zia lifted Dan over first, then followed him. Cara handed Robbie over and came last. She took off his harness and lead.

He stood crouching while it was undone, then sped forward like a slim grey arrow, past the house, past the stables, into the wildwood. Each breath was a protest against restraint. He felt free and cruel as a fox.

Now he was chasing a rabbit, all his boredom gone. Through the green twilight of the wood they sped, terror in one, joy in the other. Under the thick clammy leaves of rhododendrons, under the prickling boughs of holly, through thorny undergrowth that tore out locks of Robbie's hair and scratched his face. Neither he nor the rabbit uttered a sound. They flew silently, as though in a dream.

Then suddenly the rabbit was gone, swallowed up in a burrow. Robbie lay panting, his heart throbbing. He pulled some of the burrs from his paws and his tail. After a while he remembered his dinner, his home. He trotted along a path and was passing the orchard when he saw that the hens had been let out of their run and were strutting about among the daffodils.

He hesitated by a hole in the hedge and peered through at them. His eyes were bleak, as when he had turned his gaze away from the ducks. But now he did not turn away. He stared and stared. He was alone. There was no one to stop him.

He glided through the hedge and sprang fiercely on the nearest hen. She flapped her big red wings and ran squawking, with him on her back. She fell and still holding her by the neck, he threw her from side to side till she stopped struggling. All the other hens and the cock were in a panic, running here and there among the trees, each thinking it was its turn next. Robbie, with the face of a little gargoyle, ran after them. He whimpered in his delight.

The red feathers were scattered over the grass. Five bundles of them lay still and two more huddled in weakness and fear. The rest of the flock were safe in their run. Robbie stood looking in at them. They were all right there. That was where they belonged. In the orchard they were wild things to be pursued.

The front door stood open. He glided into the sitting-room. Dan was curled up in his basket, asleep after a good dinner, but he jumped out and came to meet Robbie. He sniffed Robbie's mouth and his tail quivered in recognition of the scent there. He grinned joyfully at Robbie.

But Robbie wanted his dinner. He went to the kitchen and found the maid. He danced about her, gently nipped her ankles in their black cotton stockings. She snatched him up and rocked him in her arms.

'Oh, baby, baby, little baby!'

His beautiful eyes pleaded but she could not bear to put him down. She snuggled her rosy cheek against him, then held him at arm's length in her hands, adoring him. He looked at her, docile yet roguish. When she put her face near enough he gave her nose a swift nip. She hugged him close.

At last his plate was set in front of him, boiled cod mixed with vegetables. He ate less daintily than usual, for he was very hungry. Dan stood watching him and, when he had finished, came to his plate and licked it thoroughly. Robbie took a big drink out of the brown earthen dish, then went back to the sitting-room and stretched himself at length on the settee. Dan returned to his basket.

For some reason the settee did not satisfy Robbie, though generally it was his favourite spot. He jumped down and came to the basket and gazed in at Dan. Dan turned up his belly and rolled his eyes at Robbie but, after a little, he scrambled out of the basket and on to the settee. Robbie drifted into the basket.

While they were still drowsy Zia came with brush and comb and began to groom them. They were to go to the photographers and already they were late for the appointment but they must look their best. The car was at the door and now Zia slid under the wheel and Cara sat in the seat behind with a little dog on either side of her. They were as pretty as pictures, she told them.

They sat looking noble, till the car went into low gear on the steep hill and they felt the threat of the engine's vibration. They yawned and drooped, then hid their faces in Cara's lap and gave themselves up to misery. But on the level their spirits returned and they began to romp in exhilaration, growl at each other, stand upright on the seat, breast to breast.

What grand puppies, the photographer said, and placed them side by side on a settee and hid his head in the camera. That was only the beginning.

Dan jumped to the floor and, when he was lifted to the settee, Robbie jumped down. They did this till they were excited and panting and spoken to severely. Then they cowered on the settee, looking like curs. The photographer barked loudly and they had hysterics. Robbie suffered the photographer to put him on the settee and admonish him but Dan raised his voice and barked: 'Don't touch me, man!' He showed his teeth in a threatening grin. Then suddenly he was well behaved and posed nobly, sometimes in profile, sometimes full-face but always fine, like the prize-winner at a dog show.

Now there was only Robbie to cope with, but Robbie had become all wriggles and gaiety. Being photographed was funnier than he could bear. He lay on his back and kicked his joy in it.

Then, at last, he sat still. But now Dan was tired. He curled himself into a tight ball and fell asleep. When he was raised he had no backbone but lolled and looked imbecile. Zia produced toffee and fed them. The trick was done! The camera clicked.

Now there was shopping and they sat alone in the car while

Zia and Cara went into the shops. It was lonely in the car. Dan attended to his paws, licking them till his nails shone like ebony. Sometimes, by mistake, licking the cushion of the car. Robbie never licked his paws. He ignored sore spots which Dan would have licked incessantly. So, to pass the time, Robbie gnawed the polished wood of the window-frame. It was awkward to get at but he managed it. They were nearly home when Cara discovered the tooth-marks. 'Which of you did this?' she demanded sternly.

Dan looked guilty, contrite, but Robbie knew nothing about it. His eyes spoke innocence from under his silken fringe. Cara smacked the top of Dan's lean flat skull. He burrowed into a corner, ashamed.

Presently Robbie's thoughts returned to the window-frame and he gave it a last gnaw as they passed through the gate.

'So – it was you, Robbie!' cried Cara. 'Oh, poor Dan, why were you so silly?' She pulled Dan from his corner and patted him. Robbie leaped lightly from the car when it stopped and, pursued by Dan, sped into the wilderness. Soon they were chasing a rabbit and Dan's screams echoed among the trees.

They came back in time for tea. They stood shoulder to shoulder, yearning towards the teapot. They had their saucers of weak tea, then got into the basket together and slept.

The gardener stood, strong and bent, in the corner of the room, the loam scraped from his boots, his hands washed clean.

'Thur's been fowls killed,' he said, 'seven on 'em. Some time this marnin', it were. I think one o' our little fellers done it.'

Cara turned pale. 'How awful! Are you sure it was one of ours?'

'Thur's been no other on t' place, ma'am. T' gates is all shut fast.'

He bent over the basket and with his gentle thick hand lifted Dan's lip and looked at the double row of white teeth laid evenly together, a little underhung but not much.

'Nubbut thure.'

As gently but less cautiously he looked in Robbie's mouth.

Quickly he folded down the soft lip. ''Tis him, for sartin,' he said quietly. 'Thur's a bit o' feather between his teeth. I'm not surprised, ma'am. He killed one once before. I caught him at it. He thinks they didn't orter be runnin' in t' orchard. But 'tis only a puppy. Don't you fret. He'll not do it again.'

Robbie looked coyly up at them. He laid a pointed paw on each side of his face and looked up lovingly into Cara's eyes.

'He'll never do it again,' comforted the gardener.

As the sun slanted in at the west window and the children were getting ready for bed, Dan and Robbie went to the nursery for their evening play. Dan romped with the children. He was rough with them, but they must not pull him about. 'Have a care how you handle me!' his warning growl came.

Robbie drifted about, always just outside the game. But, when the children caught him, he surrendered himself to be held uncomfortably in small arms, to be dandled on small hard knees.

Towards evening the air had become warmer. Without question the birds and flowers opened their hearts to summer. Starlings walked about the lawn, staring into daisy faces. Dan and Robbie lay before the door serenely facing the great spread of hills unrolled before them. Their sensitive nostrils put aside the smell of the wallflower and drank in what rich animal scents came their way.

They lay as still as carven dogs except for the faint fluttering of the hair on Robbie's crown. Dan faced the breeze with head stark, neck arched and thick like a little stallion.

When two gipsy women clumped up the drive selling mimosa the dogs did not bark but watched their coming and their going tranquilly. They were steeped in the new sweet warmth of the evening.

But when they were turned out for a last run before bedtime, it was different. The air came sharply from the highest hill. The earth sent its quickness up into them. Robbie ran into the wildwood but Dan found a hedgehog and worked himself into a rage before its prickles. Cara and Zia found him in the blackness beneath a yew tree and turned the beam of an electric torch on him. On the bright green of grass the hedgehog sat like a bundle of autumn leaves, impervious.

'Open up! Open up!' shouted Dan, his teeth wet and gleaming.

Robbie came drifting out of the shrubbery and sat down watching the pair, knowing the hopelessness of the onslaught. Dan put his nose against the prickles and started back, shouting still louder: 'Open up! Open up!'

But the hedgehog held itself close, impervious as a burr.

'Enough!' said Zia and tucked Dan under her arm.

Cara pounced on Robbie. The hedgehog was left to his dreams.

Snug in their baskets they lay in the dressing-room, the velvet darkness pressing closer and closer. Dan lay stretched as though running but Robbie's four feet lay bunched close together. His head was thrown back, his ears tilted alert for the whispering of dreams. What did he hear? The cry of a rabbit in a trap? Or some ghostly cackle from the poultry-yard?

He woke. He sat up in his basket and uttered a loud accusing bark at what had disturbed him. His own voice was comforting. He had never before barked so sonorously, so much like Dan. The comfort of the barking gave him deep peace. He kept on and on. Cara came in at the door. She turned on the light.

Robbie looked at her wonderingly, his little head pillowed on his pointed paw. Dan gave a sheepish grin and hung his head. He had got out of his basket to meet her.

'Naughty, naughty, naughty!' said Cara. 'Back to your bed, Dan! Not another bark out of you!'

Dan slunk back to his basket, curled himself close. . . .

The shadows would not let Robbie be. Out of them came mysterious things to disturb him. He went to the open window and sat on the ledge, framed in ivy. He barked steadily on an even more sonorous note. He had lovely sensations. He felt that he could go on till dawn.

But he heard the door of Cara's room open and, in one graceful leap, he was back in his basket. Small and stern, Cara entered the room. In her room Zia was lying with the blankets over her head. In shame Dan went to meet Cara.

'It is the end, Dan,' she said mournfully. 'You must go into the box-room by yourself.'

She took his basket and he humbly followed her, stopping only to nozzle Robbie as he passed. She put him in the farthest, darkest corner of the box-room where, if he did bark, he would scarcely be heard. She went back to bed. There was beautiful quiet. Zia uncovered her head.

Robbie was alone now and he gave full vent to the trouble that was in him. He forgot all but the mournful majesty of his barking as he sat on the window-ledge.

When Cara came into the room he disregarded her till she took him into her arms. Then he laid his head confidingly on her shoulder and gave himself up to what might befall. It befell that he was laid on the foot of her bed. It seemed almost too good to be true. Everywhere there was peace and slumber.

At half past seven the cook heavily mounted the stairs. She opened the door of the dressing-room and saw the one empty basket. She knocked on Cara's door and opened it.

'Half past seven, madam,' she said, 'and I can't find the puppies at all!'

'Dan is in the box-room. Robbie is here.'

Dan and Robbie met in the passage. They kissed, then pranced about each other joyfully. They nipped the cook's ankles as they descended the stairs. Another April day had begun!

SUNSTROKE

by

G. B. STERN

(from *Long Story Short*, Cassell & Co.)

'I TELL YOU I don't want to know him,' growled Shot. 'I'm not one to rub noses with every Jock, Spot, and Fido, and I didn't think you were.'

'But he's so amusing,' argued Lobo, the Afghan hound; he looked imploringly at the spaniel beside him.

Shot was three years his senior, and a dog of the world. He had come over three years ago from England with his master and mistress, and could weave long, thrilling sagas to his junior, bringing in strange words like 'The Twelfth', 'preserves', 'the birds were rising', 'down by the third butt'. At least, they were thrilling to the spaniel.

Lobo, truth to tell, one of a Riviera litter of Afghan hounds, and a birthday present from Fay Wyndham to her husband, was beginning to find them boring, especially during a heat-wave, as now. He wanted to gabble about the dog Hotsy whom he had picked up the evening before, down on the sea-road to Beaulieu: a quick, swaggering, fascinating young fellow. 'He's been on the films; he told me so.'

'What does that mean?'

'I don't know, but you have to be very talented.'

'Did he tell you that, too?'

'W-why, yes,' stammered Lobo. His ears fell with disappointment; for he had said to his new friend: 'Drop in whenever you care about it, up at our villa. I'd like you to meet my friend, Shot. He's English, like you.' And now Shot would only murmur:

'Talking through his muzzle. He's riff-raff; I've *seen* him.'

Adding something about a drink, he went round the terrace towards the trough at the back of the villa.

Inside the large, cool, green-shuttered drawing-room, very much the same scene had arisen between Godfrey Wyndham and his pretty young wife:

'I tell you, I won't have her up here,' stormed Godfrey. 'Peroxide riff-raff. How you could ever bring yourself even to speak to her —'

'I didn't begin, nor did she. It was your dog hobnobbing with hers. I whistled and whistled, but Lobo wouldn't obey. So then we had to speak, she and I. And then I found out how nice and amusing she was. She asked me in for a cocktail.'

'Couldn't you have snubbed her?'

'I didn't choose to. You know, Godfrey dear, the people *you* bring here aren't so very stimulating. I'm getting old with boredom, living on the Riviera; nothing but retired colonels and generals; your terrace is sleepy with them; it might as well be your club smoking-room in St James's. What's the good of this brilliant sun, and that incredible blue sky, and the wistaria and bougainvillaea scribbling their shadows all over the white walls, if one is never to relax and be light-hearted and have fun?'

Godfrey adored his wife, but he was conventional. He did not recognize danger signals in her voice. For the sake of his health they had transplanted themselves to this miracle of a villa on a cape above the pines, in the South of France. He had never been really well since he had lost a leg, and been gassed in the war; but he missed England. And now if Fay, sixteen years younger than himself, were going to take up with every female Tom, Dick and Harry —'

'She's on the films, isn't she?'

'That's not to her discredit. She's Dollabel Pink. And she's terribly talented.'

'I've never heard of her.'

'She's resting now.'

'Then let her rest in her own little gimcrack bijou-residence; not up here. Casetta Sans-Gêne. Did you ever hear anything like it? "*Sans-Gêne*" – as though one couldn't tell that by looking at her, without putting it over the front page! I've seen her pattering about in the wrong sort of shoes, and satin shorts, if you please, and blue ear-rings, and that frightful mongrel running along behind her. I tell you, I've *seen* her –'

'She amuses me,' Fay persisted stubbornly. The blazing heat, which had been beating down on them now for nearly six weeks with hardly even a respite between sunset and sunrise, was upsetting her normal sweetness of temper. This new friend of hers promised diversion, excitement, tales of a new sort of world. Fay repeated: 'She amuses me.'

Wyndham shrugged his shoulders: 'I'm going to get a drink,' he said briefly.

The heat-wave continued unbroken. So did the civil war between Fay and Godfrey, between Lobo and Shot. Neither Lobo nor his mistress dared go quite so far as to ignore the command that they were not to invite their infatuations up to the villa; but there were plenty of other meeting-places; often they just sat gossiping for hours at a time in the tawdry little garden at Casetta Sans-Gêne, while Dollabel, while Hotsy told their anchovy anecdotes; unloaded their store of cheap, brittle reminiscences and innuendo. Lobo, once Godfrey's inseparable companion, gave up Godfrey altogether and followed his mistress.

For it was Fay who led him straight down to the patch of queer glamour that lay around Casetta Sans-Gêne.

The Wyndhams had been invited to spend a weekend with Colonel and Mrs Tyrrell-Smythe at their house up in the hills, where it was perhaps a trifle cooler. It was a long-standing arrangement, but the day before they went, Fay remarked casually: 'Would you mind leaving me out of it this time, dear? I really don't think I can face three whole days of Sophia Tyrrell-Smythe.'

Godfrey scowled. This incomprehensible attachment to Casetta Sans-Gêne . . . Fay actually would rather remain in the company of Miss Dollabel Pink and that sickening mongrel than go with him to stay with really decent people like the

Tyrrell-Smythes; decent and nice, though a trifle heavy (he had to own that they were heavy). He was too deeply hurt to argue.

Besides, it was so hot.

He bade his valet pack a suitcase and be ready to start with him early the next morning. He would take Shot with him, not Lobo. Not Lobo the deserter. His wounded resentment extended to the Afghan.

Fay's pride would never have permitted her to ask her staff not to tell her husband, later on, that Miss Dollabel Pink (and Hotsy) arrived to spend the weekend; arrived in a humour that ran over with smiles and familiarity and impudent high laughter; but the staff did not have to be asked; they were prepared of their own accord to say nothing. This new atmosphere of careless rowdiness suited their temperaments.

They were delighted, above all, when it transpired that a not very reputable French film company recently arrived in the neighbourhood had engaged Dollabel Pink (now tired of resting) to play a small part in their not very reputable comic film *Coup de Soleil*, and that some of the scenes were to be shot next day, by express permission of Madame Wyndham, up at the Villa Antinea itself.

The film was intended to be a *risqué* comedy showing the antics of a whole village that had caught sunstroke during a heat-wave, and went mad and threw off all restraint and made love like a tribe of savages. It was the most mirth-provoking, killingly hilarious, laughter-compelling comedy of the century.

It was Dollabel's suggestion that the villa should be used for some of the sets; the producer had been mooching round and had admired the gardens and terraces so ardently that she had told him he might bring up the entire company, and she would make it 'oke' with Fay Wyndham, who owned the place. Fay was just her dearest friend.

The producer was therefore very pleased with Dollabel; he had another incident written in especially for her, just to give her her chance: 'And Madame, too, she 'ave, what you call it, a walk-in, during our café scene. That give always great pleasure to the amateur, I know it. And 'er big dog, too, that give 'er greater pleasure still, to see him, after, *sur l'écran*.'

Lobo never forgot that day of nightmare when hundreds of strangers invaded the villa, carrying with them instruments and machines of torture; when alien smells and sounds pervaded his nose and insulted his ears; when everybody, even his beloved mistress, even his hero, Hotsy, capered and leaped in obedience to some lunatic purpose which literally went on above his head, and left him bewildered and miserable, an outcast in his own wontedly quiet and stately home.

And things grew from bad to worse; for when he threw back his head and howled in protest, hands were clapped and voices barked to excite him; a sun-bonnet was ignominiously thrust on his head, and he could not shake it off; a beastly flapping pink cotton sun-bonnet. And he was chivvied about among all these strange people with their strange instruments and blinding lights, in and out of doors, up and down the terrace steps, along alleys and avenues that he just dimly remembered as peaceful green retreats where he and Shot used to follow their master, or lie in untroubled solitude while the spaniel wove his gentle, grassy, sweet-smelling remembrances of a country called England.

What happy days and what a happy friendship, compared with the din, the inescapable ignominy of the present fever-world which had burst and strewn its hideous occupants all over Villa Antinea.

In frantic terror, he tried to scramble up into Fay's arms, heaving all his great limbs into her lap; but she rejected him, too:

'Don't try and pretend you're a lap-dog, Lobo!'

And it seemed to him, moreover, that whatever Hotsy did, they all applauded enthusiastically; he seemed to understand exactly what was expected of him. Constantly he was embraced and given bones and biscuits. Yet whatever Lobo did, in his efforts either to escape to solitude or to express grim loathing of the whole business, was met with shouts of laughter.

By night time, the company had gathered itself up and passed into limbo. As the Afghan lay trembling and exhausted on the rug outside the door of Godfrey's empty bedroom, where he always stretched his huge limbs to sleep, his own hope, scarcely formulated, was that at least his master need never hear of what had been done to him this day.

Yet his devotion to Hotsy waxed even stronger, swelled by the fact that during the next week or two he was not able to see him nearly so often. Miss Dollabel Pink had not come up to the villa again after Godfrey and Shot returned from their visit; neither did Lobo's mistress go down any more to Casetta Sans-Gêne. So on the occasions when Lobo felt he simply could not endure separation any longer, he had to break away from orders and run down the hill himself in search of Hotsy.

And when he returned, he was thrashed and shut up by his master.

Two or three times, when he tenderly reproached Hotsy for not being more inclined to meet him half-way, Hotsy flung off some casual phrase even more incomprehensible to the bewildered Lobo than Shot's ponderous allusions to 'the Twelfth', or 'preserves'.

'My dear fellow, we've been on location.' Or: 'They wanted some retakes.'

Finally Hotsy told him with the utmost glee and conceit that he and Miss Dollabel Pink had both been given a long-term contract, and would shortly be off to do another picture. Lobo's heart quivered as he realized that Hotsy did not care a tail's wag about parting from him.

'One has to see the world. You're such an old stick-in-the-kennel already, although you're so much younger than I am.' He carried his tail at a jaunty angle. 'Now that Rin-Tin-Tin's dead –' he murmured, and left it at that.

The following summer might have been the same summer; the heat was as intense; but it had not begun until late in August, when the Wyndhams had already had a couple of months in England, where unluckily they encountered an earlier heat-wave. So that when they returned to their villa and their dogs, Fay was still pale and listless. Affection was cloudy between her and Godfrey. It had never been really clear and happy since the heat-wave last year had brought about her mood of restless discontent with his ways and his friends, that had concluded in that silly, infatuated friendship with Miss Dollabel Pink.

She had secretly detested Dollabel ever since the latter had invited a cheap film company to make itself at home all over the villa in Godfrey's absence. For one had learned swiftly, in those few shrill, grinning hours, what were the qualities one really valued.

But it had been impossible to share this discovery with Godfrey when he came back from the Tyrrell-Smythes. He was aloof; his mouth grim; she dared not tell him what had happened; and until he knew, the air about them must continue sultry. She longed for confession as mariners becalmed in the doldrums long for a fresh wind; hoped even that one of the servants might betray her; but they remained obstinately loyal.

It was not the human tongue that betrayed her; it was an apparatus, a machine, a few yards of perforated film. For one afternoon, a year later, some friends from England invited them to lunch, and insisted on taking them afterwards to the Miramar Palace Cinema to see a new historical film.

Preceding it, was a two-reel French comedy.

Shock, remorse, and a complete surrender to the melting joy of reconciliation can be very exhausting, especially in a heat-wave. Fay decided that she would not go down to bathe after sunset. She would lie back on the terrace, watch the pigeons flying in and out of the eucalyptus trees, and muse on happiness and love and Godfrey and her other recovered treasures. But she insisted that he should go. So, tenderly arranging the cushions in all the wrong places behind her, and returning at least a dozen times to kiss her again, he at last limped down the patch towards the sea, calling to his companions: 'Shot! Shot! Lobo! Heel, Shot! Lobo! Lobo! Good old Shot!'

Shot capered round him in circles, plunging up joyously towards his face, then whizzing ahead till nothing could be seen of him but a scurry of paws and ears. But Lobo only came as though on compulsion, sedately loping along several yards behind his master.

'Wonder what's wrong? He's been like this for months. No life in him. Nothing but sighs and sulks. He's fit enough, or I'd dose him thoroughly and hope for the best. Lord, what a complete fool he looked, careering round and round like mad with that sun-bonnet clapped on his head. Pity dogs can't see themselves; might wake him up. But I suppose films are a bit beyond their range.'

All day long, rumbles of thunder had disturbed the half-ring of hills behind the shore, and now the sun had set and the sea lay with an opal sheen on it, too still even to murmur among the rocks; a sea entranced, without resistance, surrendering to the evening but dreading the fierce onslaught of another brilliant day.

The flat rocks where Godfrey usually bathed, at the end of a small stone breakwater, were shadowed and deserted. Godfrey stripped, unscrewed his leg, and dived in; followed by Shot, who swam after him with an air of deepest anguish, paws beating the water as though in a frenzy, but in reality enjoying himself enormously.

The Afghan never went in the water, and his master had long ago given up trying to persuade him. Lobo always ran up and down the breakwater, lashing his tail; and with howls of misery, begged them to return to him. This was also enjoyable, in its way. But just as he was starting on his usual formula, he heard a gay, quick bark summoning him up to a clump of trees on a spur of the hill overlooking the water.

Lobo joyously recognized the summons. So his friend had returned. They would begin all over again, those glorious, exciting, stolen meetings of last summer.

Hotsy was rolling on his back, his four paws waving in the air, his jaws open, his stomach quivering, his pert nose shaken and convulsed. At first he could hardly get his breath to tell his huge comrade what had struck him as the best joke in the whole world. At last, however, he controlled himself enough to share it: he had seen a man –

'*En effet*, it was your master, *mon p'tit*' (Hotsy was full of French, these days) '– actually taking off one of his legs. Yes, *pouff*, so! as though it were no more than a hat, a boot. Taking it off and laying it beside him! Oh Dog, I'll die of it! You've never seen anything quite so funny. His *leg*! I tell you, he took it off and went into the sea without it. Oh Dog, oh Dog, what a pain I've got from laughing''

Lobo stood next to the terrier, frozen into stone, save for his heart bursting against its barriers with great indignant thumps. Never, never if he lived to be twenty, could he explain to this gurgling, gasping, laughing little clown *why* it was not funny that a man should take off his leg. Not in the least funny. Never could he explain it, because he did not know why, himself. He knew only that he knew, and Hotsy did not and could not and never would, and that was perhaps what Shot might have meant all along . . .

Suddenly, without a word of farewell, he bounded down the hill, galloped along the breakwater and cast himself into the sea; forgetting that he hated it and never bathed unless his master actually threw him in; forgetting all except this imperative need to join the other two, share in their swim, identify himself with their delight; belong utterly to them, lick Godfrey's wet face, lick it all over in frantic affection, scramble back on the rocks with them, an inseparable trio understanding one another.

HAVING NO HEARTS

by

Sir Hugh Walpole

(from *Head in Green Bronze*, Macmillan & Co.)

Mr and Mrs William Thrush owned a very sweet little house in Benedict Canyon, Los Angeles. That is, the postal address was Los Angeles, but Benedict Canyon is a Hollywood district if ever there was one. The Thrushes liked it for that reason, among others, and it gave William Thrush a very real pleasure when he heard the big motor wagons, between seven and eight in the morning, thundering down the Canyon on their way to location. This was about as near as he ever got to Pictures. He didn't wish to get any nearer, because he had a certain pride; not very much, but enough to make him desire to live in a society where he would be valued. Every morning he read the columns of film-making gossip in his daily paper, and always remarked to Isabelle: 'Goodness! If they don't have a time!' Then they both felt happy and a little superior too.

Isabelle Thrush had more pride than William. In fact, she had a great deal, and she spent most of her time in feeding it or inducing other people to do so. Would you say they were a happy pair? If you didn't know all about them, certainly yes. If you did know all about them, you would probably be doubtful, as William often was. There was something wrong between Isabelle and himself, although they'd been married for ten years and very seldom squabbled about anything. They didn't quarrel, because William refused to. Isabelle had undoubtedly a shrill temper, especially when she didn't get what she wanted. Of course, she couldn't get all the things that she wanted because William, who was a clerk in one of the leading banks in Los Angeles, had but a moderate salary. It happened, however, that a wealthy aunt of his had died some three or four years before and left him a pretty little sum. He invested this wisely, so that even through the depression it remained. But Isabelle had all of it and then a little more.

He asked himself sometimes, in the privacy of the night, whether she were greedy. He couldn't be sure, because he often read in American magazines about the tyranny of the American wife and how she eagerly bled her husband. Well, Isabelle wasn't as bad as that. Gosh! He'd see to it if she tried anything like that on him. And so, he decided comfortably, she was better than most American wives. Isabelle considered herself a really magnificent creature, filled with all the virtues – courage, wisdom, self-sacrifice, love and endurance. She thought that William was extremely lucky to be married to her. And this thought produced in her a kindly, motherly air when he was around, as though she were saying: 'Little man, I'll look after you. Don't be afraid.' And then: 'How lucky really you are!'

The Thrushes had no children. That was Isabelle's wish, because she said it was wicked to bring a child into the world when you weren't going to give it everything of the best. William, once when he was feeling peevish because of his indigestion, remarked to her that his aunt's money would look after the child all right. But Isabelle was indignant, indeed, and said that there was a cruel strain in his nature which he would have to watch or he'd be a real sadist.

Having no children, Isabelle thought that it would be pleasant to have a dog. Many of her lady friends had them. There were, in fact, far more hospitals for dogs in Beverly and Hollywood than for human beings. And everybody said that the dog hospitals were so perfectly run that it was worth having a dog just for that reason alone. Isabelle wanted a dog, but there were problems to be settled. She understood that unless you had it as a puppy, it never became really fond of you. On the other hand, puppies had to be trained, and one's beautiful rugs and carpets suffered in the process. Then, what kind of dog should she have? There were the darling Cockers, the adorable Scotch Terriers, the amusing Dachshunds and the great big splendid Setters and Airedales. Some very lonely women had Pekingese, and then there were French Bulldogs. She couldn't make up her mind, and used to ask William which sort he preferred. And William, while he was trying to guess what she wanted him to say, would look at her with that slow, puzzling stare, which Isabelle always interpreted as a tribute of gratified recognition of her brilliance and beauty. In reality, what he was saying was: 'What is the matter with Isabelle? She has gone somewhere and I don't know quite where.'

They lived the social life of ladies and gentlemen of moderate means in Hollywood. That is, they went to previews of celebrated pictures; in the summer they sat in the Bowl and wiped the damp off their fingers as they listened confusedly to symphonies by Brahms and Beethoven; they occasionally, with great daring, went with a friend or two to a burlesque in Los Angeles; they played bridge quite badly and gave little dinner-parties at which the coloured maid was never quite satisfactory. On the whole, it was a happy life.

Then one day, William, sitting alone and doing a crossword puzzle in the patio of his little Spanish house, had a visitor. Isabelle was out playing bridge with some friends and he was enjoying the lovely tranquil sunset, which lay like a golden sheet let down from heaven protectingly over the Canyon. In another half-hour the light would be gone, the air would be chill and sharp and he would go indoors and read his evening newspaper, turn on the heat, and wonder why he wasn't as happy as he ought to be. Then he saw enter his little garden, through a hole in the hedge, a French bulldog.

This dog sniffed around, looked at him from a distance with a very nervous expression, and then slowly advanced towards him, twisting and bending his thick body as though it were made of some elastic substance. William Thrush looked at the dog and disliked him exceedingly. He'd never had a great passion for dogs, ever since, years and years ago, his mother in a real temper had shaken him and told him he was as silly as a terrier puppy. So he'd grown up disliking dogs. And

B

being himself a short little man, with large glasses and rather bowed legs, short dogs were especially unpleasant to him.

In any case, this dog seemed to him the ugliest ever. The dog seemed to him to be so very ugly that he felt a sort of nausea. He said, 'Shoo! Go away!' But the dog was evidently accustomed to being disliked. On looking back over this first meeting, William reflected on the fact that the dog resembled himself, in that if anyone disliked him some kind of paralysis seized him and he simply stayed and stayed, although he knew that he ought to go away. So did the dog now. He didn't come up to William, but lay at full length on the grass at a short distance and looked at him with his bulging, ugly, and in some unpleasant way, very human eyes.

William went up to him that he might frighten him out of the garden. But instead of that, the dog lay over on his back, wriggling his stomach and waving his legs feebly in the air. 'You're horrible!' William said aloud. 'I don't like dogs and never have. For God's sake, get out of here!' and then had a dreadful sense of speaking to himself – telling himself to get out of the house and garden and go somewhere. The dog turned over, sat up, gave him a beseeching but intimate look, as though he said: 'I know you much better than you think I do. Nothing could destroy our intimacy,' and then went quietly out of the garden.

His wife returned later, vexed because she had lost at bridge. 'Such cards, my dear, you would have thought there was a spell on me. I don't know what to do about it. The cards I've been having lately!' He told her about the dog, but she wasn't in the very least interested, and after her absent-minded 'Really? How revolting!' went on with a long story about a shop in Los Angeles, where you could get a mink coat, or if it wasn't mink it looked very like it, by paying so small a sum weekly that you really didn't know you were paying it.

'No, you wouldn't,' said William, who was most unexpectedly cross, 'because I should be paying it.'

This upset her very much indeed. She detested mean people, and suddenly, standing there in the garden, which the sun had left so that it was cold and dead, she realized that William *was* mean, and that she had been living with a mean man for years and years, and it was quite wonderful for her to endure it. William on his part felt, oddly enough, that she had behaved to him just as he had behaved to the dog. 'Damn that dog!' he thought to himself. 'I can't get it out of my mind.'

Next morning, however, Isabelle was in excellent temper again, and for this reason: Helena Peters rang her up on the telephone and informed her that she had the most enchanting Cocker puppy. In fact she had two, a male and a female. Which of them would Isabelle prefer? It seems that the breed was perfect and its price in any kind of market would be fifty dollars apiece, but Helena was giving this dog to Isabelle and it was an act of friendship, because she loved Isabelle so dearly.

'I don't know why she's doing it,' Isabelle said to William. 'She wants something or other. Helena never gives anything for nothing – but it sounds a perfect puppy. I'll go around for it myself this morning.'

William very feebly suggested the disadvantages of having puppies – the wear and tear, the unpleasant hidden smells, the certainty that the dog would have distemper and die and so on. Isabelle waved all these objections aside. She had cherished them herself until William mentioned them. But, as was so often the case, her brain, so superior to William's, insisted that anything that he said must be foolish. So she went around and fetched the puppy.

Standing in the doorway at lunch-time, her face rosy with pleasure, the puppy lying in her arms against her dark green dress, its large amber eyes turned up to hers, its tongue suddenly licking her cheek, its soft brown body, its long silken ears, there was a picture so lovely that William, with a pang at his heart, wondered why it was that he didn't love her more dearly.

The puppy slowly turned its head towards William and looked at him. Was there in its eyes, even from the very first moment, a certain contempt? Had it hoped, young as it was, to

find William someone quite different? Did its gaze wander to
the incipient paunch, the bowed legs, and rise again to the
round, rather pathetic face in which the eyes, William's best
feature, were hidden behind the dull, gleaming glasses?

As they stood together in the cosy living-room, while the
puppy wandered cautiously from table to chair, from chair to
sofa, he was sure that Isabelle was above the puppy's social
line, and that he, alas! was below it. The puppy sat down.
'Look out!' William cried. 'He had better be put in the
garden.' Isabelle regarded him scornfully.

'*This* puppy is intelligent. Helena tells the most amazing
stories about it. It isn't, technically, house-trained, of course,
but it is wonderfully mature for a puppy. Helena says it avoids
all the really valuable rugs.'

And the puppy did seem to be wonderfully sophisticated.
Not that it wasn't a real puppy. It rushed about madly, it bit
everything and everybody within sight, played with a string as
though it had discovered the secret of perpetual motion at last,
it went suddenly to sleep in your arms in the most adorable
manner. It had everything that a puppy ought to have. The
trouble was that it knew all about its charm. It was perfectly
aware that when it lay on its side and grinned at you over its
silken ear, it was entirely bewitching. And when it pretended
to be angry, growling, showing its white little teeth and flashing
its amber eyes, no one in the world could resist it.

Isabelle insisted that it should be called Roosevelt.

'Why?' asked William.

'Well, I think he's the most wonderful man in the world, and
now, when people are turning against him and saying horrid
things about the New Deal and that he's a Socialist and everything of that sort, one has to stand up for him and come right
out into the open.'

'I don't see,' said William 'that calling the puppy Roosevelt
is coming out into the open.'

'It's a kind of demonstration. After all, isn't the puppy the
sweetest thing in the world?'

'I don't think,' said William, sulkily, 'that Roosevelt would like anyone to call him the sweetest thing in the world. He isn't at all that kind of man.'

She looked at him reflectively. What had happened to him? Was it, perhaps, that she was only now really beginning to discover him? And if she discovered him a little further, how would it be then? Would she be able to endure it?

There is no doubt that after the arrival of the puppy, they bickered a good deal. A happy marriage between two persons depends altogether on mutual charity, unless one of the two is so absolutely a sheep that he doesn't mind what is done to him. Isabelle was a woman who had charity for everyone and everybody, but it was charity of a kind. It never worked unless Isabelle's pride was properly fed first. William, unfortunately, continued increasingly to look at her with that puzzled, bewildered expression that is so justly irritating to wives.

And then the puppy confirmed her in her growing sense of injustice. People love dogs because they are so flattering. If you are unjust to your friend and feel a certain shame, your dog swiftly restores your self-confidence. It never knows that you have been mean or jealous or grasping. It encourages you to be kindly to itself, and when you respond, it loves you.

The puppy, Roosevelt, must have been born a courtier; its tact was perfectly astonishing. For instance, when it arrived in the bedroom in the morning and greeted the twin beds with little yelps of ecstatic pleasure, it almost at once discriminated between Isabelle's bed and William's. It went to William first so that Isabelle, looking enchanting in her early-morning sleepy bewilderment, was given the opportunity to say: 'Isn't he coming to Mummy then?' and Isabelle's little smile of gratified pleasure when it rushed over to her, as though William never existed, was something delightful to witness.

When guests were present, as they often were, how Roosevelt was adored! And how then he made it appear that it was really because of Isabelle that he seemed so charming. He bit at a lady's dress, or chewed playfully at the corner of a handsome purse with a side glance at Isabelle, as though he were saying to the ladies: 'It is because I love her so. It is because she is such a perfect darling. It is because I'm so wonderfully happy with her that I'm behaving like this.' William had never greatly cared for Isabelle's lady friends and generally avoided occasions when they would be present. That was one of Isabelle's complaints. But now he simply could not bear to be there. Isabelle's patronage of him was one thing, but Isabelle and Roosevelt together were more than any man could endure. And so they had a quarrel.

'You're behaving ridiculously about that dog.'

'Ridiculously?' That was something that Isabelle never would forgive. 'You've hated it,' she asserted, her eyes flashing, 'ever since its arrival. And why? Why? Shall I tell you?'

'Please do,' said William, stony-faced.

'Because it prefers me to you, because it always has.'

'Oh, damn the dog!' said William.

Meanwhile, the French bulldog made frequent appearances, but never when Isabelle was about. Greatly though William disliked it, he began, very reluctantly, to be interested in its personality. It wanted so terribly to be loved, and it was a certainty nobody loved it. Building was in process near by. And William, after he shaved in the morning, looking out of the window, would watch its approach to the different workmen, wiggling its body and leaping heavily up and down, and all the workmen repulsed it. They were good, kindly men, no doubt, as most American workmen are, but they felt about it as William did, that it was too ugly to be borne. He christened it Ugly, and as soon as he had given it a name it seemed to have at once a closer relationship with him.

'Get away, Ugly, you beastly dog!' he would say. And the dog would be apparently in an ecstasy of enjoyment at being called anything at all. Once in a fit of abstraction, sitting there wondering why it was that he was so lonely, wondering why everything was going wrong with Isabelle and what it was that she really lacked, Ugly came close to him, and not knowing what he did, he stroked its back and tickled it behind the ear. He was aware then of a wave of affection that was almost terrifying.

As soon as William realized what he had done, he moved away with an irritated murmur. The dog did not follow him, but stayed there stretched out looking at him. How unpleasant is this naked sentimentality in this modern realistic world! How we run from sentiment and how right it is that we should do so! And yet William was sentimental too. Someone loved him, and although he detested the dog, he was not quite as lonely as he'd been before.

It happened, of course, that Roosevelt and Ugly had various encounters. Ugly would come across the path into the garden, and finding Roosevelt there, hoped that they might have a game. But Roosevelt, young as he was, played only with his social equals. He did not snarl at Ugly. He did nothing mean or common. He allowed Ugly supplicatingly to sniff him, to walk around him, even to cavort and prance a little, and then very quietly he strolled indoors. And then Isabelle realized that Ugly existed.

'William, do look at that hideous dog! What's it doing here? Shoo! Shoo! Get away, you horrible animal!' and Ugly went. William found himself, to his own surprise, defending Ugly.

'He isn't so bad,' he said. 'Not much to look at, of course, but friendly, obedient, rather a decent dog.'

'Oh, you would!' said Isabelle. 'It only needs the most hideous animal I've seen in my life to come your way for you to praise it. Really, William, I don't know what's happening to you.'

William smiled at her and said very gently: 'I don't know what's happening, either.' He made then, almost as though it were under Ugly's instructions, a serious attempt to persuade Isabelle to love him again. He was very patient, thoughtful, generous. A few people in the world knew that William Thrush had an extraordinary amount of charm – even a kind of penetrating wit when he liked. But William's charm was unconscious. It failed him when he tried to summon it. And now the more he tried, the more irritating to her he became.

The breach grew wider, and Isabelle confessed to her closer

friends that she didn't know whether she could stand it much longer. Then, as nothing ever stays where it is but always advances to its appointed climax, the catastrophe occurred.

One of the troubles between William and Isabelle had always been that William liked to read and Isabelle did not. William liked long, long novels, preferably about family life. Novels that went on and on for ever and ever, in which you could be completely lost. Novels that deceived you with so friendly and profuse a carelessness that it was like a personal compliment to yourself. Isabelle, on the other hand, could not bear to read. She looked at the social column of the daily paper and sometimes a film magazine or a fashion monthly. But for the most part, as she said, she adored to read, but 'just didn't have the time to open a book'.

This had once been very sad to William, who in his young glowing days had imagined sitting on one side of the fire reading aloud to his dear little wife, who was sewing things for the baby, but nevertheless able to take it all in and speculate about the characters. Well, on this particular day, he was deep in a novel by one of those English novelists who have so many characters in their family that they have to have a genealogical table at the end of the book. To this same table he would often refer with a pleasing sense that he was staying in the most delightful house with an enormous family of cousins. He read cosily and comfortably. The door leading on to the porch was open and the afternoon sun poured bountifully in. He was aware then that something had occurred. There had been no sound, no movement, but looking up, he beheld a very horrible sight.

Ugly was advancing towards him, and one of his eyes, a blood-red ball, was nearly torn from his head. The dog made no sound whatever. He simply came towards William, only once and again lifting a paw feebly, as though he were absurdly puzzled as to what had happened to him. When he got near to William, he crouched down, and, still without a sound, looked up into his face.

William's first feeling was of nausea. He hated the sight of blood. His sensitive soul was intensely distressed by any kind of physical suffering. This seemed to him quite horrible. Then almost at once he was overwhelmed with pity. He'd never in his life before been so sorry for anything. Something in the distressed trusting patience of the dog won his heart completely and for ever. That the animal should be so silent, making no complaint, seemed to him himself as he ought to be. That was how he'd wish to behave had such a terrible thing happened to him. How, he was sure, he would *not* behave.

He said nothing, but arose from his chair, was about to take the dog in his arms and hasten at once with it to the nearest dog hospital, when Isabelle entered and Roosevelt scampered out from a room near by. She was smiling and happy. She greeted the cocker puppy with little cries of baby joy. 'Oh, the darling! The ickle, ickle darling! Wasn't he an angel to come and see his mummy?' And then she saw the other dog. Ugly had turned his head and was looking at her. She screamed. She put her hands in front of her face.

'Oh, William, how horrible! How frightful! It must be killed at once!'

William got up, took the heavy, bleeding dog in his arms, and without a word, passed her and went out.

He went into the garage, laid the dog on the old rug, got out his car, picked up the dog again, got into the car with him and drove off to the dog hospital. Here he talked to a very kindly plump little man and discussed whether Ugly should be destroyed or not. When the little man took Ugly in his arms to examine him, the dog very slowly turned his head, and, with his one eye, looked at William as much as to say: 'If you think this is the right thing for me to do, I'll suffer it.' William even nodded his head to the dog and a silent understanding seemed to pass between them.

'It seems to have no damage anywhere else,' the doctor said. 'It was done, of course, by another dog. They do that. They just take hold of one place and don't let go again. Poor old fellow!' The dog doctor caressed him. 'Not very handsome, anyway, is he?'

'Oh, I don't know,' said William; 'he's got a kind of character about him, I think.'

'Is he your dog?' asked the doctor.

'No. I don't think he belongs to anybody, but he comes to our garden sometimes. I've grown interested in him.'

'Well, I can tell you this,' the doctor said, 'I guess he'll be all right. We can sew it up so you'll hardly notice it. He won't exactly be a beauty, you know.'

'Yes, I know,' said William, who wasn't a beauty, either. He went home.

For some reason or another, Isabelle had been greatly excited by the incident. She sat there and gave William a terrific lecture, the total of which was that for ever so long now he'd been letting himself go. He was becoming soppy, almost a sissy, in fact.

'A sissy?' said William, indignantly.

'Oh, well, you know what I mean. You're getting dreadfully sentimental. You always had a tendency that way, but lately it's been terrible. All my friends notice it.'

I don't know why it is, but there is almost nothing so irritating in the world as to be told by someone that one's friends have been silently, mysteriously, observing one to one's disadvantage. William, for the first time in their married life, lost all control of himself. He stood up and raved. He said that it didn't matter whether he was getting sentimental or not, but anyway, perhaps sentiment wasn't a bad thing. What really mattered was that Isabelle was selfish, cold and unkind! That she hadn't any idea of the horrible woman she was becoming. Isabelle suitably replied. In fact, they both thoroughly lost their tempers. And while this was going on, Roosevelt sat in Isabelle's lap making little playful bites at Isabelle's dress and beautiful fingers. While he sat there, he looked at William with a really terrible sarcasm in his soft, amber eyes – sarcasm and scorn.

'I tell you what,' William cried in a last frenzy, 'I hate that dog! Puppies ought to be nice, gentle, loving creatures. Look at him! He's hard as iron and the most horrid snob.'

So then Isabelle burst into tears, went to her room and locked the door. There followed days of constrained silence, and after that William went down to the dog hospital.

'He's a patient dog, I must say,' the doctor remarked. 'Never a whine. Seems fond of you too.'

William was surprised at the pleasure that he felt at the tribute. The day came when Ugly's eye was gone, the empty space sewed up, and his whole air rather that of a drunken soldier who had been in the wars. What was to be done with him? William, realizing that the crisis of his life was upon him, decided that if Isabelle had her Roosevelt, he should have his Ugly. He went home an' told her so. This was at breakfast. She said no word and he left fo. 's work in the city.

When he returned in the la. r afternoon there was a strange silence about the house. He ha' been thinking and had decided t' in some way or anothe this awful trouble with Isabelle must be stopped. After all, sur 'v he loved her. Or if he didn't, they were at least man and wife. How miserable, how lost, he would be without her! Would he? At that ., 'alling wonder, his whole soul shook. So he returned home with t. 'ry intention of making everything all right again, although how he was to do that he didn't in the least know.

Ugly greeted him, coming in from the garden, rolling his body about, baring his teeth, showing an ecstasy of pleasure. But Isabelle was not there, nor Roosevelt. On his writing-table lay the note so essential to all dramatists and novelists who have learnt their job. What it said was that Isabelle had gone to her mother in Santa Barbara and would remain there. She wished that William would give her a divorce. She had been seeing for a long time how impossible things were. She had taken Roosevelt with her.

William read the note and felt a dreadful shame and despair. His impulse was to depart at once for Santa Barbara. And so he would have done if it had not been for Ugly. But he could not leave him just then. The dog was new to the house and the servants had no especial affection for him. In a day or two he would go. But he did not. The days passed and he did not.

A quite terrible thing happened to him. He found that he liked the house better without Isabelle than with her. He found that he adored his freedom. That he could now have liberty of action and thought, that showed him what all these years he'd been missing. He discovered a number of other things. He took long walks up the Canyon with Ugly. He talked to the dog and it seemed to him that the dog answered him. Strangest of all, he was less lonely than he had been when Isabelle was there. It was as though for years there had been a padlock on his mind. Someone, something, had all the time inhibited his thought.

A letter came from Isabelle and he made his discovery. In her letter she said she was now ready to return. Santa Barbara wasn't half the place it had once been, and her mother was in many ways unsympathetic, and, he would be glad to hear, she missed her dear old William. As he wrote his reply to her letter, he solved his problem. This was the letter he wrote.

DEAR ISABELLE,

I don't want you to come back. This sounds very unkind and rude on my part, but I've done a lot of thinking in the last few weeks and I know that I must be honest. For a long while I've been wondering what it was that was wrong between us. I admire you so much. You are far finer than I. You have been so good and so kind for so long, that it seems absurd to say that you are lacking in anything. But you are. You have no heart. That sounds like a thing you read in a novel, but I mean it just like that. I don't think you're any the worse for not having one – it is only that I have suddenly discovered while I've been alone here that that is the one real difference between human beings. Either you have a heart, or you haven't one. What I mean is, either the heart is the part of your body that functions more than any other or not. This is the one insuperable difference between people. Not whether you're a Fascist or Communist, American or French, teetotaller or a drunkard, clever or stupid. All those things can be got over quite easily. I'm not saying either that the people with hearts are preferable to those without. I think it is possibly just the opposite. The people with hearts are nearly always too sentimental, too emotional, prevent the work of the world being done, get in the way of real thinkers. The people without hearts are, as the world is now going, the ones we really want. But the difference is there. I can't help feeling emotionally about things. You can't help the opposite. But we mustn't live together any more. This is a difference that nothing can get over.

Yours sincerely

WILLIAM.

PS. – There is the same difference between Roosevelt and Ugly.

When he had posted the letter and was walking in a last cool flash of sunshine up the Canyon, Ugly ambling along beside him, he thought that possibly no one had ever written so silly a letter. And yet, he had this sense that he had made this marvellous discovery. He looked at all his friends, male and female, and saw the dividing line with absolute clearness. He looked beyond the other great figures in the world. Einstein had a heart – Hitler, even. On the other hand, Mussolini possibly not. And Simon Callahan, the manager of his bank in Los Angeles, most certainly not! Ugly, whose vision of course was now sadly dimmed, saw a golden leaf, one of the first signs of autumn, twirling through the air. He leapt rather foolishly, ran a little way and looked back at William. William smiled encouragement. Then he turned back home, Ugly delightedly following.

THE BOY AND THE BADGER

by

ERNEST THOMPSON SETON

(from *Wild Animals at Home*, Hodder & Stoughton)

In 1871, there was a family named Service living at Bird's Hill, on the prairie north of Winnipeg. They had one child, a seven-year-old boy named Harry. He was a strange child, very small for his age, and shy without being cowardly. He had an odd habit of following Dogs, Chickens, Pigs, and Birds, imitating their voices and actions, with an exactness that on-lookers sometimes declared to be uncanny.

One day, he had gone quietly after a Prairie Chicken that kept moving away from him without taking flight, clucking when she clucked, and nodding his head or shaking his 'wings' when she did. So he wandered on and on, till the house was hidden from view behind the trees that fringed the river, and the child was completely lost.

There was nothing remarkable in his being away for several hours; but a heavy thunderstorm coming up that afternoon called attention to the fact that the boy was missing, and when the first casual glance did not discover him, it became serious, and a careful search was begun.

Father and mother, with the near neighbours, scoured the prairie till dark, and began the next day at dawn, riding in all directions, calling, and looking for signs. After a day or two, the neighbours gave it up, believing that the child was drowned and carried away by the river. But the parents continued their search even long after all hope seemed dead. And there was no hour of the day when that stricken mother did not send up a prayer for heavenly help; nor any night when she did not kneel with her husband and implore the One who loved and blessed the babes of Jerusalem to guard her little one and bring him back in safety.

THE EVIL ONE

There was one neighbour of the family who joined in the search that had nevertheless incurred the bitter dislike of little Harry Service. The feeling was partly a mere baby instinct, but pointedly because of the man's vicious cruelty to the animals, wild or tame, that came within his power. Only a week before, he had set steel traps at a den where he chanced to find a pair of Badgers in residence. The first night he captured the father Badger. The cruel jaws of the jag-toothed trap had seized him by both paws, so he was held helpless. The trap was champed and wet with blood and froth when Grogan came in the morning. Of what use are courage and strength when one cannot reach the foe? The Badger craved only a fair fight, but Grogan stood out of reach and used a club till the light was gone from the brave eyes and the fighting snarl was still.

The trap was reset in the sand, and Grogan went. He carried the dead Badger to the Service house to show his prize and get help to skin it, after which he set off for the town and bartered the skin for what evil indulgence it might command, and thought no more of the trap for three days. Meanwhile the mother Badger, coming home at dawn, was caught by one foot. Strain as she might, that deadly grip still held her; all that night and all the next day she struggled. She had little ones to care for. Their hungry cries from down the burrow were driving her almost mad; but the trap was of strong steel, beyond her strength, and at last the crying of the little ones in the den grew still. On the second day of her torture, the mother, in desperation, chewed off one of her toes and dragged her bleeding foot from the trap.

Down the burrow she went first, but it was too late; her babies were dead. She buried them where they lay and hastened from that evil spot.

Water was her first need, next food, and then at evening she made for an old den she had used the autumn before.

THE BADGER THAT RESCUED THE BOY

And little Harry, meanwhile, where was he? That sunny afternoon in June, he had wandered away from the house, and losing sight of the familiar building behind the long fringe of trees by the river, he had lost his bearings. Then came the thunder shower which made him seek for shelter. There was nothing about him but level prairie, and the only shelter he could find was a Badger hole, none too wide even for his small form. Into this he had backed and stayed with some comfort during the thunderstorm, which continued till night. Then in the evening the child heard a sniffing sound, and a great, grey animal loomed up against the sky, sniffed at the tracks and at the open door of the den. Next it put its head in, and Harry saw by the black marks on its face that it was a Badger. He had seen one just three days before. A neighbour had brought it to his father's house to skin it. There it stood sniffing, and Harry, gazing with less fear than most children, noticed that the visitor had five claws on one foot and four on the other, with recent wounds, proof of some sad experience in a trap. Doubtless this was the Badger's den, for she – it proved a mother – came in, but Harry had no mind to surrender. The Badger snarled and came on, and Harry shrieked, 'Get out!' and struck with his tiny fists, and then, to use his own words, 'I scratched the Badger's face and she scratched mine.' Surely this Badger was in a generous mood, for she did him no serious harm, and though the rightful owner of the den, she went away and doubtless slept elsewhere.

Night came down. Harry was very thirsty. Close by the door was a pool of rainwater. He crawled out, slaked his thirst, and backed into the warm den as far as he could. Then remembering his prayers, he begged God to 'send mamma', and cried himself to sleep. During the night, he was awakened by the Badger coming again, but it went away when the child scolded it.

Next morning Harry went to the pool again and drank. Now he was so hungry; a few old rose hips hung on the bushes near the den. He gathered and ate these, but was even hungrier. Then he saw something moving out on the plain. It might be the Badger, so he backed into the den, but he watched the moving thing. It was a horseman galloping. As it came nearer, Harry saw that it was Grogan, the neighbour for whom he had such a dislike, so he got down out of sight. Twice that morning men came riding by, but having once yielded to his shy impulse, he hid again each time. The Badger came back at noon. In her mouth she held the body of a Prairie Chicken, pretty well plucked and partly devoured. She came into the den sniffing as before. Harry shouted, 'Get out! Go away.' The Badger dropped the meat and raised her head. Harry reached and grasped the food and devoured it with the appetite of one starving. There must have been another doorway, for later the Badger was behind the child in the den, and still later when he had fallen asleep she came and slept beside him. He awoke to find the warm furry body filling the space between him and the wall, and knew now why it was he had slept so comfortably.

That evening the Badger brought the egg of a Prairie Chicken, and set it down unbroken before the child. He devoured it eagerly, and again drank from the drying mud puddle to quench his thirst. During the night it rained again, and he would have been cold, but the Badger came and cuddled around him. Once or twice it licked his face. The child could not know, but the parents discovered later that this was a mother Badger which had lost her brood and her heart was yearning for something to love.

Now there were two habits that grew on the boy. One was to shun the men that daily passed by in their search, the other was to look to the Badger for food and protection, and live the Badger's life. She brought him food often not at all to his taste – dead Mice or Ground-squirrels – but several times she brought in the comb of a bee's nest or eggs of game birds, and once a piece of bread almost certainly dropped on the trail from some traveller's lunch-bag. His chief trouble was water. The prairie pool was down to mere ooze, and with this he moistened his lips and tongue. Possibly the mother Badger wondered why he did not accept her motherly offerings. But rain came often enough to keep him from serious suffering.

Their daily life was together now, and with the imitative power strong in all children and dominant in him, he copied the Badger's growls, snarls, and purrs. Sometimes they played tag on the prairie, but both were ready to rush below at the slightest sign of a stranger.

Two weeks went by. Galloping men no longer passed each day. Harry and the Badger had fitted their lives into each other's, and strange as it may seem, the memory of his home was already blurred and weakened in the boy. Once or twice during the second week men had passed near by, but the habit of eluding them was now in full possession of him.

FINDING THE LOST ONE

One morning he wandered a little farther in search of water, and was alarmed by a horseman appearing. He made for home on all fours – he ran much on all fours now – and backed into the den. In the prairie grass he was concealed, but the den was on a bare mound, and the horseman caught a glimpse of a whitish thing disappearing down the hole. Badgers were familiar to him, but the peculiar yellow of this and the absence of black marks gave it a strange appearance. He rode up quietly within twenty yards and waited.

After a few minutes the grey-yellow ball slowly reappeared and resolved itself into the head of a tow-topped child. The young man leaped to the ground, and rushed forward, but the child retreated far back into the den, beyond reach of the man, and refused to come out. Nevertheless, there was no doubt that this was the missing Harry Service. 'Harry! Harry! don't you know me? I'm your cousin Jack,' the young man said, in soothing, coaxing tones. 'Harry, won't you come out and let me take you back to mamma? Come, Harry! Look! here are some cookies!' but all in vain. The child hissed and snarled at him like a wild thing, and retreated as far as he could till checked by a turn in the burrow.

Now Jack got out his knife and began to dig until the burrow was large enough for him to crawl in a little way. At once he succeeded in getting hold of the little one's arm and drew him out struggling and crying. But now there rushed also from the hole a Badger, snarling and angry; it charged at the man, uttering its fighting snort. He fought it off with his whip, then swung to the saddle with his precious burden, and rode away as for his very life, while the Badger pursued for a time. But it was easily left behind, and its snorts were lost and forgotten.

HOME AGAIN

The father was coming in from another direction as he saw this strange sight; a Horse galloping madly over the prairie, on its back a young man shouting loudly, and in his arms a small, dirty child, alternately snarling at his captor, trying to scratch his face, or struggling to be free.

The father was used to changing intensity of feeling at these times, but he turned pale and held his breath till the words reached him: 'I have got him, thank God! He's all right,' and he rushed forward shouting, 'My boy! my boy!'

But he got a rude rebuff. The child glared like a hunted Cat, hissed at him, and menaced with hands held claw fashion. Fear and hate were all he seemed to express. The door of the house flung open and the distracted mother, now suddenly overjoyed, rushed to join the group. 'My darling! my darling!' she sobbed, but little Harry was not as when he left them. He hung back, he hid his face in the coat of his captor, scratched and snarled like a beast, he displayed his claws and threatened fight, till strong arms gathered him up and placed him on his mother's knees in the old, familiar room with the pictures, and the clock ticking as of old, the smell of frying bacon, and the nearness of his father's form; and, above all, his mother's arms about him, her magic touch on his brow, and her voice, 'My darling! my darling! Oh! Harry, don't you know your mother? My boy! my boy!' And the struggling little wild thing in her arms grew quiet, his animal anger died away, his raucous hissing gave place to a short panting, and that to a low sobbing that ended in a flood of tears and a passionate 'Mamma, mamma, mamma!' as the veil of a different life was rolled away, and he clung to his mother's bosom.

But even as she cooed to him, and stroked his brow and won him back again, there was a strange sound, a snarling hiss at the open door. All turned to see a great Badger standing there with its front feet on the threshold. Father and cousin exclaimed, 'Look at that Badger!' and reached for the ready gun, but the boy screamed again. He wriggled from his mother's arms and rushing to the door, cried, 'My Badgie! my Badgie!' He flung his arms around the savage thing's neck, and it answered with a low purring sound as it licked its lost companion's face. The men were for killing the Badger, but it was the mother's keener insight that saved it, as one might save a noble Dog that had rescued a child from the water.

It was some days before the child would let the father come near. 'I hate that man; he passed me every day and would not look at me,' was the only explanation. Doubtless the first part was true, for the Badger den was but two miles from the house and the father rode past many times in his radiating search, but the tow-topped head had escaped his eye.

It was long and only by slow degrees that the mother got the story that is written here, and parts of it were far from clear. It might all have been dismissed as a dream or a delirium but for the fact that the boy had been absent two weeks; he was well and strong now, excepting that his lips were blackened and cracked with the muddy water, the Badger had followed him home, and was now his constant friend.

It was strange to see how the child oscillated between the two lives, sometimes talking to his people exactly as he used to talk, and sometimes running on all fours, growling, hissing, and tussling with the Badger. Many a game of 'King of the Castle' they had together on the low pile of sand left after the digging of a new well. Each would climb to the top and defy the other to pull him down, till a hold was secured and they rolled together to the level, clutching and tugging, Harry giggling, the

Badger uttering a peculiar high-pitched sound that might have been called snarling had it not been an expression of good nature. Surely it was a Badger laugh. There was little that Harry could ask without receiving it those days, but his mother was shocked when he persisted that the Badger must sleep in his bed; yet she so arranged it. The mother would go in the late hours and look at them with a little pang of jealousy as she saw her baby curled up, sleeping soundly with that strange beast.

It was Harry's turn to feed his friend now, and side by side they sat to eat. The Badger had become an established member of the family. But after a month had gone by an incident took place that I would gladly leave untold.

THE HUMAN BRUTE

Grogan, the unpleasant neighbour, who had first flung Harry into the den, came riding up to the Service homestead. Harry was in the house for the moment. The Badger was on the sand pile. Instantly on catching sight of it, Grogan unslung his gun and exclaimed, 'A Badger!' To him a Badger was merely something to be killed. 'Bang!' and the kindly animal rolled over, stung and bleeding, but recovered and dragged herself towards the house. 'Bang!' and the murderer fired again, just as the inmate rushed to the door – too late. Harry ran towards the Badger shouting, 'Badgie! my Badgie!' He flung his baby arms around the bleeding neck. It fawned on him feebly, purring a low, hissing purr, then mixing the purrs with moans, grew silent, and slowly sank down, and died in his arms. 'My Badgie! my Badgie!' the boy wailed, and all the ferocity of his animal nature was directed against Grogan.

'You better get out of this before I kill you!' thundered the father, and the hulking halfbreed sullenly mounted his horse and rode away.

A great part of his life had been cut away, and it seemed as though a deathblow had been dealt the boy. The shock was more than he could stand. He moaned and wept all day, he screamed into convulsions, he was worn out at sundown and

slept little that night. Next morning he was in a raging fever
and ever he called for 'My Badgie!' He seemed at death's door
the next day, but a week later he began to mend, and in three
weeks was strong as ever and childishly gay, with occasional
spells of sad remembering that gradually ceased.

He grew up to early manhood in a land of hunters, but he
took no pleasure in the killing that was such sport to his
neighbours' sons, and to his dying day he could not look on
the skin of a Badger without feelings of love, tenderness, and
regret.

This is the story of the Badger as it was told me, and those
who wish to inquire further can do so at Winnipeg, if they
seek out Archbishop Matheson, Dr R. M. Simpson, or Mrs
George A. Frazer, of Kildonan. These witnesses may differ as
to the details; but all have assured me that in its main outlines,
this tale is true, and I gladly tell it, for I want you to realize the
kindly disposition that is in that sturdy, harmless, noble wild
animal that sits on the low prairie mounds. For then I know
that you will join with me in loving him, and in seeking to save
his race from extermination.

A FIGHT WITH A MOTHER PANTHER

by

JAMES FENIMORE COOPER

James Fenimore Cooper was born at Burlington, New Jersey, in September 1789, and died September 1851, being sixty-two years of age. He was one of the earliest American novelists and in many respects the most original. He wrote sea tales and Indian stories. It is to his eternal fame that he first, and best of all, pictured the real Indian, setting forth fully and enthusiastically the manly virtues of the Red Race.

His style of writing was far too verbose and pompous for our modern ideas of quick, vivid picture; but he gave the first accurate details we have of hunter life and forest life in primitive America.

The incident selected to represent him is from his story *The Pioneers*. It illustrates at once his strength and his weakness. The scene is laid in the woods about the famous Lake Glimmerglass, now called by its Indian name Otsego. The actors are, first, two young ladies, Elizabeth Temple, and Louisa Grant; second, an old and feeble but valiant Mastiff; the villain, a Mother Panther; and finally the hero, Leatherstocking. The young ladies were of the Languishing Lydia type, feeble, helpless and proud of it. Such was the approved mode of those days. Leatherstocking of the heroic rescue was the ideal type of frontiersman that Cooper so often and successfully depicted.

BY THIS time they had gained the summit of the mountain, where they left the highway, and pursued their course under the shade of the stately trees that crowned the eminence. The day was becoming warm, and the girls plunged more deeply into the forest, as they found its invigorating coolness agreeably contrasted to the excessive heat they had experienced in the ascent. The conversation, as if by mutual consent, was entirely changed to the little incidents and scenes of their walk, and every tall pine, and every shrub or flower, called forth some simple expression of admiration.

In this manner they proceeded along the margin of the precipice, catching occasional glimpses of the placid Otsego, or pausing to listen to the rattling of wheels and the sounds of hammers that rose from the valley, to mingle the signs of men with the scenes of nature, when Elizabeth suddenly started, and exclaimed:

'Listen! there are the cries of a child on this mountain! Is there a clearing near us, or can some little one have strayed from its parents?'

'Such things frequently happen,' returned Louisa. 'Let us follow the sounds; it may be a wanderer starving on the hill.'

Urged by this consideration, the females pursued the low, mournful sounds, that proceeded from the forest, with quick and impatient steps. More than once, the ardent Elizabeth was on the point of announcing that she saw the sufferer, when Louisa caught her by the arm, and pointing behind them, cried:

'Look at the Dog!'

Brave had been their companion, from the time the voice of his young mistress lured him from his kennel, to the present moment. His advanced age had long before deprived him of his activity; and when his companions stopped to view the scenery, or to add to their bouquets, the Mastiff would lay his huge frame on the ground and await their movements, with his eyes closed, and a listlessness in his air that ill accorded with the character of a protector. But when, aroused by this cry from Louisa, Miss Temple turned, she saw the Dog with his eyes keenly set on some distant object, his head bent near the ground, and his hair actually rising on his body, through fright or anger. It was most probably the latter, for he was growling in a low key, and occasionally showing his teeth, in a manner that would have terrified his mistress, had she not so well known his good qualities.

'Brave!' she said, 'be quiet, Brave! What do you see, fellow?'

At the sounds of her voice, the rage of the Mastiff, instead of being at all diminished, was very sensibly increased. He stalked in front of the ladies and seated himself at the feet of his mistress, growling louder than before, and occasionally giving vent to his ire by a short, surly barking.

'What does he see?' said Elizabeth; 'there must be some animal in sight.'

Hearing no answer from her companion, Miss Temple turned her head and beheld Louisa, standing with her face whitened to the colour of death, and her finger pointing upward with a sort of flickering, convulsed motion. The quick eye of Elizabeth glanced in the direction indicated by her friend, where she saw the fierce front and glaring eyes of a female Panther, fixed on them in horrid malignity, and threatening to leap.

'Let us fly,' exclaimed Elizabeth, grasping the arm of Louisa, whose form yielded like melting snow.

There was not a single feeling in the temperament of Elizabeth Temple that could prompt her to desert a companion in such an extremity. She fell on her knees by the side of the inanimate Louisa, tearing from the person of her friend, with instinctive readiness, such parts of her dress as might obstruct her respiration, and encouraging their only safeguard, the Dog, at the same time, by the sounds of her voice.

'Courage, Brave!' she cried, her own tones beginning to tremble, 'courage, courage, good Brave!'

A quarter-grown cub, that had hitherto been unseen, now appeared, dropping from the branches of a sapling that grew under the shade of the beech which held its dam. This ignorant but vicious creature approached the Dog, imitating the actions and sounds of its parent, but exhibiting a strange mixture of the playfulness of a kitten with the ferocity of its race. Standing on its hind legs, it would rend the bark of a tree with its fore-paws, and play the antics of a Cat; and then, by lashing itself with its tail, growling, and scratching the earth, it would attempt the manifestations of anger that rendered its parent so terrific.

All this time Brave stood firm and undaunted, his short tail erect, his body drawn backward on its haunches, and his eyes following the movements of both dam and cub. At every gambol played by the latter, it approached higher to the Dog, the growling of the three becoming more horrid at each moment, until the younger beast, over-leaping its intended bound, fell directly before the Mastiff. There was a moment of fearful cries and struggles, but they ended almost as soon as commenced, by the cub appearing in the air, hurled from the jaws of Brave, with a violence that sent it against a tree so forcibly as to render it completely senseless. Elizabeth witnessed the short struggle and her blood was warming with the triumph of the Dog, when she saw the form of the old Panther in the air, springing twenty feet from the branch of the beech to the back of the Mastiff. No words of ours can describe the fury of the conflict that followed. It was a confused struggle on the dry leaves, accompanied by loud and terrific cries. Miss Temple continued on her knees, bending over the form of Louisa, her eyes fixed on the animals with an interest so horrid, and yet so intense, that she almost forgot her own stake in the result. So rapid and vigorous were the bounds of the inhabitant of the forest, that its active frame seemed constantly in the air, while the Dog nobly faced his foe at each successive leap. When the Panther lighted on the shoulders of the Mastiff, which was its constant aim, old Brave, though torn with her talons, and stained with his own blood, that already flowed from a dozen wounds, would shake off his furious foe like a feather, and, rearing on his hind legs, rush to the fray again, with jaws distended, and a dauntless eye. But age, and his pampered life, greatly disqualified the noble Mastiff for such a struggle. In everything but courage, he was only the vestige of what he had once been. A higher bound than ever raised the wary and furious beast far beyond the reach of the Dog, who was making a desperate but fruitless dash at her, from which she alighted in a favourable position, on the back of her aged foe.

For a single moment only could the Panther remain there, the great strength of the Dog returning with a convulsive effort. But Elizabeth saw, as Brave fastened his teeth in the side of his enemy, that the collar of brass around his neck, which had been glittering throughout the fray, was of the colour of blood, and directly that his frame was sinking to the earth, where it soon lay prostrate and helpless. Several mighty efforts of the Wild-cat to extricate herself from the jaws of the Dog followed, but they were fruitless, until the Mastiff turned on his back, his lips collapsed, and his teeth loosened, when the short convulsions and stillness that succeeded announced the death of poor Brave.

Elizabeth now lay wholly at the mercy of the beast. There is said to be something in the front of the image of the Maker that daunts the hearts of the inferior beings of his creation; and it would seem that some such power, in the present instance, suspended the threatened blow. The eyes of the monster and the kneeling maiden met for an instant, when the former stooped to examine her fallen foe; next, to scent her luckless cub. From the latter examination it turned, however, with its eyes apparently emitting flashes of fire, its tail lashing its sides furiously, and its claws projecting inches from its broad feet. Miss Temple did not or could not move. Her hands were clasped in the attitude of prayer, but her eyes were still drawn to her terrible enemy – her cheeks were blanched to the whiteness of marble, and her lips were slightly separated with horror.

The moment seemed now to have arrived for the fatal termination, and the beautiful figure of Elizabeth was bowing meekly to the stroke, when a rustling of leaves behind seemed rather to mock the organs than to meet her ears.

'Hist! hist!' said a low voice, 'stoop lower, gal; your bonnet hides the creature's head.'

It was rather the yielding of nature than a compliance with this unexpected order, that caused the head of our heroine to sink on her bosom; then she heard the report of the rifle, the whizzing of the bullet, and the enraged cries of the beast, who was rolling over on the earth, biting its own flesh, and tearing the twigs and branches within its reach. At the next instant the form of Natty, the Leatherstocking, rushed by her, and he called aloud:

'Come in, Hector! come in, old fool; 'tis a hard-lived animal, and may jump agin.'

Natty fearlessly maintained his position in front of the females, notwithstanding the violent bounds and threatening aspect of the wounded Panther, which gave several indications of returning strength and ferocity, until his rifle was again loaded, when he stepped up to the enraged animal, and placing the muzzle close to its head, every spark of life was extinguished by the discharge.

The death of her terrible enemy appeared to Elizabeth like a resurrection from her own grave. There was an elasticity in the mind of our heroine that rose to meet the pressure of instant danger, and the more direct it had been, the more her nature had struggled to overcome it. But still she was a woman. Had she been left to herself in her late extremity, she would probably have used her faculties to the utmost, and with discretion, in protecting her person; but, encumbered with her inanimate friend, retreat was a thing not to be attempted. Notwithstanding the fearful aspect of her foe, the eye of Elizabeth had never shrunk from its gaze, and long after the event her thoughts would recur to her passing sensations, and the sweetness of her midnight sleep would be disturbed, as her active fancy conjured, in dreams, the most trifling movement of power.

We shall leave the reader to imagine the restoration of Louisa's senses, and the expressions of gratitude which fell from the young women. The former was effected by a little water, that was brought from one of the thousand springs of the mountains, in the cap of the Leatherstocking; and the latter were uttered with the warmth that might be expected from the character of Elizabeth. Natty received her vehement protestations of gratitude with a simple expression of good-will, and with indulgence for her present excitement, but with a carelessness that showed how little he thought of the service he had rendered.

'Well, well,' he said, 'be it so, gal; let it be so, if you wish it – we'll talk the thing over another time. Come, come – let us get into the road, for you've had terror enough to make you wish yourself in your father's house agin.'

This was uttered as they were proceeding, at a pace that was adapted to the weakness of Louisa, towards the highway; on reaching which the ladies separated from their guide, declaring themselves equal to the remainder of the walk without his assistance, and feeling encouraged by the sight of the village which lay beneath their feet like a picture, with its limpid lake in front, the winding stream along its margin, and its hundred chimneys of whitened bricks.

The reader need not be told the nature of the emotions which two youthful, ingenuous, and well-educated girls would experience at their escape from a death so horrid as the one which had impended over them, while they pursued their way in silence along the track on the side of the mountain; nor how deep were their mental thanks to that Power which had given them their existence, and which had not deserted them in their extremity; neither how often they pressed each other's arms as the assurance of their present safety came, like a healing balm, athwart their troubled spirits, when their thoughts were recurring to the recent moments of horror.

Leatherstocking remained on the hill, gazing after their retiring figures, until they were hidden by a bend in the road, when he whistled in his Dogs, and shouldering his rifle, he returned into the forest.

AN AFRICAN TIGER HUNT

by

SIR PERCY FITZPATRICK

(from *Jock of the Bushveld*, Longmans, Green & Co.)

One day, a pompous old Kaffir chief came to Fitzpatrick's camp; and, after much diplomatic lead-up, announced the reason for his call. It related to a certain Tiger, which is the African name for a Leopard. For permission to reprint this story from *Jock of the Bushveld*, I am indebted to the publishers, Longmans, Green & Company, New York and London.

THERE WAS a Tiger – it was of course the biggest ever seen – which had been preying on the old chief's kraal for the last six months: Dogs, Goats and Kaffir Sheep innumerable had disappeared, even fowls were not despised; and only two days ago, the climax had been reached when, in the cool of the afternoon and in defiance of the yelling herdboy, it had slipped into the herd at the drinking-place and carried off a Calf – a Heifer-calf too! The old man was poor: the Tiger had nearly ruined him; and he had come up to see if we, 'who were great hunters', would come down and kill the thief, or at least lend him a Tiger-trap, as he could not afford to buy one.

In the evening when we returned to camp, we found the old fellow there, and heard the story told with the same patient resignation or stoical indifference with which he had told it to the boys; and, if there was something inscrutable in the smoky eyes that might have hidden a more calculating spirit, it did not trouble us – the Tiger was what we wanted; the chance seemed good enough; and we decided to go. Tigers – as they are almost invariably called, but properly, Leopards – were plentiful enough and were often to be heard at night in the kloofs below; but they are extremely wary animals, and in the inhabited parts rarely move about by day; however, the marauding habits and the audacity of this fellow were full of promise.

The following afternoon we set off with our guns and blankets, a little food for two days, and the Tiger-trap; and by nightfall we had reached the foot of the Berg by paths and ways which you might think only a Baboon could follow.

It was moonlight, and we moved along through the heavily-timbered kloofs in single file, behind the shadowy figure of the shrivelled old chief. His years seemed no handicap to him, as with long easy soft-footed strides, he went on hour after hour. The air was delightfully cool and sweet with the fresh smells of the woods; the damp carpet of moss and dead leaves dulled the sound of more blundering steps; now and again through the thick canopy of evergreens we caught glimpses of the moon; and in odd places the light threw stumps or rocks into quaint relief or turned some tall bare trunk into a ghostly sentinel of the forest.

We had crossed the last of the many mountain streams and reached open ground when the old chief stopped, and pointing to the face of a high krans – black and threatening in the shadow, as it seemed to overhang us – said that somewhere up there was a cave which was the Tiger's home, and it was from this safe refuge that he raided the countryside.

The kraal was not far off. From the top of the spur we could look round, as from the pit of some vast coliseum, and see the huge wall of the Berg towering up above and half enclosing us, the whole arena roofed over by the star-spattered sky. The brilliant moonlight picked out every ridge and hill, deepening the velvet black of the shadowed valleys; and on the rise before us there was the twinkling light of a small fire, and the sound of voices came to us, borne on the still night air, so clearly that words picked out here and there were repeated by our boys with grunting comments and chuckles of amusement.

We started on again down an easy slope passing through some bush, and at the bottom came on level ground thinly covered with big shady trees and scattered undergrowth. As we walked briskly through the flecked and dappled light and shade, we were startled by the sudden and furious rush of Jess and Jock off the path and away into the scrub on the left; and immediately after there was a grunting noise, a crashing and scrambling, and then one sharp clear yelp of pain from one of the Dogs. The old chief ran back behind us, shouting, 'Ingwa, Ingwa!' (Tiger, Tiger). We slipped our rifles round and stood facing front, unable to see anything and not knowing what to expect. There were sounds of some sort in the bush – something like a faint scratching, and something like sobbing grunts, but so indistinct as to be more ominous and disquieting than absolute silence.

'He has killed the Dogs,' the old chief said, in a low voice.

But as he said it there was a rustle in front, and something came out towards us. The guns were up and levelled, instantly, but dropped again when we saw it was a Dog; and Jess came back limping badly and stopping every few paces to shake her head and rub her mouth against her fore-paws. She was in great pain and breathed out faint, barely-audible, whines from time to time.

We waited for minutes, but Jock did not appear; and as the curious sounds still came from the bush we moved forward in open order, very slowly and with infinite caution. As we got closer, scouting each bush and open space, the sounds grew clearer, and suddenly it came to me that it was the noise of a body being dragged and grunting breathing of a Dog. I called sharply to Jock and the sound stopped; and taking a few paces forward then I saw him in a moonlit space turning round and round on the pivot of his hind legs and swinging or dragging something much bigger than himself.

Jim gave a yell and shot past me, plunging his assagai into the object and shouting, 'Porcupine, Porcupine', at the top of his voice. We were all round it in a couple of seconds, but I think the Porcupine was as good as dead even before Jim had stabbed it. Jock was still holding on grimly, tugging with all his might and always with the same movement of swinging it around him, or, of himself circling round it – perhaps that is the fairer description, for the Porcupine was much the heavier.

He had it by the throat where the flesh is bare of quills, and had kept himself out of reach of the terrible spikes by pulling away all the time, just as he had done with the Duiker and other Buck to avoid their hind feet.

This encounter with the Porcupine gave us a better chance of getting the Tiger than we ever expected – too good a chance to be neglected; so we cut the animal up and used the worthless parts to bait the Tiger-trap, having first dragged them across the veld for a good distance each way to leave a blood spoor which would lead the Tiger up to the trap. This, with the quantity of blood spread about in the fight, lying right in the track of his usual prowling, ought to attract his attention, we thought; and we fastened the trap to a big tree, making an avenue of bushes up to the bait so that he would have to walk right over the trap hidden under the dead leaves, in order to get at the bait. We hoped that, if it failed to hold, it would at least wound him badly enough to enable us to follow him up in the morning.

The doctoring of Jess had delayed us considerably; and while we were still busy at it, the old chief came up to say that his scouts had returned and reported that there was no Tiger to be seen, but that they thought the trap had been sprung. They had not liked to go close up, preferring to observe the spot from a tree some way off.

The first question was what to do with Jess. We had no collar or chain, of course, and nothing would induce her to stay behind once Ted started; she would have bitten through ropes and reins in a few minutes, and no kaffir would have faced the job of watching over and checking her. Finally we put her into one of the reed and mud huts, closing the entrance with some raw hides weighted with heavy stones; and off we went.

We found the trap sprung and the bait untouched. The spoor was a Tiger's, right enough, and we saw where it had circled suspiciously all round before finally entering the little fenced approach which we had built to shepherd it on to the trap. There each footprint was clear, and it appeared that instead of cautiously creeping right up to the bait and stepping on the setting-plate, it had made a pounce at the bait from about ten feet away, releasing the trap by knocking the spring or by touching the plate with the barrel of its body. The Tiger had evidently been nipped, but the body was too big for the teeth to close on, and no doubt the spring it gave on feeling the grip underneath set it free with nothing worse than a bad scraping and a tremendous fright. There was plenty of hair and some skin on the teeth of the trap, but very little blood there, and none at all to be found round about.

That was almost the worst result we could have had: the Tiger was not crippled, nor was it wounded enough to enable us to track it, but must have been so thoroughly alarmed that it would certainly be extremely nervous and suspicious of everything now, and would probably avoid the neighbourhood for some time to come.

The trap was clearly of no further use; but after coming so far for the Tiger, we were not disposed to give up the hunt without another effort. The natives told us it was quite useless to follow it up as it was a real 'schelm', and by that time would be miles away in some inaccessible krans. We determined, however, to go on, and if we failed to get a trace of the Tiger, to put in the day hunting Bushbuck or Wild Pig, both of which were fairly plentiful.

We had not gone more than a few hundred yards, when an exclamation from one of the boys made us look round, and we saw Jess on the opposite slope coming along full speed after us with her nose to the trail. She had scratched and bitten her way through the reed and mud wall of the hut, scared the wits out of a couple of boys who had tried to head her off, and raced away after us with a pack of kaffir mongrels yelping unnoticed at her heels. She really did not seem much the worse for her wounds, and was – for her – quite demonstrative in her delight at finding us again.

In any case there was nothing to be done but to let her come, and we went on once more beating up towards the lair in the black krans with the two Dogs in the lead.

The guides led us down into the bed of one of the mountain streams, and following this up we were soon in the woods where the big trees meeting overhead made it dark and cool. It was difficult in that light to see anything clearly at first, and the considerable undergrowth of shrub and creepers and the boulders shed from the Berg added to the difficulty and made progress slow. We moved along as much as possible abreast, five or six yards apart, but were often driven by obstacles into the bed of the stream for short distances in order to make headway at all; and although there did not seem to be much chance of finding the Tiger at home, we crept along cautiously and noiselessly, talking – when we had to – only in whispers.

We were bunched together, preparing to crawl along a rock overhanging a little pool, when the boy in front made a sign and pointed with his assagai to the Dogs. They had crossed the stream and were walking – very slowly and abreast – near the water's edge. The rawest beginners would have needed no explanation. The two stood for a few seconds sniffing at a particular spot, and then both together looked steadily up-stream: there was another pause, and they moved very slowly and carefully forward a yard or so, and sniffed again with their noses almost touching. As they did this, the hair on their backs and shoulders began to rise until, as they reached the head of the pool, they were bristling like Hedgehogs and giving little purring growls.

The guide went over to them while we waited, afraid to move lest the noise of our boots on the stones should betray us. After looking round for a bit, he pointed to a spot on the bank where he had found the fresh spoor of the Tiger, and picking up something there to show to us he came back to our side. It was a little fragment of whitish skin with white hairs on it. There was no doubt about it then; we were on the fresh spoor of the Tiger where it had stopped to drink at the pool and pro-bably to lick the scratches made by the trap; and leaving the bed of the stream it had gone through the thick undergrowth up towards the krans.

We were not more than a hundred yards from the krans then, and the track taken by the Tiger was not at all an inviting one. It was at first merely a narrow tunnel in the undergrowth up the steep hillside, through which we crept in single file with the two Dogs a few yards in front; they moved on in the same silent deliberate way, so intent and strung up that they started slightly and instantly looked up in front at the least sound. As the ascent became steeper and more rocky, the undergrowth thinned and we were able to spread out into line once more, threading our way through several roughly parallel game tracks or natural openings, and stooping low to watch the Dogs and take our cue from them.

We were about fifteen yards from the precipitous face of the krans, and had just worked round a huge boulder into a space fairly free of bush but cumbered with many big rocks and loose stones, when the Dogs stopped and stood quivering and bristling all over, moving their heads slowly about with noses well raised and sniffing persistently. There was something now that interested them more than the spoor: they winded the Tiger itself, but could not tell where. No one stirred: we stood watching the Dogs and snatching glances right and left among the boulders and their shady creeper-hidden caves and recesses; and as we stood thus, grouped together in breathless silence, an electrifying snarling roar came from the krans above, and the spotted body of the Tiger shot like a streak out of the black mouth of a cave and across our front into the bush; there was a series of crashing bounds, as though a stone rolled from the mountain were leaping through the jungle; and then absolute silence.

We explored the den; but there was nothing of interest in it – no remains of food, no old bones, or other signs of cubs. It seemed to be the retreat of a male Tiger – secluded, quiet, and cool. The opening was not visible from any distance, a split-off slab of rock partly hiding it; but when we stood upon the rock platform, we found that almost the whole of the horseshoe bay in the Berg into which we had descended was visible, and it was with a 'Wow!' of surprise and mortification that the kraal boys found they could see the kraal itself and their Goats and Cattle grazing on the slopes and in the valley below.

Tigers do not take their kill to their dens unless there are young cubs to be fed; as a rule, they feed where they kill, or as near to it as safety permits; and when they have fed their fill, they carry off the remainder of the carcase and hide it. Lions, Hyenas, and others leave what they cannot eat and return to it for their next feed; but Tigers are more provident and more cunning, and – being able to climb trees – they are very much more difficult to follow or waylay by means of their kill. They are not big fellows, rarely exceeding seven feet from nose to tip of tail and 130 pounds in weight; but they are extraordinarily active and strong, and it is difficult to believe until one has seen the proof of it that they are able to climb the bare trunk of a tree carrying a kill much bigger and heavier than themselves, and hang it safely wedged in some hidden fork out of reach of any other animal. I have repeatedly seen the remains of their victims in the forks of trees; once it was part of a Pig, but on the other occasions, the remains were of horned animals; the Pig was balanced in the fork; the others were hooked in by the heads and horns.

A well-known hunter once told me an experience of his illustrating the strength and habits of Tigers. He had shot a young Giraffe and carried off as much as he could put on his Horse, and hid the rest; but when he returned next morning it had disappeared, and the spoor of a full-grown Tiger told him why. He followed the drag mark up to the foot of a big tree and found the remains of the carcase, fully 300 pounds in weight, in a fork more than twenty feet from the ground.

He left it there as a bait, and returned again the following morning on the chance of a shot; but the meat had once more been removed, and on following the spoor he found what was left hidden in another tree some two hundred yards away.

It would have been waste of time to follow our Tiger – he would be on the watch and on the move for hours; so we gave it up at once, and struck across the spurs for another part of the big arena where Pig and Bushbuck were known to feed in the mornings. It was slow and difficult work, as the bush was very dense and the ground rough. The place was riddled with game tracks, and we saw spoor of Koodoo and Eland several times, and tracks innumerable of Wild Pig, Rietbuck, Bushbuck, and Duiker. But there was more than spoor; a dozen times we heard the crash of startled animals through the reeds or bush only a few yards away without being able to see a thing.

We had nearly reached the kloof we were aiming for, when we had the good luck to get a Bushbuck in a very unexpected way. We had worked our way out of a particularly dense patch of bush and branches into a corner of the woods, and were resting on the mossy ground in the shade of the big trees when the sound of clattering stones a good way off made us start up again and grab our rifles; and presently we saw, outlined against the band of light which marked the edge of the timber, a Buck charging down towards us. Three of us fired together, and the Buck rolled over within a few yards of where we stood.

We were then in a 'dead end' up against the precipitous face of the Berg where there was no road or path other than game tracks, and where no human being ever went except for the purpose of hunting. We knew there was no one else shooting there, and it puzzled us considerably to think what had scared the Bushbuck; for the animal had certainly been startled and perhaps chased; the pace, the noise it made, and the blind recklessness of its dash, all showed that. The only explanation we could think of was that the Tiger, in making a circuit along the slopes of the Berg to get away from us, must have put the Buck up and driven it down on to us in the woods below; and if that were so, the reports of our rifles must have made him think that he was never going to get rid of us.

We skinned and cut up the Buck and pushed on again; but the roughness of the trail and the various stoppages had delayed us greatly, and we failed to get the expected bag. We got one Rietbuck and a young Boar; the Rietbuck was a dead shot; but the Pig, from the shooting standpoint, was a most humiliating failure. A troop of twenty or thirty started up from under our feet as we came out of the blazing sunlight into the gloom of the woods, and no one could see well enough to aim. They were led by a grand Boar, and the whole lot looked like a troop of charging Lions as they raced by with their bristly manes erect and their tufted tails standing straight up.

As we stood there, crestfallen and disgusted, we heard fresh grunting behind, and turning round we saw one Pig racing past in the open, having apparently missed the troop while wallowing in a mudhole, and known nothing of our intrusion until he heard the shooting. We gave him a regular broadside, and – as is usually the case when you think that quantity will do in place of quality – made an awful mess of it; and before we had time to reload Jess and Jock had cut in, and we could not fire again for fear of hitting them. The boys, wildly delighted by this irregular development which gave them such a chance, joined in the chase and in a few seconds it became a chaotic romp like a Rat hunt in a schoolroom. The Dogs ranged up on each side and were on to the Pig together, Jess hanging on to one ear and Jock at the neck; the Boar dug right and left at them, but his tusks were short and blunt, and if he managed to get at them at all they bore no mark of it afterwards. For about twenty yards they dragged and tugged, and then all three came somersaulting over together. In the scramble, Jock got his grip on the throat, and Jess – rolled and trampled on – appeared between the Pig's hind legs, sliding on her back with her teeth embedded in one of the hams. For half a minute the Boar, grunting and snorting, plunged about madly, trying to get at them or to free himself; and then the boys caught up and riddled him with their assagais.

After the two bombardments of the Pigs and the fearful row made by the boys, there was not much chance of putting up anything more, and we made for the nearest stream in the woods for a feed and a rest before returning to camp.

We had failed to get the Tiger, it is true, and it would be useless giving more time or further thought to him, for in all probability it would be a week or more before he returned to his old hunting-ground and his old marauding tricks; but the Porcupine and the Pig had provided more interest and amusement than much bigger game might have done; and on the whole, although disappointed, we were not dissatisfied: in fact, it would have needed an ungrateful spirit indeed to feel discontented in such surroundings.

Big trees of many kinds and shapes united to make a canopy of leaves overhead through which only occasional shafts of sunlight struck. The cold mountain stream tumbling over ledges, swirling among rocks or rippling over pebble-strewn reaches, gurgled, splashed and bubbled with that wonderful medley of sounds that go to make the lullaby of the brook. The floor of the forest was carpeted with a pile of staghorn moss a foot thick, and maidenhair fern grew everywhere with the luxuriant profusion of weeds in a tropical garden. Traveller's Joy covered whole trees with dense creamy bloom and spread its fragrance everywhere; wild clematis trailed over stumps and fallen branches; quantities of maidenhair overflowed the banks and drooped to the water all along the course of the stream; whilst, marshalled on either side, huddled together on little islands, perched on rocks, and grouped on overhanging ledges, stood the tree-ferns – as though they had come to drink – their wide-reaching, delicate fronds like giant green ostrich feathers waving gently to each breath of air or quivering as the movement of the water shook the trunks.

Long-tailed, greeny-grey Monkeys with black faces peered down at us, moving lightly on their branch trapezes, and pulled faces or chattered their indignant protest against intrusion; in the tops of the wild fig-trees green Pigeons watched us shyly – great big birds of a wonderful green; gorgeous Louries too flashed their colours and raised their crests – pictures of extreme and comical surprise; golden Cuckoos there were also, and beautiful little green-backed ruby-throated Honey-suckers flitted like butterflies among the flowers on the sunlit fringe of the woods.

Now and again Guinea-fowl and Bush-pheasant craned their necks over some fallen log or stone to peer curiously at us; then, stooping low again, darted along their well-worn runs into the thick bush. The place was in fact a natural preserve; a 'bay' let into the wall of the Berg, half-encircled by cliffs which nothing could climb, a little world where the common enemy – man – seldom indeed intruded.

We stayed there until the afternoon sun had passed behind the crest of the Berg above us; and, instead of going back the way we came, skirted along the other arm enclosing the bay to have the cool shade of the mountain with us on our return journey. But the way was rough; the jungle was dense; we were hot and torn and tired; and the shadow of the mountain stretched far out across the foothills by the time the corner was reached. We sat down to rest at last in the open on the long spur on which, a couple of miles away, the slanting sun picked out the red and black Cattle, the white Goats, and the brown huts of the kaffir kraal.

Our route lay along the side of the spur, skirting the rocky backbone and winding between occasional boulders, clumps of trees and bush, and we had moved on only a little way when a loud 'Waugh' from a Baboon on the mountain behind made us stop to look back. The hoarse shout was repeated several times, and each time more loudly and emphatically; it seemed like the warning call of a sentry who had seen us. Moved by curiosity, we turned aside on to the ridge itself, and from the top of a big rock scanned the almost precipitous face opposite. The spur on which we stood was divided from the Berg itself only by a deep but narrow kloof or ravine, and every detail of the mountainside stood out in the clear evening air; but against the many-coloured rocks, the grey figure of a Baboon was not easy to find as long as it remained still, and although from time to time the barking roar was repeated, we were still scanning the opposite hill when one of the boys pointed down the slope immediately below us and called out, 'There, there, Baas!'

The troop of Baboons had evidently been quite close to us – hidden from us only by the little line of rocks – and on getting warning from their sentry on the mountain, had stolen quietly away and were then disappearing into the timbered depth of the ravine. We sat still to watch them come out on the opposite side a few minutes later and clamber up the rocky face, for they are always worth watching; but while we watched, the stillness was broken by an agonized scream – horribly human in its expression of terror – followed by roars, barks, bellows and screams from scores of voices in every key; and the crackle of breaking sticks and the rattle of stones added to the medley of sound as the Baboons raced out of the wood and up the bare rocky slope.

'What is it?' 'What's the matter?' 'There's something after them.' 'Look, look! There they come': burst from one and another of us as we watched the extraordinary scene. The cries from below seemed to waken the whole mountain; great booming 'waughs' came from different places far apart and ever so high up the face of the Berg; each big roar seemed to act like a trumpet-call and bring forth a multitude of others; and the air rang with bewildering shouts and echoes volleying round the kloofs and faces of the Berg. The strange thing was the Baboons did not continue their terrified scramble up the mountain, but, once out of the bush, they turned and rallied. Forming an irregular semicircle they faced downhill, thrusting their heads forward with sudden jerks as though to launch their cries with greater vehemence, and feinting to charge; they showered loose earth, stones and debris of all sorts down with awkward underhand scrapes of their forepaws, and gradually but surely descended to within a dozen yards of the bush's edge.

'Baas, Baas, the Tiger! Look, the Tiger! There, there on the rock below!'

Jim shot the words out in vehement gusts, choky with excitement; and true enough, there the Tiger was. The long spotted body was crouched on a flat rock just below the Baboons; he was broadside to us, with his forequarters slightly raised and his face turned towards the Baboons; with wide opened mouth he snarled savagely at the advancing line, and with right paw raised made threatening dabs in their direction. His left paw pinned down the body of a Baboon.

The voices from the mountain boomed louder and nearer as,

clattering and scrambling down the face, came more and more Baboons: there must have been hundreds of them; the semi-circle grew thicker and blacker. The Tiger raised himself a little more and took swift looks from side to side across the advancing front; and then his nerve went, and with one spring, he shot from the rock into the bush.

There was an instant forward rush of the half-moon, and the rock was covered with roaring Baboons, swarming over their rescued comrade; and a moment later the crowd scrambled up the slope again, taking the Tiger's victim with them. In that seething rabble I could pick out nothing, but all the kaffirs maintained they could see the mauled one dragged along by its arms by two others, much as a child might be helped uphill.

We were still looking excitedly about – trying to make out what the Baboons were doing, watching the others still coming down the Berg, and peering anxiously for a sight of the Tiger – when once more Jim's voice gave us a shock.

'Where are the Dogs?' he asked; and the question turned us cold. If they had gone after the Baboons they were as good as dead already – nothing could save them. Calling was useless: nothing could be heard in the roar and din that the enraged animals still kept up. We watched the other side of the ravine with something more than anxiety, and when Jock's reddish-looking form broke through the bracken near to the Tiger's rock, I felt like shutting my eyes till all was over. We saw him move close under the rock and then disappear. We watched for some seconds – it may have been a minute, but it seemed an enternity – and then, feeling the utter futility of waiting there, jumped off the rock and ran down the slope in the hope that the Dogs would hear us call from there.

From where the slope was steepest, we looked down into the bed of the stream at the bottom of the ravine, and the two Dogs were there: they were moving cautiously down the wide stony watercourse just as we had seen them move in the morning, their noses thrown up and heads turning slowly from side to side. We knew what was coming; there was not time to reach them through the bush below; the cries of the Baboons made calling useless; and the three of us sat down with rifles levelled ready to fire at the first sight. With gun gripped and breath hard held, watching intently every bush and tree and rock, every spot of light and shade, we sat – not daring to move. Then, over the edge of a big rock overlooking the two Dogs, appeared something round; and, smoothly yet swiftly and with a snake-like movement, the long spotted body followed the head and, flattened against the rock, crept stealthily forward until the Tiger looked straight down upon Jess and Jock.

The three rifles cracked like one, and with a howl of rage and pain the Tiger shot out over the Dogs' heads, raced along the stony bed, and suddenly plunging its nose into the ground, pitched over – dead.

It was shot through the heart, and down the ribs on each side were the scraped marks of the trap.

THE SANGAM PANTHER

by

KENNETH ANDERSON

(from *Man-Eaters and Jungle Killers*, George Allen & Unwin)

NEWS FILTERED through to my home in Bangalore that a leopard, or 'panther' as it is more commonly known in India, was killing people in the vicinity of a place called Sangam, a little over seventy miles south of the city.

Man-eating panthers are rare in Southern India. To begin with, the jungles are not so extensive, or nearly so continuously mountainous, as in the north, particularly along the foothills of the vast Himalayan range. The exception is the Western Ghats, which are almost wholly covered with forest for over 400 miles, with an average breadth of ten to fifteen miles. But the other forest areas are of much smaller extent and are more or less surrounded by cultivation. This causes carnivores, and particularly panthers, to confine their attentions to the herds of cattle and goats, in which the country is abundantly rich, and to a lesser extent to the village curs, locally known as 'pie-dogs', which are, like the common monkey, the curse of the land. Prior to the advent of hydrophobia vaccine, large numbers of persons died yearly of infection from the bite of mad dogs, as these curs constantly contract rabies, especially in the hot weather. Monkeys are and always have been a major menace, doing untold damage to crops and fruit trees. The monkey has a strong religious significance to the Indians, and great objection is raised against any attempt to harm it. Panthers – at least so far as the 'pie-dogs' and monkeys are concerned – therefore perform a great service to the land.

In the Western Ghats, of which I have just spoken, the rainfall is very heavy, even exceeding 100 inches per year. They are covered with dense bamboo, long grass, and thick evergreen vegetation – the breeding-grounds of clouds of mosquitoes, ticks, leeches, flies and other animal pests.

Panthers do not like much water – and they detest the pests, in any and all their many forms! So, in the only region where they could multiply unmolested they are hardly to be found! By a natural arrangement, therefore, panthers, which are found in all the other jungles of Southern India, generally have plenty to eat and somehow do not become addicted to the bad habit of man-eating. A notable exception to this was the panther of Gummalapur, a story I have related elsewhere;[1] in that case there were special circumstances that caused it to take to man-eating.

In Bangalore news often reached us of people being mauled by panthers and tigers, more often by the former. But nobody took particular notice of these rumours as on-the-spot investigation always told the same tale. Some villager, with his matchlock, or some inexperienced hunter would let fly at a panther, generally with slugs, and succeed only in hurting it. Then, inexperienced in jungle-lore, he would attempt to follow it up, through lantana bushes or amongst rocks, and get mauled – sometimes severely – for his pains. In years gone by, over seventy-five per cent of such cases of mauling resulted in death from septicaemia. With the advent of the sulpha drugs, casualties dropped to below ten per cent.

So nobody took much notice when such news came in. Why should they? They had other work to do. Moreover, rumour is invariably much exaggerated in India! A slight scratch is magnified into a severe mauling, and a mauling into a killing. When an actual killing does occur, it is widely described in the Press as several killings.

Therefore, when I heard that a panther had killed a woman, and later killed and eaten a child, at Sangam, I did not believe it. Then the panther killed a third, and a fourth time. The Press got hold of the news and it was splashed across the front pages.

Several hunters from Bangalore, Mysore and Madras went

[1] In *Nine Man-Eaters and one Rogue*, George Allen and Unwin, 1954.

after the animal, but for a month the panther did not kill. One of the hunters succeeded in shooting a panther; and this fact, coupled with the cessation of human kills, seemed to indicate that it was the man-eater that had been shot. The hunters returned to the towns.

Then the panther killed once more, but was prevented from eating its victim, a man who was sleeping in a shed-like room with a pack of four mongrel dogs, with which he used to hunt hare and sometimes deer.

A thorn fence protected the entrance to the shed. The roof comprised loose bits of zinc sheeting, and the wall consisted of wooden stakes driven into the ground in close formation, the gaps being stuffed with thorns. The panther came at night, and with its paws contrived to open a passage between the end stake of the doorway, and the thorn fence across the entrance. The dogs panicked, barking and howling loudly and cowering to one side. But the man must have just woken.

The panther entered the shed. The dogs clustered together but did nothing, and the marauder, walking past them, grabbed the man by the throat. He died after uttering a single, piercing wail.

The people in the neighbouring hut had been disturbed by the dogs barking and growling in the shed. They wondered what was happening, but nobody would go outside to investigate. The panther then tried to drag the dead man out of the shed through the same gap by which it had entered. The gap was not big enough. So the panther itself passed through and tried to drag the man after it. But the body became entangled in the thorns and stuck fast. The panther then gave a mighty heave, which succeeded in unbalancing the fence, which fell with a crash on top of the animal. This must have frightened him considerably, for he made off, leaving the corpse still entangled amongst the thorns.

The continued noise resulting from the efforts of the panther now alarmed the people in the next hut, who had been listening breathlessly all this time. They began to shout and woke other villagers. After quite a while, some of the braver men came forth carrying lanterns, armed with matchlocks, bludgeons and staves, to find the dead man, but no panther.

The alarm now spread afresh, and news was brought to me by the village Patel, or headman, who came to Bangalore expressly for the purpose. I was at that time able to take two days' casual leave, while Sunday made a third. So I agreed to go with him and attempt to shoot the panther within those three days.

The road to Sangam ran past the town of Kankanhalli, thirty-six miles from Bangalore, from where it began to descend sharply to the bed of the Cauvery River. The last ten miles of the track was really atrocious, and my Studebaker rocked and creaked and groaned in all its joints, in protest at such bad treatment. Hairpin bends at ridiculous gradients and sharp angles (where all milestones and furlong slabs were coloured black to prevent them from being uprooted by wild elephants, who have a great aversion to anything white), betokened my approach to journey's end, and soon I reached the little Travellers' Bungalow after a short but exceedingly tough journey.

The word 'Sangam' denotes a 'joining' or 'confluence', and was most appropriate, for it marked the junction of the Cauvery River with its tributary, the Arkravarthy, which flows in almost a straight line southwards from its source north of Bangalore.

The Cauvery here flows from west to east, Sangam being on its northern bank within Mysore State territory. The southern bank of the Cauvery comes within the jungles of North Coimbatore District (Kollegal Forest Division). Some thirteen miles east of Sangam, Mysore State territory ends and is flanked by the Salem District, which thereafter holds the northern bank of the river with North Coimbatore District continuing along the southern bank. Both North Coimbatore and Salem Districts belong to the Madras Presidency.

Sangam is a beautifully wooded spot, offering in normal times first-rate mahseer fishing, with crocodile shooting among the sandbanks and rocks in any direction along the river. On the Mysore side of the forest there are spotted deer, sambar, barking-deer, wild pig, feathered game, and an occasional bear, panther or tiger. Elephants often cross over from the Coimbatore bank. Along the southern bank, in the Coimbatore jungles, all the above abound in great numbers, in addition to several fine herds of bison. Elephant and bear are particularly numerous.

After parking the car under the huge muthee trees that flanked the river and grew beside the bungalow, I walked across to the small village where the dog-keeper had recently been killed and inspected the scene for myself, in addition to being given graphic accounts of what had happened by the neighbours, who had heard so much that day, but had done nothing to help the poor fellow. The Patel, who had returned with me, joined in the voluble tale.

With much questioning and cross-questioning, it became apparent that this panther was going to be an exceedingly difficult animal to bag, as on the north bank of the river it had a very wide expanse of jungle to wander over, without taking into consideration those many square miles of forest on the southern or Coimbatore side. But the latter could reasonably be excluded, since panthers, unlike tigers, generally dislike swimming across big rivers, although they swim well when compelled to do so.

The first and apparently only thing to do was to tie out baits. With the Patel's active help, I purchased five large bull-calves. The first of these we tethered about half a mile west of the bungalow and about the same distance from the river bank; the second on a line roughly parallel with the river and a mile farther west; the third a mile farther west than the second; the fourth on the farther bank of the Arkravarthy tributary, about half a mile east of the bungalow and the same distance from the Cauvery; and the fifth a mile east of the fourth bait. Thus the five baits were roughly in a straight line, flanking the river, about half a mile inland and with a distance of four miles between the farthest bait to the west and the farthest bait to the east.

It was sunset before I returned to the bungalow. A cold
dinner appeased my appetite, eaten on the small bungalow
veranda and washed down with two steaming mugs of tea.
After lighting my pipe, I sat with my back to the wall, listening to the subdued rush of the river as it sped along its rocky
bed. It was a dark night and fairly cloudy. Such stars as
could be seen peeping occasionally between clouds would
be insufficient for night-watching, so I went inside and fell
asleep.

Early next morning we checked the baits. They were all alive.
I walked up the road down which I had come the previous day,
climbing up the hairpin bends and ghat section. There were no
panther tracks to be seen. A herd of spotted deer and three
sambar – singly and at different places – had crossed the road
during the night, but no other animals had passed.

When returning to the bungalow, instead of coming back
along the road, I cut down the hill through the jungle and came
on to the dry bed of the Arkravarthy, where I turned southwards and walked in the sand, looking for possible pug-marks.
There were none to be seen, but the same herd of spotted deer
that had crossed the road had also traversed the sands. In due
course, I passed my bait no. 4, and came to where the Arkravarthy joined the Cauvery.

A day and a half, out of the three days at my disposal, had
now passed, and I had not even seen the panther's pug-marks.
The situation seemed hopeless.

After lunch, I decided to walk in an easterly direction, downstream along the Cauvery for about three and a half miles, to a
gorge where the river narrowed to about twenty feet. At this
spot it roared through a chasm, known as Meke-Dat. The
meaning of that word, in the Kanarese language, is 'the goat's
leap'. Legend records that, years and years ago, a jungle-sheep
pursued by wild dogs on the Coimbatore side and driven to the
brink of the river, performed the prodigious feat of leaping
those twenty feet to safety on the Mysore side.

Here, all other sounds are drowned by the roar of the turbulent waters, hurling themselves through the narrow opening,

and a man can hardly hear himself even when he shouts his very loudest.

I sat on the edge of the rocks and watched the troubled, racing river. A hundred yards away, downstream, where the surface had become placid again, an occasional fish broke water, leaping into the air, as if evincing sheer exuberance and the joy of living. A fish-eagle circled in the ethereal blue of a clear sky. After a while, I rose and retraced my steps to the bungalow. I had still not found any panther tracks.

The night was clear. Although there was no moon, there were none of the previous night's clouds and the starlight was enough in the jungle to enable one to see for a few yards.

The watchman in charge of the bungalow owned a 'pie-dog' – the name by which mongrels in India are known – and against my custom and only because time was so short, I asked him to lend it to me till midnight. He hummed and hawed at first, but when three rupees had changed hands he agreed.

While walking along the road that day, I had noticed a rock at its edge hardly a mile away. I took the dog, tied it at the foot of the rock and walked away down the road. When out of sight of the dog, I turned to my right and cut into the jungle, coming back to the rock on its 'off' side. Silently I clambered up, and lay flat on its top. The rock was still warm from the sun that had been shining on it all day.

Thinking it had been abandoned, the dog began barking, whining and howling by turns. Dogs are too intelligent, and it is unfair to tie them out as bait. Unlike cattle and goats, they sense danger at once and, even if not attacked, go through hours of mental agony. I have known a dog which was tied out as bait for a panther, although it was not harmed, become so nervous that it fell sick the following day and died within a week.

I watched from the top of the rock. Nearly an hour passed, and then a shadowy, grey shape came scampering down the road. It moved fast till about ten feet from the dog, then it stopped. Could it be the panther?

The stars shed just enough light to prevent the darkness

from being total, but no more than that. I could just see the grey shape looking at the dog. The dog growled furiously as it turned round to face the intruder. It must be a panther, I thought, as I aligned my rifle in its direction, preparatory to depressing the switch of my torch which was fastened along the barrel.

'*Ha! Ha! Ha! Ha! Ha!*' said the intruder, followed by a disparaging but loud, '*Cheey! Shee-ay! Shee-ay!*'

It was a hyena, the common striped hyena of Southern India. The dog growled still more ferociously; then began to bark frenziedly.

Now began an amusing drama, such as watchers by night are sometimes privileged to witness in a jungle. The hyena darted off the road into the undergrowth, where he began to say, '*Gudda! Guddar! Garrar! Gurr-rr-aa!*' ending with his usual disparaging '*Cheey-ar! Shee-ar!*'

The dog faced the noise and barked loudly. The hyena reappeared on the road, beyond the dog but watching him, and cackled, '*Ha! Ha! Ha! Gudder! Garrar! Shee-ay!*'

Unlike his African cousins – the spotted and the brown hyena, the former being the familiar 'laughing hyena' we have all heard about – the Indian hyena is generally a silent animal, hunting alone or at the most in pairs. Spotted hyenas move in packs. As a rule, all hyenas are cowardly animals, although they are extremely strong for their size and have enormously powerful jaws, which can easily bite through a man's arm, bone and all.

Quite rarely, they display extraordinary courage, of which I once saw an example. I had been sitting over a panther kill. The owner turned up and began to eat. I had held my shot, as I wanted, if possible, to learn the sex of the animal before killing it. This was because I had been told a male and female panther lived in the vicinity, and that the female was accompanied by two cubs about six months old. I wanted to make certain I did not shoot the mother.

While I hesitated, a hyena had arrived on the scene, and his arrival, on that occasion, had been dramatic. He came as if from nowhere, and the first I knew of his arrival was when he had scampered boldly up to the panther, voicing the same medley of sounds I have just described. The panther, sprawled across its kill, had glared at the newcomer with blazing orbs, snarling and growling furiously. The hyena had approached to within five feet, just beyond reach of the panther's paw-sweep, and had set up such a cacophony of hideous sound as to resemble a chorus of the demons of hell.

The panther had added to the noise by growling still louder, and every now and then striking at the hyena with its claws. The latter just rocked backwards, out of reach of each blow, after which it would feint with a short rush forward, while gradually working around to the rear of the panther. At first the panther had turned around correspondingly, to keep the hyena in view, growling even more loudly while making short jabs and slaps with its paws in the direction of the hyena. But the hyena, always out of reach, had haw-ed and sneered, gargled and gurgled with unabated zeal.

Frightened – or perhaps just disgusted – at the unseemly racket, the panther had finally risen from its kill and then walked slowly away with many a backward glance, amidst snarls, at the hyena, who continued his weird din till the panther had vanished in the undergrowth. Then he had fallen upon the kill himself, with the greatest – and, no doubt, thoroughly deserved – enthusiasm.

But the hyena which I continued to watch from the rock was undoubtedly a little scared of the mongrel dog. Frequently he would disappear to one or other side of the road. Then would come a pitter-patter amongst the dried leaves as he doubled back and forth, this way and that, to reappear at all places while continuing to make his unseemly, weird and often comical sounds.

The lesson I learnt from these two experiences was that hyenas try to frighten their opponents with their continuous, unseemly cackle. The first hyena had frightened the panther off its own kill, while this one was trying to frighten the dog, perhaps just to clear it off the road or into the undergrowth, where he could pounce upon it more easily.

But the dog was tied up, and so could not move away, which the hyena could not understand. An hour of this sort of thing ceased to be amusing to me, and I realized the racket, especially the part played by the hyena, was almost certain to drive away any panther in the vicinity, man-eater or otherwise. So, groping for a small piece of rock, I hurled it at the hyena. My aim fell short of its mark, and the stone thudded on the hard surface of the road. The hyena jumped nervously, and scampered into the bushes, while the dog stopped barking and began to whimper. I thought I had rid the scene of a most unwelcome visitor.

Perhaps a quarter of an hour had passed when I heard the furtive pitter-patter again, shortly followed by the hyena's queer notes. The dog barked and growled. I threw another stone at the hyena. He stopped, only to start again after ten minutes. Once more a stone; once more silence, followed by a new beginning. Only after about the fifth stone did the hyena feel that the spot had somehow become unhealthy, and with a final, 'Ah! Ah! Ah! Chee-ay! Shee-ay!' took himself off. It was past ten o'clock.

My watch showed five minutes to midnight when I heard the approach of human voices. A little later, I saw the twinkling lights of two lanterns, illuminating from that distance the walking feet of many men. The dog saw them and stopped its moaning.

When the party drew level with the dog, I counted eleven men, two of whom were carrying lanterns, and all of whom, except one, carried staves and lathis of some sort or another. The one exception was armed with a matchlock. They had obviously come in search of me. I answered their call and came down from the rock.

The men told me that, scarcely an hour earlier, the panther had made its way into one of the huts of the very village where the dog-keeper had been attacked by burrowing through the thatched wall, and had seized one of the five sleeping inmates, a woman about twenty-five years old. She had shrieked aloud as she found herself being dragged away, waking the other four persons in the room, who were her father, two brothers and mother.

Meanwhile, the panther was trying to drag her out through the opening in the thatch, by which it had entered. The girl struggled violently. The panther dropped her and bit her viciously. One of the brothers struck a match to lighten the darkness of the hut's interior. Her father, with commendable bravery and presence of mind, hurled the only missile which came to his hand, at the panther. The missile happened to be a brass water-pot of some weight, and it struck the panther full on its side. Man-eaters, whether tigers or panthers, invariably have a streak of cowardice in their natures and this panther was no exception to the general rule. Leaving its victim, it had dashed out of the hut through the opening in the thatch.

The screams of the mauled woman and the general pandemonium had awakened the whole village. The menfolk came out with lanterns, armed as best they could. The party of eleven had then come to the rest-house to find me, and the watchman from whom I had borrowed the dog had directed them to where I was sitting.

Telling one of the men to untie the rope and bring the dog in tow, we hastened back to the bungalow, and I brought out my first-aid kit from the back seat of the Studebaker. We then hurried on to the village, where an appalling sight awaited me. The poor girl had been bitten right through her right shoulder, and again in the abdomen, where the panther had seized her the second time when she had struggled to escape. One breast and her chest right down to the side were in ribbons where the foul claws had buried themselves deep in her flesh, raking it open with their downward sweep. Her jacket and sari were torn to pieces, and she lay in a welter of blood, blissfully unconscious after her experience.

I saw at once that such meagre first-aid equipment as I had was totally inadequate to meet the situation, but we quickly washed the wounds with a strong solution of potassium permanganate and roughly bandaged her chest and abdomen with strips torn from another sari. Her father, two brothers, and three willing men from the village then carried her on a rope-cot to the Studebaker. Placing her as comfortably as possible in the 'dickie', I took her three male relations aboard and set out for the town of Kankanhalli, which boasted the nearest village hospital. We reached there after three-thirty in the morning, when I awoke the doctor and handed over the injured woman. Her condition appeared to be very low, owing to the great deal of blood she had lost.

By four-thirty, I was in the bathroom of the Travellers' Bungalow at Kankanhalli, where I removed my blood-soaked clothing and took a cold bath. I had no change of clothing with me, having left them behind at Sangam in the confusion of the moment. So I borrowed a clean dhoti and a blanket from the bungalow-waiter.

Dawn was breaking when I knocked at the Post Office, awoke a most obliging Postmaster from his sleep, paid the necessary late fee and dispatched an urgent telegram to Bangalore requesting extension of leave for four more days.

When I returned to the bungalow I found the younger brother of the injured woman awaiting me in tears. He had come from the hospital to tell me his sister had just died. Shortly afterwards, the father came to ask me to take his daughter's body back in the car to Sangam for cremation by the banks of the River Cauvery, in which the ashes would eventually be scattered. It was a request I could not refuse. The bungalow servant told me he wanted his dhoti and blanket back. So I had to dress again in my blood-smeared clothes.

We drove back to the hospital, placed the still, limp body of the girl in the back seat, and set out on the return journey to Sangam, delayed by two hours at the Police Station, where we reported the occurrence.

After a bath in a quiet pool beside the river, free from crocodiles, a change into fresh clothing, a cold lunch and two big mugs of tea, I lay back in a rickety old armchair to review the situation. My loaded pipe, from which the comforting smoke arose in spirals to the roughly-tiled low roof, helped a great deal to soothe my ragged nerves after the events of the previous night and to prevent my eyes from closing with sleep.

What should I do with the remaining four days and five nights at my disposal, to rid these poor village-folk from another, and God only knew how many more repetitions of these terrible events. Facts appeared to indicate that: (1) the panther would not take animal baits, (2) it had a wide range of cover, and (3) it was predisposed to dragging people out of huts. Then, while I pondered, I fell asleep.

At 3 pm I awoke and a possible line of action appeared to have presented itself while I slept. It was this:

The small village of Sangam, with about a dozen huts, had been constructed in the usual fashion, on both sides of a central lane. I remembered that on the southern side of this lane, and not far from the river bank, a small herd of cattle belonging to the villagers were corralled in a common enclosure, surrounded by a fence of bamboo, intersticed with cut lantana brambles. The only dogs left in the village, which had belonged to the man who had been killed, were enclosed in the shed-like room where he had been slain, which room happened to adjoin the larger cattle enclosure on its western side. The idea came to me that, if I posted myself at night in the midst of the cattle, not only would I be perfectly safe from unexpected attack, as the cattle would grow restive and give ample warning should the panther approach, but this very restlessness, and the fact that the dogs too would join in the alarm, would help me to learn of the panther's presence, should he enter the village. Meanwhile, I would keep my five live-baits tied out on the off chance that one of them might be taken instead.

With this plan in view, I dressed warmly for the night, wearing a khaki woollen 'balaclava' cap to keep off the dew. My usual night equipment included, this time, a large flask of tea, some biscuits, and my pipe, as I knew that smoking, in this case, would do no harm.

Because of the panther's presence, the villagers were inside their huts, behind doors barricaded and reinforced with freshly-cut thorns, long before six o'clock. I took up my position in the middle of the cattle enclosure. About me was a space of about fifty yards in every direction, with nearly a hundred nondescript cattle scattered around.

At first the animals resented my presence and crowded to the corners away from me, leaving me isolated in the centre of the pen. I started trying to make friends with them. One kicked over my flask of tea and nearly broke it! Moreover, some of the bulls were rather truculent and made short jabs at me with their horns if I came too close. After an hour in each other's company, the situation eased a little, and I was able to make my way guardedly to the centre of the herd, about half of whom were now resting on the ground. I got down also.

As the hours dragged by the silence was unbroken, except for an occasional snort from one of the animals, or the trampling of another as it altered its position. One cow became friendly and insisted in nuzzling her muzzle against my chest as a gesture of companionship. Eventually she flopped down contentedly on the ground beside me.

Then cattle ticks began to bite me, in many places and mercilessly. I scratched myself vigorously, although I knew that by doing so I would only increase the irritation. It grew colder, and soon I was glad to nuzzle myself, in my turn, up against the warm body of the cow who had chosen to open this strange friendship with me. Now and again, one of the herd would 'moo' contentedly, or snort, or flop down to the ground, or struggle to its feet.

The hours still dragged by, and the ticks continued to bite. At one o'clock a sambar belled on the small hill to the north of the village. It was a doe that had called, and she called again and again. Then her call was taken up by a kakar, whose hoarse bark resounded across the nullahs which furrowed the lower slopes of the hillock.

The sambar doe had stopped belling by this time, while the kakar climbed up, giving occasional vent to his guttural call. Whatever it was that had alarmed them had come down the hill.

Some twenty minutes later spotted deer began their warning cries, answering one another from the jungle that slopes from the base of the hill to the edge of the river. Either a tiger or a panther was afoot, and the next few minutes would tell whether the carnivore was just a normal animal or the marauder I was awaiting.

It was almost pitch-dark when the cattle grew restless. With one accord, those lying on the ground scrambled to their feet, and I did the same, keeping close beside the friendly cow. Some of the bulls snorted, and the herd were all turned towards the lane that divided the small village and passed by the thorn hedge that bordered the cattle stockade.

The animals became very restless and began to gather in a mass at the farther end of the stockade, away from the hedge and lane. The four dogs in the neighbouring shed had been barking furiously; they now began to whimper. Whatever had frightened them was passing down the lane at that very moment.

I had got myself wedged in the midst of the cattle and had to watch carefully against being impaled on one of the many horns that were nervously tossing about me. I began to force myself through the herd to reach their front rank, hoping that I might be able to see something, but the darkness and the hedge revealed nothing.

I could hear the dogs howling and whimpering in the shed in which they were locked. My ears were attuned to catch the slightest sound, but the noise made by the cattle and the dogs gave me little chance. Some minutes later, I caught the faintest of scratching noises. Listening carefully I located it as coming from farther down the lane. They became louder and more impatient. Then I realized that the panther was scratching at a door of one of the huts some distance away.

Breaking through the remainder of the cattle, I approached the fence on tiptoe, hoping to be able to peep over it and catch a glimpse of the panther when I switched on the torch at the end of my rifle. The inmates of the hut at which the panther was scratching chose that very moment to set up a bedlam of shrieks and shouts; the silence was broken by the most frightful din.

Thinking that the man-eater had succeeded in forcing his way into the hut, I threw discretion to the winds and rushed for the bamboo-and-thorn door that formed the entrance of the stockade. At dusk I had firmly wedged a huge Y-shaped log into place, and it took some precious moments to release its base from the big stones against which I had jammed it.

Dragging it aside and switching on the torch, I heaved the clumsy door back and stepped into the lane. Nothing was to be seen in any direction.

Keeping my back to the thorn fence to guard against attack from the rear, I shone the beam in all directions, but I still saw nothing. The panther had disappeared into thin air. Meanwhile the shrieks and shouts continued unabated.

Then it occurred to me that perhaps the panther was inside the hut all this time, mauling and killing the inmates, and with this alarming thought in mind I began carefully to cover the intervening twenty yards.

When I came abreast of the entrance, I found it was shut fast. I called out to the inmates. At first, due to the noise they were making, they could not hear me. Then I called again, louder and many times. Then the hubbub gradually subsided.

I shouted to the occupants to open the door. They would not do so. Then a tremulous voice from inside asked whether I was a man or devil. I called back that it was I, and that the panther had gone. The voice replied that the inmates would open the door only when morning came. Meanwhile, my torch beam clearly showed the fresh claw-marks on the door of the hut, where the panther had just tried to effect an entrance.

I returned to the stockade, reclosed the door, replaced the Y-shaped log and the stones and went back to the spot where I had been lying against the ¦cow when the alarm ¦had begun.

To my horror, I found that the milling feet of the herd had smashed my thermos and it was now impossible to drink the hot tea for which I longed. My biscuits also had been devoured, and as I watched her ruefully, the friendly cow devoured the last of the paper in which they had been wrapped. Fortunately, I had kept my pipe and tobacco in my pocket, and with this I spent the rest of the night in comparative comfort, once again nestling against the side of the cow.

I returned to the bungalow at dawn, tired and disappointed. Worst of all, my body was a mass of tick-bites and itched abominably. Further, I knew only too well that each bite would fester during the coming ten days, and that I was in for a most uncomfortable time.

A cold bath and change, followed by hot tea, tinned bacon and bread and butter helped to ease my gloom, and by 7.30 am I was asleep. I awoke for a lunch at midday, and slept again till 3 pm. Then I got up and began to work out another plan.

It would be impossible to sit with the cattle again, for if I was to get bitten once more by as many ticks as in the previous night, I might end with a dose of tick fever. Yet it was undeniable that both the cattle and the dogs had helped admirably in giving me the alarm when the panther had passed down the lane.

At last I had a fresh idea, that appeared to be the only compromise in the situation. The roof of the dog-shed consisted of scraps of zinc sheeting. I decided that I would lie on that roof, suitably camouflaged and overlooking the lane, so that I should be able to shoot the panther if it walked down the lane again. The cattle and the dogs would still help me by giving the alarm. I could protect my rear and both flanks by heaping stacks of cut thorns on to the roof. Any heavy body, like the panther, that leapt upon the zinc roof would necessarily give its presence away by the noise that would follow. Not only did this appear to be the only solution, but actually a good solution of the problem.

So I hurried towards the village, carrying my night-kit, biscuits and tea (poured into an empty beer bottle, borrowed from the bungalow watchman). After telling the villagers of my new plan, willing hands soon stacked piles of cut thorn branches on to the zinc roof of the dog-shed in the form of a square. Others brought dried straw, which they placed on the roof within the square of thorns for me to lie on.

At 6 pm I took up my position. There were two disadvantages that almost immediately began to show themselves: the first, that having to face the lane all the time, I would have to lie so that my legs would be slightly higher than my head, for the zinc roof sloped slightly downwards from back to front, to allow rain-water to flow off easily; the second, that I would have to remain lying on my stomach for most of the time, since my slightest movement sounded distinctly on the zinc roof. But the advantages were that I was safe from surprise attack from the rear; that I had a clear and unobstructed view of the lane and could hear distinctly, particularly if the cattle or the dogs became uneasy; lastly, that I was away from those awful ticks.

But that night was a peaceful one, without any indication whatever that the panther had come within two or three miles of the village. Back at the bungalow next morning I had another bath, and another daylong sleep. Each day I had had my five live-baits checked by a group of men, but none of these beasts had been harmed.

That night I took up position on the roof once more. It was past 2 am, and there had been no alarms from the surrounding jungle, and I felt very drowsy. Suddenly, as in a dream, I heard the cattle begin to stir restlessly. One of the four dogs in the shed beneath me growled. Then all four of them began to bark or howl together.

Peering forward slowly, I began to scan the village lane in both directions. Starlight was not good at that moment, only enough to prevent the night from being obscure. The lane to right and left appeared as a faint blur and of a slightly lighter shade than the surroundings. I could hear nothing and see nothing.

Then I caught the faintest of sounds. It appeared to be a hiss such as a cobra might make. Yes, there it was again! And it came from in front and directly below me. Was it the hiss of a snake or the faint noise a panther makes when he curls back the skin of his upper lip?

I peered downwards and at first could see nothing. Seconds later a faint elongated shape registered itself on my vision in that difficult light, a smudge of infinitesimally lighter shade than the surrounding blur of the lane. I stared at it, and thought I saw it move. The hiss was repeated more distinctly this time. It appeared to come from this lighter smudge. The dogs inside the shed below me now started to whine and whimper. The cattle were very restless.

I realized that I could not point my rifle downwards from where I lay. I would have to move forward another foot per-haps, till my head and shoulders completely cleared the edge of the zinc sheet on which I was lying. I began to do this, but despite my utmost care, the straw rustled and the zinc creaked faintly.

There came an ominous growl from that lightish smudge, and I knew that I was discovered and that within the next few seconds the panther would probably jump on to the zinc roof – and on to me.

Kicking myself forward the remaining six inches, I lowered the rifle over the side of the roof and depressed the torch-switch. Two gleaming orbs reflected the light from a spotted body, crouched for the spring. Only a single shot was required at that point-blank range and the spark of life slowly faded from those gleaming orbs: from fiery white they became a dull orange, then a faint green, then an empty glimmer, and finally a purplish blue as the light was reflected back by the now lifeless retina.

It was an old female that I saw next morning, with canine teeth worn down almost to their stubs. Her coat was extremely pale; even the rosettes were ill-formed and dull. Her claws were blunt and worn. There appeared to be no other signs of deformity of any sort about her, or indication of an earlier wound. It seemed that only old age, and the prospect of gradual starvation through her physical incapacity to kill animals, had

caused the Sangam panther to make war on the human race –
a war which, however ghastly and fearsome while it lasts, invariably ends in the death of the feline. Modern firearms and
the human intellect are heavy odds against the jungle instinct,
cunning, and the pangs of hunger.

A BROWN OWL

by

H. M. TOMLINSON

(from *Out of Soundings*, by permission of Messrs A. P. Watt)

ONE NIGHT, the night of my arrival home after a long absence,
I was introduced to Joey. It was the first time I had ever
looked straight at a large owl, desiring friendship, but wondering whether or not I was going to get it. That owl, sitting on
the table, was not a bird. I should call it a gnome. The other
members of the family sat round, and laughed. They knew the
creature. Evidently he was on intimate terms with them,
though there was no laughter in his direct and impish stare at
me. His flat face, with its enlarged and challenging eyes, was
odd. He stared at me briefly, then turned his head away wearily,
as if he had seen all he wanted. I was dismissed. He began
larking with those he knew. He walked about with a jaunty
and rolling gait, like a sailor who knows what he is expected to
do to make people happy. He made them happy. His conduct,
in a guise of the utmost gravity, was ridiculous. Presently I
tried to join the party. He gave me another stare, and its meaning was plain: You still here? Without warning he flew at me,
his grappling hooks in front of him. I drew back, to more
laughter; for it appeared that this was his fun.

Joey's plumage is beautiful, though at first you might not
notice it. The beauty of a shadow, with its tones, needs more
than a careless glance. This soft swarthiness has regular mark-
ings of hazel and buff. When he sits within a greater shadow, his
eyes may blaze like orange glow-lamps. Now that he and I
know each other he will sit on the back of a chair near me, when
I am writing. He shakes his feathers loose, half closes his eyes,
and at times makes a contented noise, if spoken to. Or he will
come to one's shoulder to sit there, occasionally nibbling round

D

one's ear with his sickle-like beak. But there is no need to worry
about that. He knows what his beak can do, but he is a perfect
gentleman. His claws can close like a vice, but not on us. It is
certain that a bird cannot be a Christian, but the simple truth is
that Joey is more like the real thing than most of us try to be.
If you offend his dignity certainly he resents it, but he never
retaliates, and he never harbours resentment. He is magnani-
mous without knowing what that means.

In fact, I think I would sooner write about that owl than
about ships or anything else that I may happen to understand
in a small measure. He fascinates me because, beyond Freud
or Jung, he appears to hint that life is a riddle which we had
better give up. No good even dreaming about it. Besides, like
the Sphinx, he gives no help, but merely sits looking to
futurity with those awful eyes of his.

We have been told W. H. Hudson was afflicted by letters
from numerous correspondents who were moved, not so much
by the order of his prose, as by the inexplicable behaviour of
their pets. They supposed that Hudson could guess hidden
springs, not mentioned in the manuals, which actuated most
animals. Their faith in Hudson's gift of insight is not surprising. I myself once interrupted his meditations with just
such a problem; but he was a sceptical man, who well knew
the poverty of common observation, and the vanity of human
desire which so readily recognizes what naturally it prefers to
believe is there. Hudson always coldly directed reason on those
pets, and reason is not invariably fair to poor instinct. Yet what
he himself could make of the twitching ears of a deer we learned
from his enchanted *Hind in Richmond Park*. Let us not marvel
over the magic carpet. That would be Axminster, or what not,
compared with those ears. They got Hudson to South America
and elsewhere, they reminded him of music he had heard as a
boy, of inexplicable premonitions he had felt as a man; indeed,
those ears persuaded a reader, who watched their nervousness
with Hudson's eyes, to believe that their extraordinary movements would presently waft apart the black curtain which
hangs between this world and whatever may be on the hither

side of it. That is fairly remarkable for a deer in Richmond Park.

We enjoy good stories about animals, but we rarely believe them unless they are our own. Luckily, there is no need to believe a good story before we enjoy it. Those yarns by our neighbours who would have us believe that good morality, noble conduct, subtle intelligence, which are our prerogatives, are at least nascent in humble creatures, are very pleasant, and that is as much as we ought to expect of them. We doubtless conceded more to animals, for reasons we forgot long ago, while we still used totems, than we do now, when natural history is the lesson most enjoyed in the elementary schools of the cities. We knew more about animals before we stuffed them for museums, and even before we had a settled Government. The settled Government it was, perhaps, that settled it. Our fear of the wilderness diminished. It was no longer necessary for us to watch the outside dark in apprehension when we had quite forgotten what could come out of it. It may not be of much importance that we have grown deaf and blind to the finer communications from the night, for we get along very well without them now we have our wireless installations. But there, anyhow, the communications are for such as Hudson, and for primitives who still live beside the wild, and even in it, and who may neglect its signs at their peril. It gave me a chill once when I spoke at night innocently, but without restraint, of Rimau, the tiger, to some forest Malays, and saw the embarrassment caused by my careless ignorance. They did not like it. His name may not be mentioned. I but wanted some information, yet it was certain then that they knew more than they were going to give.

Since then I have enjoyed the good fortune of a close friendship with this fellow Joey, who is but a Wood, or English Brown Owl. I do not propose to tell any tall stories about him, because as there are not any I should have to make them up; nor to pursue, biologically, the problems of memory, joy, love, sorrow, fear, and so on, to their remote physiological springs in a bird, for I am ignorant of the way. I could not put that

owl's mind, should it exist, under the microscope. But at least
he has caused me to put my own there for a brief examination,
with what result I need not confess. After all, ignorance, like
everything else, is relative. It is possible that our confidence in
our scientific understanding of this broad matter of life cannot
be fully justified. Joey is a warning. My assurance fails me
under that inscrutable contemplation of his; which is beautiful
to see, though there is an element of terror in it, if you dare his
glance long enough. It occurs to me, while observing him, that
there may be a ridiculous side to our science, when we are explaining what we know of these lower creatures; creatures
quite incapable of forming a systematic and orderly government. An orderly government? We had better be careful,
because even with our unique gifts, by which we form complex
communities, we should ponder afresh in the neighbourhood
of an anthill or a beehive.

As for this bird Joey, we have examined diligently all the
evidence about the Brown Owl in the ornithological text books;
but I must say that, except for his coloration, and his language
– or some of it – and the length of his primaries, and his weight
and dimensions, he is still outside those books. He sits above
and beyond, beautifully meditative, quietly interested in our
strange behaviour, not altogether unwilling to assist us in the
careful measuring of his primaries – for we grow more and
more concerned with the need to establish beyond cavil his
ordinary owlship; but he is outside. He is beyond us. If he
knows no more of us than we know of him then he knows very
little.

We at home have seen in him the reason why the ancients
chose him as the symbol of learning and wisdom. The reason is
obvious enough. It is not because his eyes are deep with
shadows, and are better to look at than most eyes; they certainly give, in repose, a hint of mild but unusual wisdom. But
they seem to tell him, without fail, all he wants to know about
anything which takes his interest, and his interest is constant
and alert. He has an inspection which begins with an instant
and piercing glance, while his body is motionless, and thus he

may remain for a full minute, meditating whatever it may be, with a stern fixity which would draw out the innermost secret of a diplomatic note. Satisfied at last that it is worthless, he turns his head with an expression of tedium, and the object is thus contemptuously dismissed. But that first challenging glance, that night stare of his, though I am used to it, and know that Joey is incapable of treachery, is still somewhat startling when he fixes it on me. You feel like a sinner whose very thoughts are manifest. He sees through you; and thereupon he relaxes, puffs his feathers, and languidly half closes with bluish veils those dark and luminous orbs. But let anything stir in the shadows – I think he can hear a shadow move – and he becomes as tense as a taut spring, and his eyes are judgement itself.

When he sees a matter quite novel to him he has a curious habit of moving his face in a circle; and if the object really astonishes him, as when he saw his first aeroplane, then his whole body sways to enlarge the radius of the circle. It is a comic spectacle of eager curiosity, altogether different from his still glance of doom when a mouse is present though unperceived by our crude senses. I used to think that rotary performance of his head was a foolishness of his till once I caught myself shifting my head about to get a name to something nondescript on the floor which glinted in the lamplight. So now I know that when Joey plays that caper he is but obtaining evidence of an object from different angles; he is trying to give it solidity. He could teach any young writer a point or two at that game.

That he reasons things out there can be no doubt. I should rate his intelligence as high as that of a good cat, and his manners and morality much higher. He has a sense of fun. He is very good natured. Even when badly irritated he never strikes with his full force, but appears to remember in his extreme annoyance just how far his sickle beak may be struck into a hand without drawing blood. Yet it can execute a rat with a single swift puncture through the skull between the ears. The rat has no chance at all. Joey looks very satisfied with himself when he has nailed so big a victim, and evidently expects that we will admire him. He lifts his flat intelligent face to us with a new expression of languid and fatuous good humour; but one foot has the rat's middle in a vice of steel; it would be useless for the unlucky creature to struggle, and it does not. But Joey, I must say, shows no cruel enjoyment, as would a cat, in fooling with his prey. He stoops down and very early dispatches it.

He has never yet shown anger, but only a kind of fierce resentment, which he expresses with a sound which mixes a whistle and a warble, in a high key, his wings outspread and his head held low. And he will do what most cats will not. If he is out after dark, and you call quietly his name into the night, then presently a great noiseless shadow sweeps swiftly at you; and you may be used to him, but control is necessary or you will dodge; and so he alights on your shoulder, nibbles your ear in salutation, and questions you in friendly little undertones. It is amusing to watch a strange cat in its prowl come upon Joey where he is hunched in deep thought on the garden border. The cat sees at once that this is a bird. So near, too. A bird? What a bird! The cat's mingling of desire and fear is plain in its attitude. It would attack, but dare not. Joey does not move, but looks at the trespasser as a constable would at a loafer. The cat slinks off, Joey's haughty glance following it.

One curious trick he has, which, so far as I know, the natural history books do not record; perhaps because, in the wild, the trick is invariably successful. It is not always easy, by daylight, to pick him out of the shadows of a tree, even when you know he is somewhere there. But if a noisy stranger comes into the garden that owl instantly understudies a dead stump. He elongates stiffly and shuts his eyes; he might be aware that it is his eyes you see first, when looking for him. When he has become a stump of dead wood then he is nothing but that. You may even push him, but he does not relax, nor open his eyes. He is a stump. There is no owl.

He is fond of a bit of fun, but only after dark. Like a cat, he will pounce on small moving objects. Suppose that you secrete a matchbox, tied to a length of string, under the table-cloth, Joey will spy its first effort to get slyly away. However, he looks elsewhere. He pretends that he has been unobservant. He looks everywhere but at the suspicious movement. Then, with his odd walk, that curious rolling gait, like that of a stout and light-hearted seaman, he strides not directly towards the movement, but only obliquely, as though he had just thought of something more important than play. Yet as soon as he is beside the object he is on it so quickly with his talons that there is no getting used to his suddenness. We used to play this game by moving our hands under the table-cloth. Now we prefer a matchbox and string.

There was a time when we thought he had had enough of us, and was about to choose a home in alien trees. But he remains, and he seems to have lost his desire for the wild. He keeps close to the household. He seems to prefer to stay within sight of the place he knows; for he is a sociable creature, and at times comes to the window to intimate that he wishes to sit, for a spell, within the family circle. When admitted he becomes maudlin with his demonstrations of affection, though never servile, like a dog. He stands no nonsense even when most maudlin. It should be added that he was found, two years ago, an orphaned fledgling. He would have died of starvation but that a youth of the house, who had a way of his own with animals, got a blow-pipe, filled his mouth with milk, and blew it into Joey. The dodge worked. Joey has never forgotten, by the look of it, the one who gave that first kindly attention with a blow-pipe. For the youth has gone overseas, and now Joey sits humped and not at all playful, contemplative, friendly, but by no means inclined to accept me as a substitute for his companion. His particular friend used to be the first to greet him in the morning. Joey came eagerly to the opening of the door. He comes eagerly now, but it is odd to see his sudden relapse into indifference, when the familiar sound of that opening door is no longer followed by a sight of the one he most favoured. I thought, once upon a time, that I would like to try my hand at a novel; but that blessed owl is a salutary warning. I know next to nothing even about him, and his share of life's mystery does not amount to much.

There was a memorable occasion when we were visited by Thomas Hardy. I believe that great man had a special regard for owls; the author of *The Dynasts*, we may fairly suppose, would know why the owl is Athene's familiar. In any case, the venerable poet and Joey unexpectedly confronted each other. It was a strange experience for the rest of us, who stood and watched them. They did not speak; they regarded each other intently, but I do not know what passed between them. Presently the poet turned sadly away; and the owl directed his gaze elsewhere as though entirely satisfied.

*

I had written all that, and I think I had an intention to continue it, perhaps as an attempt at a purely ornithological study. But a day came when Joey's young friend returned from overseas. Joey looked at him, and understood, but did not move. He was not demonstrative, but he began to watch for the coming and going of his old friend. He regained his humorous spirit. Then, with surprising suddenness, he deprived me of my one chance to contribute to ornithology. We stood round him one morning while he stared at us from the ground; he was on his back, and that had never happened before. He stared at us with what appeared to be bright and haughty knowledge. His young friend, so recently returned, knelt to lift his head. The brown owl nibbled his fingers in greeting. Then he shut his eyes and returned to Athene.

THE VULGAR ASSASSIN

by

ROBERT C. RUARK

ON THE premise that even a wart-hog thinks another wart-hog is pretty, if the moon is right and the sex divergent, and that the hyena in full voice adds glamour to the night scene of Africa, even the most unattractive animal seems to have something to recommend it. And actually the wart-hog is almost beautiful in its extreme ugliness, while the hyena excites a certain pity with his dog's head, bear's body, and crippled hind end.

But up to now I have failed to find anyone with a kind word for the crocodile, including the Romans who named him *Crocodilis vulgaris*. Even the people who kill him for his hide hate him and the work that translates him into a lady's handbag or a pair of sporty pumps. Certainly there is no imagination sufficiently elastic to conceive of the croc as worthy of sporting attention, unless one fishes for him in a manner I'll describe later. He is indeed so utterly awful as an adult that he has no close confidants, possibly because of a halitosis so overpowering that even his best enemy wouldn't come close enough to tell him. This halitosis I can vouch for, since I once propped a croc's mouth open for a picture and nearly fainted from the rush of stinking breath from his cargo of putrid meat.

A fact like that is obvious, but in reality nobody really knows the definitive truth about the crocodile. A lot of arrant nonsense has been written about him, a flock of exaggerations have been set down as gospel about his size and habits, gustatory and otherwise, and he has become legendary to most of the native tribes who live in constant fear of him.

You can call a croc stealthy, cruel, frightening, wicked, awful, powerful, canny, deceitful, omnivorous, intelligent, amphibious, slimy, determined, reasonable, unreasoning menacing, hungry, cowardly, brave, cannibalistic, dentally miraculous (as soon as he loses one tooth another replaces it), quiet, noisy, and enigmatic. And you may always refer to 'crocodile tears' when spurious sympathy is demonstrated by the banker just before he forecloses the mortgage.

Beyond this it is difficult to generalize, except that there is no such thing as a sympathetic croc, a charitable croc, a lovable croc, a pretty croc, a kind croc, or a cute croc. The crocodile is an individual, a callous criminal, and surprisingly little is accurately known about his breeding, length of life, and family habits. It is still not generally believed by scientists that he can, and does, hibernate under water – in one instance may have lived in hibernation for as much as eighteen months.

I have heard story after story about crocodiles nipping off an arm or a leg, as a shark might shear off a member. This is *not* so. If a man lost an arm or a leg to a crocodile, it would be because he was tied or chained to a stone or a tree the croc couldn't haul into the water, together with the man; then the limb would be pulled out of the body. No man is powerful enough to cling to a tree or a rock and thereby lose a leg when the croc sets his teeth and yanks.

The truth is that old Mamba can neither chew nor properly bite. He has a rudimentary tongue that is fastened securely to his lower jaw, so what he ingests must be swallowed whole. His lower jaw is immovable, and the upper lifts like a man-hole cover with spikes in it. He can maul but he can't munch. This is why he stores his food in muddy underwater caverns until it is rotten enough to be torn into edible bits. And this is why the flesh he consumes is generally so foul (unless it's a small fish or animal or child) that his breath is worse than any hyena's.

The vast rows of teeth are awe-inspiring; if they worked together as cutting agents a grown crocodile could snap a cow in two. But they perform only as the jaws of a steel trap, to clamp and hold. The teeth fasten on to the prey and lock; the croc has a lower fang that grows straight up at the end of his lower jaw and fits into a hole in his snout tip, effectively locking the jaws. (Note to Ed.: I have hand-operated this business, using a just-shot croc, and if bonuses ever are given for research, I qualify.)

The *mamba* kills by vicing on to his prey and dragging it into water, where he sinks to the bottom and drowns his victim. The variety of victims is almost limitless. It certainly could include a young elephant – although I have no eyewitness accounts to offer – since the trunk of a drinking elephant would make a tempting target. But there are several documented cases of crocodiles drowning full-grown African buffalo, and on the Tana River, in Northern Kenya, a crocodile dragged a mature rhino into the drink. Certainly a fearful toll is exacted among young hippo, and any ordinary animal that comes to the water's edge is a fair prospect.

As an offensive weapon, the heavy, sharp-horned tail – as big at its base as the body – is a vicious flail, comparable in use to the elephant's thick trunk as a fighting tool. A flirt of this spined extension is enough to break the legs of an ordinary animal on land. Waterborne, the croc uses it with tremendous efficiency against native canoes. He will charge a dugout, swim by close alongside, swerve, and knock the boat galley-west with a swish of that tail, which approximates a limber, pointed, jagged, iron train rail used as a quirt.

I'm not acquainted with the mechanism that submerges the crocodile. This I know from first hand: a croc shot dead in the water will sink and remain on the bottom for several days, rising finally to wash ashore. A mortally wounded croc will not choose to die in the water. After several hours he will swim in, haul himself ashore on the shingle, and expire there. Of the scores of crocs shot on Lake Rudolf in recent years, the mortally wounded have a way of turning up next morning to die on their favourite lee shore.

My friend Harry Selby, the professional hunter who runs a fishing camp at Rudolf, and I were croc shooting one day a year or so ago at a favourite sunning site of the saurians on Molo Island, down the beach a piece from a small fishing village of the decimated Molo tribe. A small mountain tops the beach, and we stalked over the lava cobbles – if you can imagine some cobbles as big as houses – to the summit. There was one big croc lying below on the shale in a line of his snoozing relatives, which looked like dirty driftwood. Selby made a long shot with a .243, a remarkably flat little rifle, and dotted the big chap beneath the eye bumps.

'I think that got him,' Selby said, 'but I'll give him the other half.'

The croc moved just as Selby fired again, the distance being downhill and about three hundred yards on the flat. The bullet struck too far aft, and the croc made the water and disappeared. Harry shrugged. 'We'll find him on the beach tomorrow,' he said. 'That's a dying croc. Maybe he doesn't know it yet, but he'll come ashore to die.'

We sat and smoked a cigarette, and away off in the distance a pair of knobs showed out of the water. It was a good six or seven hundred yards.

'Maybe that's our boy,' Selby said. 'I'll have another bash at him.'

He took very careful aim, bracing the rifle with his elbows on his knees, aiming just under the knobs. I saw the bullet smack in the right place, making a little splash. The croc turned over, sun flashed on his belly as he thrashed, and then he quit flailing the water and slid into the deep.

'That is a stone-dead croc,' Selby said. 'He'll sink straight to the bottom and wash up in four or five days. But the other – if it was another. We'll just fish a while and watch. That other chap'll head for the beach.'

We fished for a couple of hours, then ran the boat down to the end of the island. There was a big croc on the beach. Selby glassed him.

'That's our boy,' he said. 'The first one. You want to go ashore and finish him off?'

I said sure and jumped down into the dinghy with one of the native sailors. We rowed as close as we could get to shore, and I held the scope on the croc. Blood was trickling from a head wound, all right, and there was another hole a little behind the shoulder. Harry had told me to shoot him 'behind the smile', the point where his mouth ends in a cynical grin, so as to nail him in the spine and anchor him. (The other shot is for the brain, about two inches below the eye knobs.)

The boat was bobbing up and down in the breeze, the boat boy trying to hold it steady with a paddle stuck into the mud. I waited for the down bob and squeezed as the crosshairs rode on to the top of the smile. The croc's legs shot out and I could see him quiver, exactly as a brain-shot elephant quivers.

'That did for him,' Harry shouted. 'Wade ashore and finish him off, then come on back to *The Lady*. We'll bend a line on him and tow him home.'

Largely by accident I had immobilized the critter with the spine shot, but he was still very much alive. They don't die easy, these chaps. He was already incipiently dead from Selby's first two shots, but the awful grey-yellow snake eyes were still open and malevolent. He was breathing. I poked the rifle muzzle close to his head and blew the brainpan off. It took the best part of an hour to lay a line on him and to tow him home, but when we horsed him up on to the beach with the Land-Rover his heart was still going. This wasn't surprising. Denis Lyell, who wrote a book called *The Hunting and Spoor of African Game*, once butchered the heart out of one, laid it on the hot metal deck of a launch, and held a watch on it. The severed heart was still palpitating at the end of three-quarters of an hour.

This fellow of mine was a big croc, about twelve feet long, and a male. There is no certain way to tell a big female crocodile from a male except at close hand, which means a dead crocodile. The male's sexual organs retract into his body and are covered by a flap over the vent, so that his underside is completely smooth.

The Molo fishermen cut this one up; they, like some tribes on the Zambezi, greatly esteem the croc as a delicacy. I fiddled with the idea of trying a piece of him fried, figuring he'd be fishy at worst, and not worrying too much about his carrion-eating habits. But a whiff of that foetid, reeking breath, when we were taking the pictures, put me off crocodile – or any other food – for quite some time.

So we had proved that a mortally wounded croc comes ashore to die. A few days later the Molo reported that the other croc (the second one) had washed in. He was torn up pretty badly, but the head was intact, and Harry's long-shot bullet had taken him just under the eyes and had blown his brains out. So we had also proved that a stone-dead croc will sink until such time as bloat-inflation fetches him to the surface and makes him lighter than water. But why does it take him so long to surface? The one I shot was easily waterborne behind the boat, and was tremendously bloated an hour or so after death.

The tenacity of life shared by most reptiles is of considerable importance in the procurement of crocodiles for the hide market. He must be killed and collected immediately unless he's harpooned.

We slit the belly of the first croc and found him full of fish, with a few stones for digestive aid. The fish diet was not unusual, because Rudolf is practically solid with the giant Nile perch and the tasty tilapia, and few animals inhabit its edges. Baby hippo and fish would seem to comprise the basis of the Rudolf croc's diet, as the fishing Molo never seem to be taken, although, wading naked in the water, they net tilapia in croc-filled shallows. The children are never taken either as they drink and play at the water's edge. And the solitary fishermen spear perch from a raft made of two logs lashed together that floats half submerged.

A crocodile will eat literally anything, and his digestive juices must have the consumptive force of corrosive acid. Certainly the bones and small horns of his prey are dissolved. He kills untold thousands of Africans annually, and since he cannot munch the bones, some special agent must dissolve them. You will find old bracelets and any number of stones in a croc's belly, but seldom bones unless the meal has been a recent one. Since he can't chew the bones into smaller bits, his digestive juices must resemble those of a boa constrictor or a python, which also eats its dinner whole.

One thing, one other nail to add to the general loathsomeness of the beast. *He dotes on hyenas!* Jack Bousfield, a professional crocodile hunter from Lake Rukwa in Tanganyika, once took a hyena by accident in a croc snare, and the crocs consumed it. Thereafter Bousfield shot hyenas for bait, and says that the crocs fancy it above any other he has ever tried.

It is from Bousfield, who has been in on the killing of some 45,000 crocodiles for the market in the last thirteen years, that I have much of my crocodile information. Bousfield, operating at Lake Rukwa, employs three other shooters and a native staff of about thirty men to work with nooses, nets, and harpoons and as skinners and boatmen.

Jack says that two-thirds of what you hear about crocodiles is myth; for a start, they do not like rotten food if they can find a meal small enough to swallow while it's fresh. Hyenas, he says, are about the right size for a big croc.

The size of crocodiles has been subject to much distortion. The biggest Bousfield ever killed was a bit over 18 feet, and a big mature croc will run 13 or 14 feet. They are deceptively heavy. Average weight may be about a thousand pounds, with a very old, very big croc possibly weighing close to a ton. Body structure is divided into rough thirds – head, torso, and tail – and the croc is enormously heavy in the shoulders. His fantastic strength comes from even weight distribution, powerful shoulders, and tremendous leverage from the long, heavy tail.

Crocodiles mate at night, and lay their eggs in August and September. The egg is about the size of a sea-turtle egg; like the sea turtle, the croc parents dig a two-foot hole in the sand, close to water. The eggs are laid in a perfect pyramid of layers, each carefully covered with sand. A clutch can be as small as thirty eggs; 120 is an extremely large setting. Average is somewhere from forty to seventy. One lusty male can service forty or fifty cow crocs. Bousfield says he can generally identify the male by size; he refrains from shooting it, since the cows are prone to hang around the area when the bull is standing at stud.

A female croc in egg is never less than 8 feet long, with the exception of the pygmy croc of Uganda. Once pregnant, she eats at night and sleeps all day. As hatching time approaches, the expectant mother goes into a coma and is relatively easy to hunt. The sun does the incubating and the mother rouses herself just before hatching time – December – and usually uncovers the babies. If she isn't there to sweep the sand off her scaly chicks, they scratch out of the shell and claw up to the surface.

They are around 7 or 8 inches long when born, and they see first light with a full set of teeth. Once they are hatched, the old lady shows no further active interest beyond curiosity, but Papa takes a definitely nonpaternal view of his kiddies. He loves nothing better than a fresh meal of his own progeny. As a matter of fact, the baby croc has a pretty thin time, both before and after birth. The big monitor lizards dote on the eggs, and hyenas, jackals, and marabou storks scratch up the nests. After birth, big catfish, meerkats and fish-eagles haunt the shallow water in which they live. Bousfield reckons that no more than five per cent make it from egg to maturity.

The baby croc eats insects during his first year, then changes over to rats, mice and birds. He has grown rapidly; at a year he's about 18 inches long. He keeps growing at an average rate of 9 inches a year, sometimes as much as 18 and as little as 5, until he reaches 7 feet. Then the growth slows down from almost nothing a year to about 2 inches. Growth varies considerably with the individual croc.

Somewhere in his second year Junior switches his hunger to larger game, such as rabbits, and in his third he graduates to fish and any carrion he can locate. He doesn't start hanging out with the big fellows until he has achieved a length of about 4 feet.

During the first couple of years the baby crocs are scared stiff of everything, particularly Papa. They stick together in packs, and if the band becomes scattered they call each other like a bunch of noisy kids. Bousfield can imitate the call of a young croc, which is a kind of piggish, grunting squeal, and has had considerable success in attracting adults to his gun. The mothers come, he says, from a sort of idle maternal curiosity, the old boys are looking for a meal, and younger crocs are seeking companionship. Bousfield swears that after a season of calling some of the crocs get to recognize his voice and won't heed his siren song any longer.

Chameleonlike, young crocs change colour according to environment. On a sandy beach they tend to yellow. They adapt to the greenish-brown-black of sudd, the floating thick skim of vegetation that is so frequently seen on slow African waters. But they are never marked in black, as are the old fellows.

As to hibernation, Bousfield says crocs will live in sealed holes if a lake dries. He sometimes hunts hibernating crocs by crawling into such holes with gun and light (ugh!) and says that the tunnel runs about eighteen feet with a dome at the end. He once came upon four sleeping adult crocodiles at the end of a tunnel on a lake that had been completely dry for nearly two years, and reckons that the four beasts had been snoozing for a minimum of eighteen months. Crocs hibernate beneath water level, too, which bespeaks some sort of strange conversion of the unconscious breathing apparatus.

There is no possible way of estimating the life expectancy of a wild crocodile, but Bousfield says that he is certain they reach an age of several hundred years. In any case, he adds, neither he nor anyone he knows has ever seen a crocodile that might conceivably have died of senility.

Growth being almost imperceptible after a critter reaches 7 feet, it stands to reason that a bull crocodile of 14 or 15 feet has been around for quite a spell. The largest bull that Bousfield has ever taped was 18 feet 3 inches, and the biggest cow about 13 feet.

Professional crocodile hunting on a large scale is a risky business, expensive to organize, and frighteningly dependent on the caprice of fashion. Bousfield reckons that his fleet of boats, motors, skinning-and-packing facilities, plus house and quarters for the natives, needed an original investment of about

$25,000. The hides are sold by belly-width, and must be free of 'buttons', or calcium deposits in the hide. There are nine different grades of skin, and a prime croc today (subject to market whim) is worth about $12, as opposed to its peak of $20 in 1954. The net profit on a prime hide is from $2 to $2·50.

Bousfield shoots crocodiles from a flatboat at night in the dark of the moon, aiming between the eyes, which are picked up by an electric torch. He shoots at close range, and the native boys make a mad dash to slip a noose on the beast while it still thrashes wildly before swimming off and sinking. Noosing traps are also used as well as heavy nets rigged around stockades of poles. Jack's record catch for one netting was fifty-two crocodiles, and it took twenty-two boys to haul in the nets. Netted and noosed crocs are killed by the boys, who use blunt pickaxes to bash out their brains.

Our vulgar friend is amazingly at home on land, and can travel like a streak on his short, bowed lizard's legs. He does *not* crawl or slide on his belly, but runs with daylight showing between him and the ground. Whether he can smell I cannot say for sure, but he has magnificent eyesight and excellent hearing equipment. Certainly the croc feels no compunction about crossing dry land to come to a camp where meat is hanging, which leads me to believe that he can smell. Also, they've been known to drag carcases of their fellows several hundred yards to get them into the water, no doubt intending to store them in a cave until sufficiently rotten to be mangled into edible portions.

Because they eat each other, crocs fight continually among themselves. Lyell relates that in Uganda a smaller crocodile was chased out of the water by a larger one on to a small pier. It was so frightened that it refused to go back into the water, even when it was attacked by natives who eventually killed it.

The menace of the crocodile is one aspect that has never been overexaggerated. The rapidity with which that innocent log turns into a monster when he is coursing food is amazing to see; a convoy of crocodiles logging knots as they speed through the water leaves a definite speedboat wake, and the nose, as Bousfield has said, does create a beautiful bow wave, A croc is not so nimble on land as in water, but a scared one heading for the deep travels amazingly fast. He does not waddle or slink; he scurries. And his approach from water to a victim on land, or his attack on one in the water, is fantastically swift, silent, and conclusive. Perhaps you may frighten a croc with a splash or a commotion, but while you're doing it a cousin will likely take you by the leg.

I can understand the natives' fearful reverence of old Mamba, god of the river. The unblinking eyes, the silence of his greasy slide through the water, the utter inexorability of his single-minded purpose, the finality of that steel-trap grip of massive jaw, and the ultimate horror of being drowned and taken to that stinking cave in a mudbank to await the monster's hungry pleasure . . . No, thank you very much. I prefer to play tag with cow elephants accompanied by calves and old gentlemen rhino in the breeding season.

The crocodile, even as the hyena, writes his own epitaph. The hyena's laugh is mirthless and can achieve the shriek of a damned soul. The crocodile smiles, but the smile is sardonic and is only fit for an aiming point, because the croc is smiling at his ultimate unmourned end. For if the aim is good, any killer of the croc who professes either sorrow or sympathy for the deceased could well be accused of shedding crocodile tears.

MR HAMBLE'S BEAR

by

MARGERY SHARP

SHERRARD HAD forty-five minutes to wait for his train, so as
the day was fine he checked his suitcase and turned out into the
Euston Road. He had three days' leave from his work at the
Admiralty, and was about to spend two of them in unpleasant
travel, in order to keep a luncheon engagement in Scotland.

As he strolled along, finding the minutes pass slowly and the
wind colder than he had thought, the sight of a tobacconist's
reminded him that he was short of cigarettes. The tiny shop
did not look as though it stocked his rather expensive brand,
but pausing outside it he was struck by the oddity of the
window. The boxes and packets, the dummies and display-
cards, showed no attempt at arrangement: they were simply
piled in one corner, leaving the rest of the space bare. The
original legend on the fascia had been smudged out with what
looked like tar, and the name 'Hamble' roughly substituted.
The whole establishment, in fact, had a take-it-or-leave-it air
which Sherrard found unusual. He liked the unusual. He went
in.

Behind the counter sat a large unshaven old man wearing a
knotted handkerchief instead of a collar. His jacket needed
cleaning, or perhaps burning. His features were heavy and sad.
But he had the aura of one who is his own master, and Sherrard
rightly guessed him to be Hamble in person.

'Balkan 333?' inquired Sherrard.

'No,' said Mr Hamble.

'Well, what have you got?' asked Sherrard.

'Nothing much,' said Mr Hamble.

Sherrard looked round and saw that this was true. Even for
wartime, the place was very poorly stocked. But there was a
box of cigarette-holders, and as the lady he was going to visit

lost about one a day, Sherrard began making a selection. To do so he put down on the counter a couple of books he had in his hand: a Euripides, in the original Greek, and a work on philosophy. They seemed to arouse Mr Hamble's interest. He looked at them, he picked them up, he flipped open the covers, noted the prices, studied the title-pages; then set them down again and considered Sherrard with new attention.

'You appear,' said Mr Hamble, 'to be a man of education.'

He spoke with a peculiar measured cadence, like a man unaccustomed to much talk, unaccustomed particularly to the give-and-take of conversation. The remark being a rather difficult one to answer, Sherrard merely nodded.

'And also,' pursued Mr Hamble, looking at Sherrard's suit, man of the world.'

'I've seen a good deal of it,' said Sherrard.

Mr Hamble examined him thoughtfully for some minutes, and appeared to come to a decision.

'Do you mind,' he asked, 'if I tell you a rather remarkable story?'

Sherrard said not at all, he would be delighted.

'It's an animal story,' said Mr Hamble apologetically.

Sherrard said he would still be very glad to hear it. Mr Hamble settled himself comfortably against the counter, and cleared his throat.

'As a small child,' began Mr Hamble, 'I frequently spent my holidays with a maiden aunt who lived in a small villa on the Italian Riviera. One day, as I was running back through the garden in response to the luncheon-bell, I was surprised to see in my path a bear. Bears, in the imagination at least, are by no means unfamiliar objects to a small boy, and I dare say I should have taken it quite calmly but for the fact that it walked upon its hind legs, and also wore a small Homburg hat. I fled, howling. In but a few moments, of course, all was explained: the animal belonged to a band of gipsies who were exhibiting it through the neighbourhood, and hoped to offer us a private show. In this they were disappointed, my aunt being a strong supporter of the Royal Society for the Prevention of Cruelty to

Animals. Her reactions were vigorous but inconsistent: she at once gave the bear-leader a lira to let the animal down on all fours, threatened to report him to the police, and sent the whole party round to the kitchen for scraps. Later, that afternoon, in a secluded grove, I came upon them again, enjoying her bounty, in which the bear had his part. He was eating a cold leg of pigeon, and to do so had thrust back his furry muzzle, revealing a physiognomy very like that of his master (or accomplice).

'This incident made a deep impression on me, and for many years after I was a good deal confused in my relations with all the larger quadrupeds. At home in London, when taken to the Zoo, I was quite convinced that all lions and tigers, apes (and of course bears) were really human persons exercising a profession as regular as that of butcher or baker. This theory was strengthened by our annual visit to the pantomime, where Puss In Boots, or Red Riding Hood's wolf, always doffed their masks to share in the final applause. Gradually, of course, the misapprehension was dispersed, and I was able to laugh with my parents at my earlier fancies. But I tell you all this so that you may understand why I have always been particularly attentive to, and perhaps easily influenced by, the personalities of animals.'

Sherrard said he understood perfectly.

'Years passed,' continued Mr Hamble, 'my parents died, leaving me but ill provided for. I had never been clever, but I found myself a niche in the second-hand furniture trade. My aunt also passed on, and from her I received a sum sufficient to set up a small business of my own in Praed Street, Paddington. My first independent purchase was a stuffed bear.'

He paused, evidently awaiting comment. Sherrard said he thought it very natural.

'It was *not* natural,' corrected Mr Hamble. 'The market for stuffed bears – upright – is extremely restricted. I did not intend bidding for it. My lips moved as it were of their own accord. "Five pounds!" I cried; and the animal was mine.

'It cost another ten shillings in transport. I set it up on the pavement outside my shop, hoping to gain some advantage in the way of publicity. I placed a small Homburg hat on its head. It attracted, as I had hoped, considerable attention. Business looked up, and I rapidly disposed of a set of croquet mallets, a Windsor chair, and a steel engraving of the Empress Josephine.

'For the first week my new acquisition remained, so to speak, passive. Then one particularly sunny day I noticed that the Homburg hat looked very shabby, and I replaced it by a hard straw. Several passers-by noted the change with approval. The weather broke, it rained every day, and I grew very tired of either hauling the bear inside or wrapping him in dust-sheets. I remembered a mackintosh cape, Inverness style, which had belonged to my father, and put that on him instead. You would have been surprised to see what a change it made. He still looked most like a bear, but he also looked rather like a German professor. My charwoman reported that he had given her quite a turn, and I noticed one or two customers murmur a word of apology as they brushed by. Perhaps the most curious point was that when the rainy spell ended, and I took the cape off, the bear looked not more, but less, natural. He looked unclad – like a German professor in his combinations. Fortunately, amongst a variety of second-hand clothes, I possessed an academic gown, which fitted him very well. I did not know what faculty it belonged to, but as I did not know either what the bear was professor of, this hardly mattered. At any rate, he was again decent.

'I ought to mention that he was already, in a small way, a public figure. Everyone in Paddington knew him, and the variety of his hats (for he had several others besides those I have mentioned) were a constant source of friendly interest; but this gown, by attracting the notice of the students of London University, opened wider spheres. I had observed for some time the presence of a new type of customer – young men in flannel trousers, tweed jackets, and large mufflers – who bought, if they bought anything, second-hand books: at last two of them approached me with an offer of five shillings for the loan of the bear for Saturday afternoon. They wished, they said, to take him to a football match. I thought it over; the

bear had certainly done his best, he had brought me innumerable fresh customers, and it seemed hard that he should never
have any pleasure. I decided to let him go – refusing, however,
the five shillings. His new friends were delighted, and off he
went in their car, wearing a large purple muffler and a knot of
purple ribbon. I put in an umbrella after him, in case of rain.'

Mr Hamble paused.

'Perhaps,' he inquired, 'you know something of the ways of
students?'

'I've been one myself,' said Sherrard.

'You surprise me,' said Mr Hamble. 'Though no doubt
some of them turn out well. However, I knew nothing of them
then, though I afterwards learnt a good deal. If I *had* known, I
dare say I should not have been so amenable.'

'I hope he got back all right?' said Sherrard.

'He got *back*. He got back well after midnight, smelling
strongly of drink, with his gown torn, and having lost his
umbrella. I was extremely annoyed, and I spoke pretty sharply
to his companions; but they were in no state to appreciate the
justice of my remarks. In fact I doubt whether they heard
them, for a day or two later, they returned, quite unabashed,
with an invitation to a Club dinner. This time I was harder to
persuade, but they assured me it was to be a most decorous
function, sanctioned by the University Authorities, and that
the Club was one for the advancement of Theological Philosophy. I have mentioned already that the bear strongly resembled a German professor, and this seemed just the sort of
thing he would enjoy. I let him accept. But I stipulated that I
should call for him myself, at ten-thirty, and I actually did so,
though I had some difficulty – the debate was still in full
swing, and he was taking the chair – in getting him away.

'This incident too had consequences. The taxi fare was six
and six – to me a not unimportant sum. In fact, I considered it
far too much, and I very nearly decided he should not go out
again. Then it occurred to me that it was really he who had
sold the croquet mallets, the Windsor chair, and the steel engraving of the Empress Josephine, at a profit of fifteen shillings;

he was therefore entitled to at least that sum. Next day I began a separate account for him – on one side his personal sales, on the other taxi-fares, new clothes, and so on. I counted as his all sales made to customers who looked at the bear before they looked in the window; and he did so well that he was soon able to buy himself an opera hat, a silk muffler, and a new umbrella – all very necessary, for from this time his engagements rapidly increased. Were you in London in '38?'

Sherrard said no, he had been abroad.

'Then you can have no idea,' said Mr Hamble impressively, 'how very popular he became. Perhaps it will help if I tell you that on certain occasions – Boat Race night, and the Cup Final – he had to have a special policeman detailed to look after him. Like a Cabinet Minister. He was the acknowledged patron of London University, without whom no academic function (of the lighter sort) was complete. He attended every sporting event, and usually finished the evening with the victorious team. He became a familiar figure on the news-films. He was several times kidnapped by medical students, for the medicals (always a turbulent element) wished to appropriate him entirely, and this led to a standing feud between the Colleges and the Hospitals. Each side wished to adopt him outright, but against this I set my face. I did not wish him to degenerate into a mere rowdy.

'My own life, of course, became more and more bound up with his, for I kept to my rule of always calling for him, and this rather cut me off from the social enjoyments of my neighbours, who were nearly all whist-players, and who disliked my having to leave in the middle of a hand. Soon I ceased to frequent them, and without regret. Tradesmen's card-parties had small charm for me; I breathed, vicariously, a wider air. I did once suffer a slight disappointment. A Miss Armiger, a lady friend in the clothing branch, one day came in with a couple of passes for the theatre, and asked me to be her escort. I looked at the date; it was impossible. We were engaged two deep – I had to call for the bear at nine, after a dinner at University College, and take him on to a smoking concert at Guy's Hospital, and fetch him again at half past ten. I refused Miss Armiger's invitation with deep regret, and while I was still explaining the circumstances, she left the shop.

'But let me,' said Mr Hamble, 'abridge. For a time all went well. Business continued to prosper. I did not perhaps keep our accounts as carefully as at first, and the bear was a bit extravagant, but I took pride in his appearance, and my own wants were few. The change in our relations came about very gradually. I began to feel a slight reluctance to turn out so frequently and so late at night. It annoyed me to hear people refer to the establishment as "The Bear's" instead of "Hamble's"; and one evening in November – the fifth – as I sat waiting to go and fetch him from a Guy Fawkes dinner, these dissatisfactions came to a head. I had had a hard day's work, the fire burned brightly, there was a programme on the wireless I should have liked to hear. But at ten-fifteen I would have to go out. For the third time that week. It suddenly came over me that the people who called my shop "The Bear's" were right: it wasn't my shop at all, it was his. I was working twelve hours a day to support him in a life of idle pleasure. He still pulled his weight, in a sense; but of his many friends fewer and fewer made any substantial purchase. I got out my books: in the last two weeks he had sold only a couple of sixpenny novels, and his taxi fares alone amounted to thirty-five shillings.

'And there were other points – trifling, perhaps, that rankled. He was always losing umbrellas. It seemed absolutely impossible for him to go out with an umbrella and bring it back. And he lost not only his own, but mine as well, whenever I lent them him. And as I sat thinking over these things, and feeling how hard it was that in a few minutes I should have to leave my fire and go out, I suddenly came to an astounding decision.

'"All right," I said, "you can get back by yourself," and I locked up and went to bed.'

Mr Hamble turned to Sherrard beseechingly.

'I assure you,' he said, 'I assure you, I never thought of anything more than his spending the night on the pavement, and having lost his umbrella, and it coming on to rain. That was the very worst I anticipated. And in the morning – for it *did* rain – I hurried down at half past six with a large towel. But he wasn't there. He hadn't come home. I waited till nine, and then I hurried to the College where he had dined. It was built round a quadrangle, in the centre of which, as I entered, I observed the remains of a large bonfire. I observed them quite idly. At the lodge I made inquiry of the porter, giving the names of the bear's particular hosts; only to be told that they were one and all in the hands of the police. They had gone, explained the porter, too far: a bonfire in the quad might pass, but not the carrying of flaming torches through the London streets. They had all been arrested. "Was there a bear arrested with them?" I asked. The porter shook his head; I felt a foolish relief. At least they had had the decency, I thought, not to implicate him. "Then, where is he?" I asked. "I have come to take him home." The porter shook his head again – but this time pityingly: and he pointed through the lodge-window to the heap of ash . . .'

'What!' cried Sherrard, genuinely shocked. 'He'd been burnt?'

'Cremated. I knew without another word. I asked, "What time did they light it?" – and the porter answered, "About half past ten."'

There is always something a little absurd in the emotions of the stout. Mr Hamble was very stout indeed, and the object of his affection a stuffed bear; yet Sherrard did not find his distress wholly ridiculous. It was too sincere. To give the old man time to recover, he picked out six cigarette-holders and laid a note on the counter in payment. Mr Hamble violently blew his nose.

'That's all,' he said abruptly. 'I never so much as riddled through the ash for his eyes. I hadn't the heart. In a day or two they came round, those students, full of regrets and explanations. I wouldn't listen to them. I sold the business, moved here, set up as a tobacconist; and I've never prospered since. I expect,' said Mr Hamble, 'I haven't had the heart.' He looked at Sherrard earnestly. 'Now, as a man of education,' he said, 'and a man of the world – what d'you make of it?'

Sherrard hesitated.

'It's certainly a remarkable story,' he said. 'It's one of the most remarkable stories I've ever heard.'

Mr Hamble moved his big shoulders impatiently.

'I know *that*,' he said. 'What I mean is – looking back over the whole matter – for I am always looking back over it – would you say I had been fooled?'

'Fooled?' repeated Sherrard.

'I gave him,' said Mr Hamble, almost shyly, 'a lot of affection. One doesn't like to be fooled in one's affections.'

Sherrard took a moment or two to think this over.

'If it's any consolation,' he said at last, 'I don't believe your case is unique. A good many men have a bear of sorts.'

'I never heard of another,' said Mr Hamble jealously.

'Not an actual bear, as yours was. It may be a golf-handicap, or a stamp collection, or Basic English. With women it's very likely to be a house.'

Mr Hamble pondered.

'I take your point,' he said. 'I once knew a man ruined a very nice little business collecting pewter snuff-boxes. Ugly clumsy things they were. No one wanted them, and he wouldn't have sold if they had.' Mr Hamble shook his head. 'But affection,' he said, 'is different.'

'Put it another way,' said Sherrard. 'The Frenchman says in every love-affair there is one who kisses and one who is kissed. Many people believe that the one who kisses has the best of it.'

Mr Hamble looked at him shrewdly.

'And what,' he asked, 'may be *your* bear?'

Sherrard counted his cigarette-holders; six of them, at half a crown each.

'My bear,' he said, 'has golden hair and brown eyes, and is unshakeably faithful to the memory of her late husband. Shall I catch my train to go up to Scotland to have lunch with her, or shall we both go out and get a drink?'

It took Mr Hamble an appreciable time to answer, and even then he did not do so in words; but he reached up to a peg behind him, and from it took down a small Homburg hat.

HIS FIRST FLIGHT

by

LIAM O'FLAHERTY

THE YOUNG seagull was alone on his ledge. His two brothers and his sister had already flown away the day before. He had been afraid to fly with them. Somehow when he had taken a little run forward to the brink of the ledge and attempted to flap his wings he became afraid. The great expanse of sea stretched down beneath, and it was such a long way down – miles down. He felt certain that his wings would never support him, so he bent his head and ran away back to the little hole under the ledge where he slept at night. Even when each of his brothers and his little sister, whose wings were far shorter than his own, ran to the brink, flapped their wings, and flew away he failed to muster up courage to take that plunge which appeared to him so desperate. His father and mother had come around calling to him shrilly, upbraiding him, threatening to let him starve on his ledge unless he flew away. But for the life of him he could not move.

That was twenty-four hours ago. Since then nobody had come near him. The day before, all day long, he had watched his parents flying about with his brothers and sister, perfecting them in the art of flight, teaching them how to skim the waves and how to dive for fish. He had, in fact, seen his older brother catch his first herring and devour it, standing on a rock, while his parents circled around raising a proud cackle. And all the morning the whole family had walked about on the big plateau midway down the opposite cliff, taunting him with his cowardice.

The sun was now ascending the sky, blazing warmly on his ledge that faced the south. He felt the heat because he had not eaten since the previous nightfall. Then he had found a dried piece of mackerel's tail at the far end of his ledge. Now there was not a single scrap of food left. He had searched every inch, rooting among the rough, dirt-caked straw nest where he and his brothers and sister had been hatched. He even gnawed at the dried pieces of spotted egg-shell. It was like eating part of himself. He had then trotted back and forth from one end of the ledge to the other, his grey body the colour of the cliff, his long grey legs stepping daintily, trying to find some means of reaching his parents without having to fly. But on each side of him the ledge ended in a sheer fall of precipice, with the sea beneath. And between him and his parents there was a deep, wide chasm. Surely he could reach them without flying if he could only move northwards along the cliff face. But then on what could he walk? There was no ledge, and he was not a fly. And above him he could see nothing. The precipice was sheer, and the top of it was perhaps farther away than the sea beneath him.

He stepped slowly out to the brink of the ledge, and, standing on one leg with the other leg hidden under his wing, he closed one eye, then the other, and pretended to be falling asleep. Still they took no notice of him. He saw his two brothers and his sister lying on the plateau dozing, with their heads sunk into their necks. His father was preening the feathers on his white back. Only his mother was looking at him. She was standing on a little high hump on the plateau, her white breast thrust forward. Now and again she tore at a piece of fish that lay at her feet, and then scraped each side of her beak on the rock. The sight of the food maddened him. How he loved to tear food that way, scraping his beak now and again to whet it! He uttered a low cackle. His mother cackled, too, and looked over at him.

'Ga, ga, ga,' he cried, begging her to bring him over some food. 'Gaw-ool-ah,' she screamed back derisively. But he kept calling plaintively, and after a minute or so uttered a joyful scream. His mother had picked up a piece of the fish and was flying across to him with it. He leaned out eagerly, tapping the rock with his feet, trying to get nearer to her as she flew across. But when she was just opposite to him, abreast of the ledge, she halted, her legs hanging limp, her wings motionless, the piece of fish in her beak almost within reach of his beak. He waited a moment in surprise, wondering why she did not come nearer, and then, maddened by hunger, he dived at the fish. With a loud scream he fell outwards and downwards into space. His mother had swooped upwards. As he passed beneath her he heard the swish of her wings. Then a monstrous terror seized him and his heart stood still. He could hear nothing. But it only lasted a moment. The next moment he felt his wings spread outwards. The wind rushed against his breast feathers, then under his stomach and against his wings. He could feel the tips of his wings cutting through the air. He was not falling headlong now. He was soaring gradually downwards and outwards. He was no longer afraid. He just felt a bit dizzy. Then he flapped his wings once and soared upwards. He uttered a joyous scream and flapped them again. He soared higher. He raised his breast and banked against the wind. 'Ga, ga, ga. Ga, ga, ga. Gaw-ool-ah.' His mother swooped past him, her wings making a loud noise. He answered her with another scream. Then he saw his two brothers and his sister flying around him curveting and banking and soaring and diving.

Then he completely forgot that he had not always been able to fly, and commenced himself to dive and soar and curvet, shrieking shrilly.

He was near the sea now, flying straight over it, facing straight out over the ocean. He saw a vast green sea beneath him, with little ridges moving over it, and he turned his beak sideways and crowed amusedly. His parents and his brothers and sister had landed on this green floor in front of him. They were beckoning to him, calling shrilly. He dropped his legs to stand on the green sea. His legs sank into it. He screamed with fright and attempted to rise again, flapping his wings. But he was tired and weak with hunger and he could not rise, exhausted by the strange exercise. His feet sank into the green sea, and then his belly touched it and he sank no farther. He was floating on it. And around him his family was screaming, praising him, and their beaks were offering him scraps of dogfish.

He made his first flight.

MADEMOISELLE KIKI

by

JOHN COLLIER

(from *Pictures in the Fire*, by permission of Messrs Rupert
Hart-Davis and A. D. Peters)

LA CAILLOT, on the dreary coast west of Marseille, has the
smallest harbour in the south of France. Its horseshoe basin
shelters a score of fishing boats, and the owners of these boats
spend their evenings in the Café Roustand.

Beside the café there is a little angular space with a street
lamp and a wind-bitten tree. In front lies the roadway, and beyond it the lapping waters of the harbour. Inside, there are six
or eight tables, and the usual small zinc bar near the door. Near
one end of this bar stands a rack of postcards, showing views of
La Caillot. These are mostly in a rather faded sepia, and have
been there for some time. One of them includes the figure of
the present proprietor, at a rather earlier age, standing with a
hoop in his hand, and a vacant expression on his face. Beyond
the rack comes the last foot or so of the counter, and it is here
that Kiki sleeps the whole day through. Kiki is a cat in her
middle years, but looking rather older owing to the ravages of a
passionate temperament.

Had the cat world its Kinsey, he could tell us some remarkable things. For example, there are certain spells in the life of
the female of that species when she becomes more than ordin-
arily interested in the conversation of the opposite sex. These
spells are very variable both in their frequency and their dura-
tion. Sometimes they occur twice in the year, sometimes thrice,
and in the ardent south instances have been known of the
manifestation recurring as often as four or five times. Kiki,
though no prude, would have disdained such intemperance. In
her case the condition prevailed only once in every year. It

E

must be admitted, however, that it lasted, except in leap years, for three hundred and sixty-five days.

Now Kiki, though unusually large and powerful, could not be called a beautiful cat. Her angular frame seemed to have been draped in a ragged, patchy and discoloured fur gleaned from some rubbish heap, and her sides were so knobbly and uneven as to suggest that this fur was stuffed with old bed-springs from the same source. In the amorous discourse of cats, a vitally important part is played by the vocal prelimina-ries. In this respect Kiki suffered a disadvantage greater even than that of her appearance. No such dismal, dolorous, and uninviting croak has ever been heard as that which issued from Kiki. It effectively chilled the hot blood of the male cats of La Caillot, a feat otherwise accomplished only by death or the mistral.

Nevertheless, the grim, gaunt, hideous scarecrow of a female lived the life of Reilly, and enjoyed the highest consideration both of the human kind and of her own. In La Caillot, the or-dinary run of cats are nothing but anonymous scavengers, but no fisherman left Roustand's at closing-time without a very civil *bon soir* to Mademoiselle Kiki. Still more to the point, every evening one or other of them would stop at his boat on his way to the café, and bring up, in a strip of net or an old can, a mess of such sorts of fish as were too bony or flavourless to be marketable. As often as not some rich sardines or delicate merlans, which had been a little trodden upon in the bottom of the boat, were included in the offering.

Such distinction, in a community so utterly neglectful of its cats, needs a little accounting for. The fact is, that when an exceptionally fierce and icy mistral was on its way, and all the local cats kept huddled in whatever shelter they could find, regardless of their hunger and all other earthly appetites, Kiki, foreseeing a lonely midnight, would lift her bristly chin and utter cries of disappointment and fury such as would set the flesh crawling on a man's bones in precisely the same way as did the bitter wind itself. When the record mistral of 1951 was on its way down the valley of the Rhône, and even before it began to flatten the wastes of reeds on the Carmargue, Kiki had raised a banshee wail that was long remembered. It was remembered also that early next morning two of the open boats were blown out to sea and never returned. Much the same thing happened in the big blow in 1953, and Kiki was credited with supernatural powers. When she uttered her most piercing cries the fishermen took warning, stayed at home, listened to the fury of the wind, and agreed that Kiki deserved all the fish she could eat.

They brought her, in fact, rather more than she could eat, but not more than she had a use for. Late in the evening, when the last customer had departed, Roustand would set the chairs on the tables, turn down all the lights but one, and bring from the kitchen a wide platter heaped with the daily tribute of fish. This he would carry outside, and set it down in the little angular space under the tree. Kiki, you may be sure, was close beside him, and had her nose to the platter the moment it clinked upon the ground.

The honest Roustand then re-entered his café, secured the door, extinguished the remaining light, and betook himself to bed.

With the extinction of this last light, there remained only the weak and rather ghastly radiance of the street lamp, and the round, flat and greenishly shining eyes of some half a dozen tom cats, seated on the low wall, or under the bench, or between the cases of empty bottles or in various other points of vantage. There are grades even among the downtrodden cat population of La Caillot, and these represented the lowest grade. These toms were hams.

Not one of the hungry wretches dared to creep over to take a share in the magnificent banquet on which Kiki proceeded to regale herself in full view of them all. Being more powerful than any of them because she was better fed, the Amazon uninterruptedly continued to feed better. Her audience observed with breathless interest the way she took each fish by the snout and crunched it between her side-teeth until she got down to the tail. The more philosophic among them might have noted that riches are not always a guarantee of beauty; the knobbliness of the harridan's sides was not smoothed out by the rich lining of fish. In fact, the existing lumps and bumps seemed to project more hideously than before. There is, however, no evidence that this observation was ever actually made.

By the time Kiki had finished her meal the sizeable platter was somewhere about half empty. At this moment a suppressed exclamation of impatience might have been heard from one or more of the famishing watchers. Kiki paid no heed to this unmannerliness, but embarked on a leisurely toilet, for all the world like some elderly charmer who lingers at her dressing-table in full confidence that her riches will keep her gigolo kicking his heels below.

When at last she considered herself ready, she moved a pace or two away from the platter, and, sadly out of tune, she hummed a few bars of the feline equivalent of *Parlez moi d'amour*. Her calculating admirers, creeping stealthily forward, their bellies low to the ground, soon ringed her about, turning their round and unwinking gaze upon her hideousness, and uttering amorous cries which were so insincere, so contrary to every normal instinct, and brought forth with such desperate, competitive effort, that they sounded like the desolate howls of the lost souls in Hell itself. It was largely because of this hideous racket that the cats of La Caillot were held to be more raucous than those of other places, and were accordingly more execrated and less fed, which in turn laid them under all the greater compulsion to vie with each other in the nightly concert. It will be seen that Kiki's circle of admirers was in every sense a vicious circle.

Kiki alone enjoyed the music, and listened with the air of a connoisseur. In the end, the voice of one or another having attracted her by some resonant suggestion of virility, she advanced her nose to within an inch of that of the chosen swain, and breathed upon him a fragrant reminiscence of her recent meal, rich with the promise of the second course yet to come. She then gratified him with a single harsh croak of approval, on which the rest of the infernal choir at once fell silent, for they realized the game was up.

Everything being well understood by everyone concerned, the business of the evening was then transacted with no concessions to false modesty or sentimental preliminaries. At this juncture a peculiar phenomenon was to be observed, such as makes it all the more regrettable that Dr Kinsey never turned his attention to the behaviour of cats. Naturally Kiki was entirely preoccupied; so was the drudging mercenary whom she had chosen as her cavalier of the evening. The platter, still well garnished with the remaining fish, thus lay unguarded, yet not one of the rejected suitors, ravenous as they were, stole over to enjoy a free meal. This was in no way due to any nice scruples of honesty, but entirely to the obsessive *voyeurism* of their species, examples of which may be witnessed by whoever walks after midnight through the back streets and vacant lots of any great city. The round eyes of the rejected were fixed unwinkingly on the spectacle of the unhallowed mating, and the circle, also a vicious one, remained unbroken. Now and then a low moan would issue from under the skeleton ribs of one or another of the watchers, for there are few of us so besotted with our vice or folly as not to be dimly aware of the price we are paying for indulging in it, but these cats were spellbound, fascinated and hypnotized, and they remained riveted to the spot.

After a certain interval Kiki would sit up, stroke her whiskers, glance around her, and stroll back to the neglected platter. Her lover was permitted to accompany her; he did so with no very noticeable signs of shame or embarrassment. The others, their virtue and their appetites undiminished, wandered disconsolately off on a round of the garbage cans of La Caillot, which are by no means notable for the richness and profusion of their contents.

Thus it was that the unlovely Kiki lived as pleasantly as the sleekest little tabby that ever lapped milk. The only exception was on those nights when the presage of the icy mistral kept the hungriest toms crouching in their lairs, and it was on those nights she set up that dolorous and discontented cry which gave warning to the fishermen, who therefore repaid her out of their catch, and thus enabled this faded Cleopatra to fee her Caesars and her Anthonys. Here is yet another vicious circle; perhaps there are more of them in the world than is generally realized.

This state of affairs had continued for some years when a lady of a very vivid complexion sold a large house she owned in Marseille and bought a small one at La Caillot, which happened to be her birthplace. There she proposed to end her days in retirement and respectable ease. She brought with her her own cat, who was called Papillon. He was a neat, trim, cheerful and well-cared-for animal, as clean as a new pin, nicely marked, and with a coat like satin, and he proudly carried the adornment of a fine red collar, made of patent leather.

No one is absolutely perfect; this Papillon had suffered a certain little deprivation, a mere trifle, nothing to make a fuss about; on balance it may have added very considerably to his general comfort and well-being, but it was something quite unknown in this very primitive village, where the cat is hardly regarded as a domestic animal, and therefore never domesticated.

Very well, on the first night he was set at liberty, Master Papillon came mincing down to the port, for all the world like a male milliner on holiday; the living principle of plumpness and the incarnation of urbanity and self-esteem. He arrived outside the café at the very moment when Roustand was setting down the big platter of fish, and he estimated that there would be plenty to spare for such a visitor as himself, who had a thousand interesting little stories to recount, of curious things he had happened to witness in Marseille. So he uttered a bird-like chirrup of satisfaction, lifted his tail, and came tripping across to join in the banquet.

Kiki, though momentarily stupefied by his impudence, soon saluted him with a stinging blow in the face, such as he had never dreamed of in all his life before. He began to gibber and back away, but he was wrong even in this. He should have made a full and helter-skelter retreat, for Kiki, feeling he didn't retire with sufficient respectful speed, fell upon him like a thunder-bolt, and drubbed him with two fistfuls of fish-hooks until he fled scampering up to the house of his protectress, leaving half his handsome coat puffing about the quay.

All the same, he had sniffed at the fish, and its fragrance haunted him. It was not long before he ventured out again. The regular circle, had they had the attention to spare, might have noticed his wistful face peeping from behind the tree. He soon understood very well what was going on, having seen something rather similar in Marseille, and the next night he edged up and took his place among the suitors. These regarded him with more of astonishment than hostility. This was less due to his citified air, his general sleekness and his shining collar, than to something at once subtler and more profound, which completely baffled and nonplussed these rugged mer-cenaries. An intruder of their own kind would quickly have been sent packing, but they felt that Papillon was somehow different. It was something on which they could not put a finger, partly of course because they hadn't a finger among them, and partly because there was nothing for them to put it on even if they had had one. Papillon, therefore, was suffered to remain.

Kiki, finding him among the others, saw him with a new eye. She was vastly impressed by his collar, which perhaps put certain social ideas into her head, to which even the drabbest of her sex are not altogether immune. She also noticed how extremely well-fed and plump he was, and she was not the first to be misled by appearances. Like his rivals, she was vaguely aware of something different about him, but he came from Marseille, and, 'What the hell!' thought Kiki. 'Who knows?'

Accordingly she approached her nose to that of Papillon, and uttered her hoarse croak of approval. The vain cockney, with a flirtatious smirk, piped a wooing or two, and proceeded to imitate, to the best of his ability, the conduct that was rewarded by the fish.

The fascinated onlookers shifted their round eyes, exchanged glances and edged nearer, as if in need of spectacles. Kiki was patient for a while, for she believed she was being introduced to sophisticated ways, but after one or two rather broad hints had been disregarded she became completely disillusioned. She faced around, and with one sweep of her paw she sent the hapless eunuch rolling in the gutter. In less time than it takes to tell, she had chosen his successor, and all proceeded as it had done so often before.

Papillon picked himself up, trembling with mortification. He removed certain unsavoury matter from one of his ears, and looked about him, and saw what was going on. His eye fell upon the neglected platter of fish. Now Papillon, if not altogether a tom, was for that very reason not a Peeping Tom. He was under no such obsessive compulsion as the others were, and nothing that he saw seemed to him of the least interest compared with the platter of fish.

He crept towards the feast, at first in hope of snatching a single sardine and bounding away with it, but he quickly realized the tremendous advantage he possessed over the rough-necks he had almost been tempted to envy. He saw them shoot brief and agonized glances in his direction, he heard some low growling sounds and noticed a convulsive start or two, but nothing could break the spell that bound them, and they remained riveted to the spot. Papillon, reflecting that it takes all sorts to make a world, devoured the last morsel at his leisure, licked the platter clean, and strolled away up the hill beyond any possibility of pursuit.

Shortly afterwards, the interested circle broke up, and Kiki, followed by her expectant paramour, came over towards the platter. They looked with a blankness absolutely beyond description at the equally blank and empty surface of the dish, upon which not so much as a single scale remained.

What followed was altogether without precedent. The bilked gigolo, using a vile expression, struck Kiki a savage blow on the ear. The unhappy debtor, conscious of the moral weakness of her position, had not the spirit to resent it, but cowered down with her ears close to her head. The enraged tom then withdrew to join his less successful rivals at the garbage cans.

The next evening, instead of six admirers, Kiki had only five. The defrauded hireling of the previous night had decided not to show up, either because of his very natural resentment, or because he thought it better to get first go at the garbage than to risk further labours of love that might be equally unrequited.

His judgement was justified. As soon as all was in train, Master Papillon sauntered easily upon the scene. He met with insouciance the hopeless glare of the immobilized Kiki, and he listened to the moans of the hypnotized circle as a diner-out listens to the agreeable strains which a wandering violinist draws from the agonized cat-gut. At the same time he was busily at work on the platter, and again he devoured the fish to the very last crumb.

The next night, the number of Kiki's suitors was reduced to four, and the night after that to only three, and by the end of the week there was not even one.

Kiki spent the next few days in a condition of shock and depression that was truly pitiable to witness. She sat with her eyes closed and her mouth half open, moving only when now and then she raked her paw from behind her ears to the tip of her nose, as if trying to comb an idea out of her bewildered head. And in the end she succeeded in doing so. She got up, stretched herself, and sallied out in the early afternoon, and went up the little hill in search of Papillon.

Papillon, observing her through the window of his well-warmed house, showed no very strong desire to take a walk in the January air. However, the hour arrived when his mistress urged upon him the necessity of a little constitutional, and he came trembling out into the presence of the cat he had wronged. You may imagine his relief when he found himself greeted with the utmost cordiality, and offered all the advantages of a warm though platonic friendship. His distrust was finally melted by an invitation to a complimentary place at the fish platter; he accepted with alacrity and joined her there that very midnight.

It is true that, when she saw him snugly devouring his

portion, his hostess was unable to repress a low rumbling in her throat, but this she may have explained as being due to the presence of a bone there. Alas, it was the very bone she had to pick with poor Papillon!

For some time these two were inseparable, and the whole town wondered at their friendship, and none more than the disappointed mercenaries, who, skulking around, were affronted by the sight of Kiki and her confidant taking their meals together. At other hours the oddly assorted pair were to be seen visiting various corners of the port, or sitting, their noses almost touching, for hours at a stretch, engaged in the endless quiet conversation of their kind. Unquestionably Kiki was hearing the most extraordinary stories about Marseille, and Papillon was being fully instructed in the amenities of La Caillot.

There came a day when two incredibly elongated clouds stretched themselves across the sky, and a chill came into the sunlight which made the flesh creep and crawl upon the bones. It was obvious that a mistral was on its way; the only question was, how long and how fiercely it might blow. Kiki sniffed the foreboding air and led Papillon out upon the jetty, where they spent another hour or so in the shelter of the sea wall. It was then that Kiki, deprecating her own hospitable platter, spoke fervently of her youthful voyages as a stowaway, and the flavour of the fresh caught sardine eaten while it was still leaping and quivering in the bottom of the boat.

Papillon, whose pleasures were confined to those of the table, was all the more an epicure on that account. He wiped a spot of eager saliva from his lip, and hastened to take a sniff at the boats that offered such divine opportunities. Kiki gave a three star recommendation to a crazy old hulk called *Les Frères Gobinet*, the least sea-worthy boat in all the port, and the infatuated greenhorn leapt aboard and concealed himself.

Kiki then returned to the Café Roustand, where the fishermen were gathered, debating whether to put to sea or not in face of the oncoming mistral. 'Don't worry,' said one of them as he caught sight of her. 'Look at Mademoiselle Kiki. She is calm; she is tranquil; she is completely at her ease.

You may take it from me the blow will die down before midnight.'

'I'm not so sure,' said another. 'It looks like being a regular hurricane.'

'If that was the case,' said a third, 'Kiki would be howling worse than the wind itself. She knows her stuff. She never fails. I've gone by Kiki for seven years now. She is better than a barometer; she is better than the radio, and I for one am not going to miss the catch.'

The discussion continued for some time, but Kiki's placid demeanour ultimately convinced even the most sceptical, and soon after midnight they one and all repaired to their boats.

Before dawn the worst mistral in living memory swept over the Bouches du Rhône. The fishing fleet was blown far out to sea, and when at last it limped back to port it reported the loss of *Les Frères Gobinet* with all hands.

Kiki was justly blamed. 'The dirty old bitch has deceived us,' said the fishermen. 'She knows no more about the weather than that post. She ought to be slung in the port.'

In spite of these hard words they still brought up the nightly mess of fish, because they had always done so. Kiki, as she had always done, ate but half the platterful, and it became known among the underprivileged of the cat world that a share of the remainder might be enjoyed by the industrious and deserving. The veterans of the informal little club resumed their midnight congregation, and Kiki raised her voice in complaint only when the approach of the bitter wind threatened an interruption of proceedings. This restored her reputation as a weather prophet, thus assuring a continuance of the offerings, and the vicious circle was intact again.

THE APE

by

V. S. PRITCHETT

(from *The Collected Stories of V. S. Pritchett*,
Chatto & Windus)

THE FRUIT robbery was over. It was the greatest fruit robbery, and from our point of view the most successful, ever known in our part of the jungle. Not that we can take all the credit for that, for it was not ourselves who started the fight but our enemies, a colony of apes who live in another tree. They were the first to attack and by the time the great slaughter was over, hundreds of their dead, of both sexes, lay on the ground, and we had taken all their fruit. It was a fortunate triumph for us.

But apes are not a complacent or ungrateful race. Once we were back in our tree binding up our wounds, we thought at once of commemorating our victory and thanking our god for it. For we are aware that if we do not thank our god for his benefactions he might well think twice before he sent us another fruit robbery of this triumphant kind. We thought, therefore, of how we might best please him. We tried to put ourselves in his place. What would most impress him? There were many discussions about this: we screamed and screeched in passionate argument and the din grew so loud – far louder than the noise we make in the ordinary business of eating or defending our places in the tree or making love and dying – that at last our oldest and wisest ape, who lived at the very top, slyly observed: 'If I were god and had been looking down at this tree of screeching monkeys for thousands of years, the thing that would really impress me would be silence.' We were dumbfounded. Then one or two of us shouted: 'That's got it. Let silence be the commemoration of our victory.'

So at last it was arranged. On the anniversary of the day when the great fruit robbery began, we arranged that all of us would stop whatever we were doing and would be silent.

But nothing is perfect in the jungle. You would think that all apes would be proud to be alike, and would have the wisdom to abide by the traditions of their race and the edicts of their leader. You would think all would destroy the individual doubt with the reflection that, however different an ape may fancy he is, the glory of the ape is that as he is now so he always has been, unchangeable and unchanged. There were, however, some, and one in particular as you will see, who did not think so.

We heard of them from a pterodactyl, a rather ridiculous neighbour of ours.

The pterodactyl lived on a cliff just above our tree and often, scaly and long-necked, he would flop clumsily down to talk to us. He was a sensationalist and newsmonger, a creature with more curiosity than brains. He was always worried. What (he would ask us) is the meaning of life? We scratched our heads. Where was it all leading? We spat out fruit pips. Did we apes think that we would always go on as we were? That question was easy. Of course, we said. How fortunate we were, he said, for he had doubts about himself. 'It seems to me that I am becoming – extinct,' he said.

It was all very well of us to make light of it, he said, but 'if I had not lived near you such an idea would never have entered my head'. We replied that we did not see what we had done to upset him. 'Oh, not you in particular,' he said. 'It is your young apes that are worrying me. They keep talking about their tails.' – 'No livelier or more flourishing subject,' we said. 'We apes delight in our tails.' – 'As far as I can see,' the pterodactyl said, 'among your younger apes, they are being worn shorter and will soon be discarded altogether.' – 'What!' we exclaimed – he could have touched us on no more sensitive spot – 'How dare you make such a suggestion!' – 'The suggestion,' the pterodactyl said, 'does not come from me but from your young apes. There's a group of them. They caught me by the neck the other day – I am very vulnerable in the neck – and ridiculed me publicly before a large audience. "A flying reptile," they said.

"Study him while you can for the species won't exist much longer – any more than *we apes shall go about on four legs and have tails*. We shall, at some unknown time in the future, but a time that comes rapidly nearer, cease to be apes. We shall become man. The pterodactyl, poor creature, came to the end of his evolutionary possibilities long ago."'

'Man!' we exclaimed. 'Man! What is that?' And what on earth, we asked the pterodactyl, did he mean by 'evolution'? We had never heard of it. We pressed the pterodactyl to tell us more, but he would only repeat what he had already said. When he had flopped back to his cliff again we sat scratching ourselves, deep in thought. Presently our old and wisest ape, a horny and scarred old warrior who sits dribbling away quietly to himself all day and rubbing his scars on the highest branch of all, gave a snigger and said, 'Cutting off their tails to spite the ape.' We did not laugh. We couldn't take the matter as lightly as he took it. We, on the contrary, raged. It was blasphemy. The joy, the pride, the whole apehood of us apes is in our tails. They are the flag under which we fight, the sheet-anchor of our patriotism, the vital insignia of our race. This young, decadent post-fruit-robbery generation was proposing to mutilate the symbol which is at the base of all our being. We did not hesitate. Spies were at once sent down to the lower branches to see if what the pterodactyl had told us was true and to bring the leader into our presence.

But before I tell what happened I must describe what life in our tree is like. The tree is a vast and leafy one, dense in the ramification of its twigs and branches. In the upper branches, where the air is freer and purer and the sunlight is plentiful, live those of us who are called the higher apes; in the branches below, and even to the bottom of the trunk, swarm the thousands of lower apes, clawing and scrambling over one another's backs, massing on the boughs until they nearly break, clutching at twigs and leaves, hanging on to one another's legs and tails and all bellowing and screeching in the struggle to get up a little higher and to find a place to sit, so that when we say, as we do, that the nature of life is struggle and war we are giving a faithful report from what is going on below us.

We in the upper branches eat our fruit in peace and spit out the pips and drop the rind upon the crowd below. It is they who, without of course intending to do so, bring us our food. Each of them carries fruit for himself, but the struggle is so violent that it is hard for them to hold the fruit or to find a quite place where they can eat it. Accordingly we send down some of our cleverer apes – those who are not quite at the top of the tree yet and perhaps will never get there because they have more brain than claw – and these hang down by their tails and adroitly flick the fruit out of the hands of the climbers. Very amusing it is to watch the astonishment of the climbers when they see their fruit go, because a minute before, they were full of confidence; then astonishment changes to anger and you see them grab the fruit from their nearest neighbours, who in turn grab from the next. Failing in this, they have to go down once more to the bottom to get more fruit and begin again; and as no part of the struggle is more difficult than the one which takes place at the bottom, an ape will go to any lengths, even to the risk of his life, to avoid that catastrophe. So for thousands of years have we lived, and only when fruit on our own tree is short or when we can bear no longer the sight of an abundance of fruit on another tree, occupied by just such a tribe of apes ourselves, do our masses cease their engaging civil struggle and at an order from us higher apes above, go forth upon our great fruit robberies. It is plain that if in any respect an ape ceased to be an ape, our greatness would decline, and anarchy would follow, i.e. how would we at the top get our food? – and we should lose our tree and be destroyed by some stronger tribe. Our thoughts can therefore be imagined when the spies brought before us the leader of that group of apes who were preparing to monkey with our dearest emblem. He stood before us – and that is astonishing, for we apes do not habitually stand for long. Then he was paler than our race usually is, less hairy, fearless – very un-apelike that – and upright on his hind legs, not seeking support for his fore-legs on some branch. These hung at his side or fidgeted with an aimless embarrassment behind his back. We growled at him and averted our eyes from his stupidly steadfast stare – for as a fighting race we are made subtle by fear and look restlessly, suspiciously around us, continually preparing for the sudden feint, the secret calculation, the necessary retreat, the unexpected attack. Nothing delivers an ape more readily to his enemy than a transparently straightforward look; but this upright ape had already lost so much of his apehood that he had forgotten the evasions of a warrior race. He was not even furtive. And in another way, too, he had lost our tradition. He spoke what was in his mind. This, I need hardly say, is ridiculous in a warrior whose business is to conceal his real purpose from his enemy. I note these facts merely as a matter of curiosity and to show how this new ape, from the very beginning, gave himself helplessly into our hands. We had supposed him to be guilty of race-treachery only, a bodily perversion which is, perhaps, a sin and not a crime – but the moment he spoke he went much farther. He accused himself of sedition from his own mouth. He spoke as follows:

'Since my arrest has given me an opportunity of speaking to higher apes for the first time in my life, I will speak what (perhaps unknown to you) has been in the minds of us who are lower in the tree for hundreds of years. We think that there is no greater evil than the vast fruit slaughters. Now there could be no slaughter if our teeth and claws were not sharp, and they would not be sharp if we were not perpetually engaged in struggles. We believe that a crucial time has arrived in the evolution' (we pricked up our ears at that word) 'of the ape. Our tails, that used to swirl us (as they waved above our heads) into bloodthirsty states of mind, are shortening; we have not shortened them ourselves by any act of will. If we apes will work to order our lives in a new way, the struggle will cease, no more great fruit slaughters will be necessary and everyone will have all the fruit he needs and can eat in peace in his appropriate place in the tree. For we do not think that even you in the higher branches for whom unconsciously we labour, really benefit by the great slaughters. Some of you are killed as thousands of us are, many of you are maimed and carry unbeautiful scars. From what we below hear of your private lives and talk in the upper branches, your privileges do not make you either sensible or happy.'

We were ready to fall upon him after this blasphemous speech, but our oldest ape, steeped in the wisdom and slyness of his great age, silenced us. 'And when there is a shortage of fruit for everyone in the tree, high and low alike?' he asked. 'If our teeth and claws are not sharpened,' replied the new ape, 'we shall not want to attack other trees but, when we need fruit, we shall go to the others and instead of tearing them apart we shall talk to them, stroke them and persuade them. They, seeing how gentle our hands are, will like being stroked and will smile and coo in their pleasure; for, as all of us apes know from intimate experience, there is nothing more delightful than a gentle tickling and scratching – and then they will share their fruit with us.' – 'What a hope!' we laughed. And some cried with disgust, 'That ape's a pansy!' But a shout went up from the lower branches where a mass of his supporters were gathered. 'You'd better do as he says,' the cry came, 'or soon there will be none of us left to bring you your fruit.' 'Yes,' said the leader, 'another fruit robbery and there will be no more workers for you to steal from.'

'Now,' we whispered to our oldest ape on the highest branch, 'now let us kill him.'

'Remember,' said the old one, 'that he has followers. They are too many for us and we are unprepared.'

This was true, so, reluctantly, we let the leader go and swing back down the branches to his own people.

After he had gone we gathered in conference in the upper branches. When we were seated, our oldest ape said: 'No doubt to you there seems to be something new, startling and dangerous in the speech you have just heard. I expect you think it the speech of a revolutionary. So it is – but there's nothing new in that. From the beginning of time there have been revolutions, and what difference do they make? None whatever. Everything goes on afterwards exactly as it went on before. Do not worry therefore about revolutionaries. I have seen dozens of such people and with a little art they can be made to die very comfortably of their own enthusiasm. And, in one way, I agree with what that strange ape said. He said that violence is wasteful. It is – for to exterminate our own workers would mean that we would be without food or would have to go down out of our comfortable places in the tree and get it for ourselves. That would indeed be a calamity. No, I think if we wish to remove the danger from this particular movement we should support it.'

'Support blasphemy and treachery?' we cried with indignation.

'Ah!' exclaimed the old ape wistfully. 'There speaks the honest warrior. But I am old and political and it would seem to me a mistake to let all that enthusiasm get out of our hands. After our last great fruit robbery we are rather tired, you know, and enthusiasm is not easily come by again.'

'But our tails!' we shouted.

'Your honour and your tails!' said our weary and ancient one. 'I guarantee to show you such a display of tails wagging, curling, prehensile and triumphant as you have never seen before.'

'Well, if your plan will safeguard our sacred tails and preserve us from evolution,' we said, 'there may be something in it. Tell us what it is.'

'It is very simple,' he said. 'First of all we shall announce the end of all fruit robbery . . .'

'Impossible,' we interrupted.

'It is never impossible to *announce* anything,' he said. 'I repeat we shall announce the end of all fruit robbery. But the lower ape is an emotional creature. It is useless to argue with him – indeed we know that the free interchange of ideas in open argument is extremely dangerous, for the lower apes are hungry and hunger sharpens the mind, just as it sharpens the claws. No, we must appeal to his emotions, for it is here that he is untrained and inexperienced. So when we announce the end of all fruit robbery we must perform an act which shall symbolize our intention. That is easy. Almost anything would do. The best, I think, would be merely to alter the date of the commemoration of our last robbery from the anniversary of its call to battle to the day on which it ended and when peace was declared. I'll lay you a hundred to one in pomegranates that you will see the tails wag on that day.'

We who listened were doubtful of the success of a trick so simple and, moreover, we were disappointed not to have the opportunity of killing the rebel ape. But when we heard the enthusiasm in the lower branches, we realized that our oldest ape had judged rightly. Those short-tailed evolutionists were so diddled that they shouted for joy. 'Peace!' 'The end of all fruit robberies.' 'To each according to his needs' – we above heard their delirious cries and winked. And when the inquisitive pterodactyl came down to see what it was all about, we slapped him on the back and pulled his wings about merrily and nearly choked him with pomegranate seeds, which do not agree with him. 'Cheer up, you're not extinct yet,' we said. And even that cheerless reptile, though he said his nerves couldn't stand monkey tricks any more, had to smile.

And the ceremony took place. We appointed the day, and just before noon the yelling ceased and all the struggling and climbing. Just where they were, on whatever twig or branch, our apes coiled their tails and squatted in silence. The only movement was the blinking of our eyes, thousands of eyes in the hot rays of the sun. I do not know if you have ever seen a tree full of apes squatting in silence on their haunches. It is an impressive sight. There was our oldest ape on the topmost branch; a little beneath him was our circle of privileged ones, and below, thick in the descending hierarchy, were the others.

And then, before a minute had gone by, an event occurred which filled us with horror. The lengths to which blasphemy will go were revealed to us. Taking advantage of the stillness of the multitude, an ape leapt up the tree, from back to back, from branch to branch, and burst through our unprepared ranks at the top. It was the leader to whom we had spoken.

'This is a fraud,' he shouted. 'You are pretending to

commemorate peace when all the time you are planning greater robberies. You are not even silent. Listen to the grinding and sharpening of your claws and teeth.'

It was, of course, our habit. We do it unconsciously.

Too startled for a moment to act, we hesitated. Then: 'Lynch him. Kill him,' cried the crowd with a sudden roar. We hesitated no more and at least a score of us leapt upon him. You would think we had an easy task. But there was extra-ordinary strength in that creature. He fought like a god, skil-fully, and he had laid out half of our number with a science and ferocity such as we had never seen before our numbers over-whelmed him. Some spirit must have been in him and we still wonder, not without apprehension, if that spirit is lying asleep in his followers. However that may be, we threw him down at last upon the branch. Our oldest ape came down to look upon the panting creature and then what we saw made us gasp. He was lying on his face. There was a backside bare and hairless – he had no tail. No tail at all.

'It is man!' we cried. And our stomachs turned.

THE GOAT

by

GERALD BULLETT

(from *Ten Minute Tales*, J. M. Dent & Sons)

THE THEORY advanced by some audacious thinkers, that men
are more sensible than goats, simply will not do. All human
history is against it. When we were first married, six months
after the First World War, Lucy and I, just turned twenty-
three, set up house together in a wooden bungalow which I,
behind her back, had had built to my own design and paid for
(partly) with my army gratuity. It stood in the middle of an
Essex field, of which one acre, fenced round with barbed wire,
was all my own. It was solitary and inaccessible, except to the
most rugged and adventurous spirits, which was just how
we liked it. It was also cheap, which we liked still more. A
mud track led from the edge of our acre to a deep-rutted lane,
at the top of which, two miles away, stood the nearest shop:
a small general store which was also the post office.

We were not entirely without neighbours, for in the con-
tiguous acre lived Mr Curricle, the man who had sold me mine
and built me my bungalow. It was his advertisement in a
weekly paper that had brought me to this spot: 'Bungalows
while you wait, 1-acre plots, freehold, from £395 inclusive,
I'm your man, Curricle.'

He proved as good as his word. He *was* our man. We had no
fault to find with Mr Curricle, except that he had oddly forgotten to mention that we should have to fetch our milk every
morning from a distant farmhouse. This meant that breakfast
got later and later as the weeks went by, and half the morning would be gone before I could get to my study and begin
work.

'What you want,' said Mr Curricle, 'is a goat.'

'Do I? I wonder.'

'Nothing like goat's milk,' said Mr Curricle. 'Look at me.'

I looked at him obediently: a wizened little man in his middle fifties.

'Sweet as a nut,' said Mr Curricle. 'Me, I never drink anything else.'

But it was not the ambition to be like Mr Curricle that decided us to keep a goat. It was the glorious prospect of being independent, self-supporting, living on the produce of our own acre. We had water from a newly dug well, the hardest and dirtiest water in England. We grew potatoes, carrots, cabbages, and largely lived on them. We planned to have fruit: the apple-trees were already four feet high. And now, with a goat, we should have an inexhaustible supply of milk, butter, and cheese. The goat would be a real treasure. Why hadn't we thought of her before? She would do everything for us except lay eggs. And eggs, the best in Essex he assured us, were to be had, luckily, from Mr Curricle himself, who was the owner of a dozen exemplary hens and a strutting rooster.

Mr Curricle, the best of neighbours, organized the whole affair. He knew where we could buy the best goat in England, and he told us how to get there. The goat-farm was situated on the Essex coast, within a mile or two of the open sea. We arrived on bicycles, dusty and eager, one September afternoon, and were handsomely entertained by three strapping young women in a room whose ample windows overlooked a broad estuary. Strapping but pretty. It was still a novelty in these days, let me remind you, to see girls in knee-breeches and bobbed hair. They welcomed us kindly, gave us tea, talked goat for three-quarters of an hour, and then took us to meet Linda, whom they felt sure we should like.

'She's quite a character, is Linda,' they said.

I could see that for myself, as soon as I set eyes on the animal. I had never seen a more ornamental goat. And from the sly, satirical look she gave me I guessed that she would be a companion about the place, as well as a source of milk, butter, and cheese. She would save us no end of trudging through muddy lanes in search of supplies, and her presence in our acre would give it just the touch of domesticity it lacked.

Lucy wasn't quite so sure, but she needed only a little persuasion, and we rode home in high spirits. A new life was about to begin for us.

And so it was, and so it did. We started off in fine style. Mr Curricle, helpful as ever, drove over and brought Linda back with him in his dog-cart, and showed me, by demonstration, how to milk her. Watching him, I could see it was ridiculously easy.

'You've a bargain here,' said Mr Curricle. 'She's got spirit, this goat has, and a mind of her own. Intelligent. That's what she is.'

'Yes, indeed,' I said. 'And a wonderful milker. My only doubt is whether she'll be happy with us. I suppose it wouldn't do to let her run loose?'

'No,' said Mr Curricle. 'I wouldn't recommend that. She'd eat everything in sight, including the barbed wire fencing. Keep her on a short tether – and near the house, for company like. She's almost human, this goat is. Mustn't let her feel lonely and start fretting. Talk to her, mister. Tell her some of those stories you're always scribbling. Make a real friend of her, that's the way to get the best results. I did you a good turn when I put you on to goats,' said Mr Curricle, 'though I says it myself.'

I believed him, and said so. His optimism was infectious.

'Later on,' said Mr Curricle, 'if you take my advice, you'll get a billy and breed from her. Why, before you know where you are you'll have a goat-farm of your own and be supplying all the neighbours, let alone winning first prize at the shows. Very profitable line. A long sight better than writing, and, what's more, useful.'

Mr Curricle had a poor opinion of literature. He thought it a harmless eccentricity but no occupation for an able-bodied young man.

Next morning, when I rolled up my sleeves and approached

Linda with my milking-pail, she didn't look quite so friendly.

'Come along, old girl,' I said, remembering Mr Curricle's exhortation. 'We want some milk for breakfast. You've got it. We want it. It's all fair enough.'

'Who are you calling old girl?' said Linda's bleak eye.

'Well, Linda then,' I said, 'if it's standing on your dignity you are.' I thought a touch of stage-Irish might help to create the right homely atmosphere. 'Come along now. Stand still, do.'

She stood still for ten seconds, then jerked away and began going round in her narrow circle, pulling hard on the chain. I followed her placatingly, with soothing noises. I smothered her with flattery, expatiating on her beauty, good temper, and general excellence. I knew, I said, that she was a good goat at heart. It was only a question of our getting to know each other. She said nothing, continued to dodge and duck and keep just out of my reach; and her silence, which in so talented a creature struck me as unnatural, was oddly intimidating. At last I lost my temper, shortened the tether, cornered her, and in the course of half an hour's gruelling hard work managed to extract from her perhaps a teacupful of the precious milk.

I took it, in sombre triumph, to Lucy, who was waiting impatiently in the kitchen.

'Looks good, doesn't it?' I said heartily. 'Not *quite* as much as we hoped for, but she'll do better next time.'

'That'll be wonderful,' said Lucy. 'We'll make what's left over into butter.'

I didn't altogether like her tone, and when the next milking-time came round, at four o'clock in the afternoon, I thought it best to solicit Mr Curricle's help. Linda behaved like an angel, and he got about a pint in no time.

'That's the style,' said Mr Curricle. 'Easy as kiss your hand.'

As soon as his back was turned I thought to have a little conversation with Linda. But the look she gave me made me think better of it. Something was evidently rankling in that goatish mind. We hadn't yet arrived at an understanding.

*

That conjecture was amply confirmed during the long hours of the night. Lucy and I went soberly to bed. I had had a profitless day, no work done; and Lucy, usually so buoyant, seemed to have something on her mind. Our friend Linda, lest she should feel lonely, was tethered just outside our bedroom window. Resolved to let bygones be bygones, I had wished her a cordial good night and expressed the hope, in Lucy's hearing, that we should all feel better in the morning.

'There's one thing,' I said, as I got into bed, 'she's a nice quiet animal.'

'Is she?' said Lucy.

We lay side by side in the darkness, waiting for sleep. The sweet smell of the countryside, delicately flavoured with Linda, floated in through the window. The silence was deep and blissful. Dreams gathered about me, and just as I was dropping off into deep sleep a noise from outside jerked me back to a consciousness of where I was. It was dear little Linda rattling her chain. She continued to rattle it, at cunningly calculated intervals, throughout the night. It was a masterly performance. She would wait till we were relaxed by a long silence, and nearly asleep, and then, with careful malice, get up on her four feet, plunge about, and rattle her chain, with a noise like crashing fire-irons.

'There's a devil in that goat,' I said, as the clock in the next room struck three.

'Such a nice companion,' said Lucy.

Day followed day in the same monotonous pattern. Linda continued to dislike me, and I am bound to confess that I did not learn to love Linda. Soon Mr Curricle was visiting us twice a day to perform his good offices, and what could I do but give him most of the milk-yield by way of recompense for his trouble? We gave up having porridge for breakfast, restricted our consumption of coffee to one cup each, and tried without much success to pretend that we enjoyed salted tea. Sweet as a nut, Mr Curricle had said. But we could not agree with him. We began to think wistfully of cows.

At last I resolved to have it out with Linda.

'Look, Linda, my dear girl,' I said, 'this can't go on.'

'Can't it?' said Linda, in effect. 'We shall see.'

'It's time we had a frank talk,' I said. 'What's on your mind? What have you got against me?'

'As if you didn't know!' sneered Linda. 'I had a kid back there, only just weaned. And weaned too soon, what's more. Separating mother and child! You ought to be ashamed of yourself!'

Having no answer for that, I said: 'Come, Linda, be reasonable. You give milk to old Curricle fast enough. Why this invidious distinction between us?'

'That's neither here nor there,' said Linda. And not another word could I get out of her.

Next morning, by heaven's mercy, she was gone, taking her chain and tether-post with her. We never saw her again.

'It's my belief she's gone back where she came from,' I told Lucy. 'I see her point.'

'Oh, you do, do you?' said Lucy.

'They're nice girls, those three sisters. I should quite like to see them again myself,' I said. 'I mean I should if I were a goat,' I added hurriedly, seeing the frost in her eye.

'You *are* a goat, dear,' said Lucy.

BEDROOM SCENE

by

JOHN GLOAG

(from *It Makes a Nice Change*, by permission of the Author and A. D. Peters)

MR LIONEL BUCKBY was the only passenger to leave the train at Brown Earth. The station was deserted. It was a dark night. There were no lights. The train steamed away, and the hoarse baying of the locomotive, whistling for grade crossings, drowned out the diminishing sound of its tolling bell. In all his journeying in the States Mr Buckby had never felt so isolated, so small, and so abjectly neglected as he felt at eleven o'clock on that autumn night in the heart of the Middle West. He picked up his suitcase and wondered whether he ought to find somewhere to wait. His host had promised to meet him, but perhaps he had mistaken the time.

He put the heavy suitcase down again. There didn't seem to be anywhere to go. No glimmer of a town, only the dim, unlit outlines of a sort of shack which marked the position of the station. There wasn't even a seat. Then he saw the flicker of headlights in the distance, and presently a huge car came roaring up. His host alighted and was introductory and apologetic.

'I'm Julian Scumber,' he said, 'and I'm real sorry you've been kept waiting. I've come from Cold Green, and there's been a crash back there on the road. A lot of circus stuff on the move, and some of it's got badly mixed.'

As he spoke a large, dark shape lolled through the open window of the car. It yawned at them, and Mr Buckby started back at the sudden sight of such a well-armed mouth.

'Get in, Razzle,' said Mr Scumber.

'Er – an Alsatian?' inquired Mr Buckby nervously.

'Mixture,' said Mr Scumber; 'with a bit of timber wolf in it, I guess. But get in Mr Buckby – I'll fix your traps.'

Presently they were driving along a straight wide road through flat country, while the hot breath of the great beast in the back of the car puffed on to the back of Mr Buckby's neck. He disliked dogs, and Razzle obviously knew this, and Mr Buckby wondered whether his dislike would be actively resented by the hundred and fifty pounds of fur and muscle that was so infernally close.

Mr Scumber drove fast, and he chatted with respectful but continuous energy.

'I'm flattered that you should make the journey out here to look at my collection,' was the burden of his talk, in different (but not very different) arrangements of words. His guest occasionally interposed a weak repetition to the effect that he had always heard that Kane Hill, Mr Scumber's house, contained the finest collection of Colonial furniture in America. To which the reply was: 'Yes, *sir*! And it's a big thing for me that such an eminent expert as you should make the journey to take a look at it.'

'Not at all,' Mr Buckby would say in a tone from which all suspicion of geniality was extracted, for Razzle was sniffing the back of his neck at short intervals, as though prospecting for a suitable locality for biting. Curse the brute! Would the drive never end?

It ended at the summit of a steep little hill, approached by a winding road through a wood. The car halted, and soon Mr Buckby was warming himself at a fire of sweet-scented apple-wood that blazed in a comfortable open fireplace. Razzle lay sprawled on the hearthrug; a sleek, glossy black, handsome creature, with tall ears, alertly upraised, and a friendly face. Electric light made Mr Buckby bold enough to pat his head, but Razzle was unresponsive, and looked inquiringly at his master as if to say: 'Am I to stand this sort of thing, boss, or shall I let him have it?'

Mr Scumber regarded him with affection.

'He's a good dog,' he observed; 'he's the only one we like to have around the house; the scale's a bit too large for comfort with his breed.'

Mr Buckby took this in with gradually increasing discomfort.

'Have you other dogs like him, then?' he asked.

'Three,' said Mr Scumber carelessly.

'Oh,' said Mr Buckby.

'Did I tell you I think I've got a Nicholas Disbrowe chest?' said Mr Scumber, settling down to the full enjoyment of a collector's secondary pleasure, which is talking about his collection. And when his guest was thawed by the fire and internally illuminated by some rye whisky, he indulged the collector's primary pleasure, which is showing his collection.

Mr Buckby did his best, but he was less interested in the rather crude mid-seventeenth century 'finds' which thrilled Mr Scumber than in the later Colonial work. There was an indisputable Duncan Phyfe work table, an airy delicate shape, with little lines of inlaid brass flashing in the ruddy mahogany. It represented the peak of American achievement in furniture design before the bad taste of the nineteenth century washed away all the Colonial traditions.

'French-looking stuff,' was Mr Scumber's dismissive comment; 'now look at this – this has age, sir. *And* human associations.'

Mr Buckby examined a clumsy assembly of oak boards with a little carving hacked out on the front of them. It was an ill-proportioned, inconvenient cupboard.

'I like a thing to have hundreds of years of use back of it,' said the collector fondly.

Mr Buckby would like to have said that age and use were poor substitutes for good design; but he shrank from an ill-mannered display of his own taste, and he was humbly reticent also about his suspicion that the exhibit was younger than its owner supposed. He was determined that nothing he said or did in this large friendly country, with its infinite hospitality, should spread the belief that Englishmen were sniffy and consciously superior strangers. The result was that he managed to feel at home wherever he went, and if it wasn't for that confounded dog he'd feel at home here. Razzle pattered round with them, as Mr Scumber went from room to room.

'I'm more sorry than I can say that Mrs Scumber's in California,' he had been told; 'she loves talking about antique furniture. She wouldn't have let you off easily.'

Mr Buckby was relieved. People had been talking to him about antique furniture for nearly twenty years; writing to him about it, and making him write and talk about it; all because he had a flair for identifying the right stuff. Unfortunately that flair was unallied with any commercial sense, so he remained a humble, incorruptible expert; and the rewards that await the dealer seldom came to his pockets.

It was an hour after the thirty-two clocks in the collection at Kane Hill filled the house with melodious chimes for nearly five minutes, as they all struck their own interpretations of midnight, when Mr Scumber glanced at his watch and said: 'Mr Buckby – I just must ask you to forgive me. I've been keeping you up, sir, talking about this collection of mine, when you've had a long journey. I'll show you your room right away.'

It was a big bedroom, with a balcony outside the tall window. The moon had risen, and the tree-tops of the belt of woods that encircled Kane Hill resembled silver flakes fluttering in a dark morass. The balcony was protected by fine mesh wire screens.

'Slide them back if you want to,' said Mr Scumber, when Mr Buckby fiddled with one of them; 'there aren't any mosquitoes now.'

So Mr Buckby, who liked fresh air, and had an irrational idea that he wouldn't get so much of it through wire netting, opened the screens, and when his host left him he stood on the balcony for some time before undressing. It was only a few feet from the ground, and the hill sloped steeply from it down to the woods. Those woods were very dark and still. The whole country was silent, although now and then he thought he heard a far-off wailing sound, which probably came from some distant freight train, the faint echo of a whistle.

There was a small fire in the bedroom, more for display than for heat, for two radiators provided a hot-house temperature until Mr Buckby turned them off. A bathroom opened out of the bedroom. It had a small window, which Mr Buckby threw open after he had enjoyed a steaming bath.

Just as he was ready to get into bed he heard a deep snort, followed by a soft, labial sound. It seemed to be in the room, and it seemed only prudent to look under the bed, although it was nearly a minute before Mr Buckby could decide whether he wanted to do so.

There was nothing under the bed.

He examined the interior of the wardrobe. He glanced into the bathroom – just to make sure. It was empty. Then he decided he would open the bedroom door, and after a few seconds he turned the handle, and opened the door about three inches. Another snort greeted him, and the light from the bedroom disclosed the ample black outlines of Razzle lying upon the doormat just outside. The dog sat up. There was an unpleasant suggestion of a sentinel about his pose.

Mr Buckby hastily shut the door. There was a thud immediately afterwards, as Razzle lay back against it.

'I suppose he'll stay there all night,' said Mr Buckby to himself. Well, anyway the brute couldn't get in; and with this comforting thought in his mind, he got into the canopied double bed and switched out the light.

The air was cold and sharp with autumn scents, and sweetened by the burning wood in the fireplace. Mr Buckby sank into a deep, refreshing sleep, from which he was awakened by a scrabbling, scratching noise in the balcony.

He sat up in bed and looked at the luminous dial of his watch. It was three o'clock.

The bed creaked as he sat up, and immediately the noise in the balcony stopped. The moonlight shone through the window. He could see the thin metal uprights from which he had pushed the wire screens, black and sharp against the pallid sky. Shadows were spotted all over the bedroom, and the lower part of the balcony was a black mystery. If anything was there it was well hidden.

His hand fumbled for the switch, but he paused. If he switched on the light, wouldn't he be illuminating himself for the benefit of the intruder, if there was an intruder.

The scratching was suddenly resumed.

'Mice!' said Mr Buckby to himself; 'or even rats,' he added; but he remained sitting up in bed, tense and watchful. And then, did he imagine it, or did the balcony momentarily upraise itself? A humped shape seemed to rise into view against the moonlight and to sink down again immediately.

He couldn't be quite sure whether it was imagination or not. It was so vague. Just a sudden elevation of some curved, bulky object; some crouching body.

'A burglar, perhaps,' was Mr Buckby's next idea; and his apprehension was subdued slightly; although with an American burglar one had to be careful. They shot on sight; or were apt to; usually with a machine gun; or so he had been given to understand by Hollywood; but maybe he was mixing them up with gangsters. Were there independent burglars in the States, or did they always belong to a gang? Anyway, they were bound to be pretty lethal if disturbed in a bedroom during the practice of their profession. Lord! What should one *do*? His hand was still on the switch, and accidentally he turned on the light.

There was a low, muttering snarl.

Momentarily he was dazzled, and then he saw Razzle sitting in the balcony, scratching himself.

Wait a minute, though. Was it Razzle?

The creature seemed larger, and was a dirty grey-black. It must be one of the other brutes that Scumber kept roving about the place. Damn all people who kept dogs! Great, noisy, disturbing, frightening brutes; smelly, too. There was a harsh, sour smell of decay creeping into the room.

The visitor sat up and licked his lips. Its jaw was dark and dripping, and it rasped a long pink tongue over those dank surfaces of fur with apparent relish. Mr Buckby had an unpleasant notion that it had just eaten something raw and bloody.

'I expect it's been hunting rabbits,' he explained, and the

theory that it had been hunting something was supported when he noticed that some mangled furry shape lay at its feet, torn and oozing redly from rents in its grey matted fur. It was odd, fleecy sort of fur.

He thought that Scumber might have trained his dogs more thoroughly. It was a bit steep that they should come and finish their meals in the guest rooms. Well, what should he do? The dog never looked at him directly; but as it moved its head he caught a flash of green in its eyes; pale green lights with a hot red spot in the centre of each.

Should he order it out of the room?

He had no ideas about ordering dogs to do anything; only a conviction that they would never take the slightest notice of anything he said to them. Besides, was it exactly polite to shout commands at one's host's possessions? It might be a custom of the house for a guardian dog to slip in and look after the safety of the guest. After all, he was in America, and there were gangsters and thugs and hi-jackers (although he hadn't the remotest idea what *they* were), and you never *knew*. There was always the unexpected adventure, ready to engulf people who had a fondness for comfort in new and unwanted experiences.

He decided to address the creature.

'Get out!' he said sternly.

The brute yawned in his face, and shifted about in the balcony, and then stretched full length, and began to arrange itself for sleep.

'No,' said Mr Buckby, aloud. 'No, I can't have that, you know.'

He got out of bed.

'Go on, good dog – get outside,' he commanded.

He was answered by a growl, and the grey dog stood up. It seemed as large as a calf.

'Oh, Lord!' said Mr Buckby, wishing that he had never got out of bed. He stood irresolute. He wanted to call somebody to turn this beast out of the bedroom; but it would look so ill-mannered, and, also, Razzle was probably the other side of the door.

F

The brute yawned again and a carrion reek came from its throat. That was too much. It was unendurable, and at the risk of being thought peculiar, and even fussy, Mr Buckby put on his dressing-gown and slippers, and was about to venture out for assistance. They would certainly make allowances for a foreigner, and he would be properly apologetic about it. He glanced at the balcony again, and saw the brute had disappeared. For a moment he wondered whether it had jumped out the way it came, and then he saw it had come into the room. It was now between him and the bedroom door.

Mr Buckby retreated to the bathroom, and locked himself in. There was nothing else to be done. No doubt the brute would leave the room again after it had slept. Meanwhile he had his dressing-gown, thank goodness and the bathroom was warm. He could sit on the stool and doze. Wait a minute, he could do better than that. There were lots of towels, and if he wiped out the bath, he could improvise a shake-down with all those large luxurious bath towels in the bath itself.

He closed the window. And, wrapped in his dressing-gown, and with three hand towels over him and two big, dry bath towels under him, he dropped off to sleep, feeling exhausted.

It was long past dawn when he woke, and for a moment he could not remember why he was sleeping in the bathroom. He had an uneasy space, wondering whether the whole thing was a nightmare, and his couch in the bathroom the result of an over-dose of rye whisky. No – the peculiar discomforts of the night had been too real. He opened the window. Then he had to make up his mind to open the door.

He unlocked it, and heard a faint, menacing snarl, and the bed creaked as some weight was released from it. He locked the door again. Not even daylight gave him the courage to cope with the savage hound. Ill-mannered though it might be, he must keep a look-out through the bathroom window, and call for assistance when he saw anybody. It was eight o'clock. Breakfast, he remembered, was at half past. Perhaps somebody would call him.

At twenty past eight, he saw Mr Scumber walking up the hill from the woods. He hailed him.

'Good morning!' cried Mr Scumber. 'Glad to see you're up. I've been out after the dogs – can't find any of them this morning. Hope you've slept well.'

This was easy. Ignoring the last remark, Mr Buckby gave a little nervous laugh, and said: 'One of your dogs spent the night with me – he's still in the bedroom.'

'What!' exclaimed Mr Scumber. 'Why didn't you turn him out? Hi, Razzle –'

'It isn't Razzle,' interrupted Mr Buckby.

Mr Scumber put a little silver whistle to his lips and blew three short blasts.

Nothing happened.

'Say, just stir him out of that,' said Mr Scumber; 'he's no business in there.'

'Oh, well, I didn't like to seem unfriendly,' said his guest. 'Perhaps he's taken to me.'

Mr Scumber whistled again, and walked round out of sight to the balcony.

'Come on!' he shouted.

'Mind if I come in,' he called up to Mr Buckby, walking round to the bathroom window again.

'Do.'

And from the bathroom Mr Buckby heard his host come striding along the corridor, and open the bedroom door.

There was a snarl from the bed, and the door was slammed.

'Where are you, Mr Buckby?' shouted Scumber.

'In the bathroom.'

'Just you stay there – I'll be right back.'

He heard him running down the corridor, and he was back in a few seconds. The bedroom door was flung open, and a roaring snarl was cut short by two revolver shots.

Mr Buckby emerged from the bathroom.

His host was standing over a gigantic dusty grey shape that had collapsed over the bed. On the balcony floor were the partially devoured fragments of a sheep.

'Oh, dear,' said Mr Buckby, 'then it wasn't your dog?'

Mr Scumber looked surprised.

'Dog – nothing!' he said. 'It's a wolf – I guess it got away from that circus smash I passed when I was meeting you. D'you mean to say it's been in with you here all night?'

'Not exactly,' Mr Buckby explained; 'I slept quite well in the bathroom.'

'But – why didn't you call me up?'

'Well, I, er – I didn't like to be a nuisance, and I did think it was one of your dogs, perhaps.'

'Say, you must have had a hell of a night.'

'Not at all,' Mr Buckby assured him. He was rather embarrassed. 'I wonder,' he said, hoping to turn the conversation, 'whether it hurt any of your dogs?'

'Not likely,' said Mr Scumber; 'I guess they've bolted. They're too tame to be much use in an emergency.'

ON GUARD

by

EVELYN WAUGH

(from *Mr Loveday's Little Outing*)

MILLICENT BLADE had a notable head of naturally fair hair; she had a docile and affectionate disposition, and an expression of face which changed with lightning rapidity from amiability to laughter and from laughter to respectful interest. But the feature which, more than any other, endeared her to sentimental Anglo-Saxon manhood was her nose.

It was not everybody's nose; many prefer one with greater body; it was not a nose to appeal to painters, for it was far too small and quite without shape, a mere dab of putty without apparent bone structure; a nose which made it impossible for its wearer to be haughty or imposing or astute. It would not have done for a governess or a 'cellist or even for a post office clerk, but it suited Miss Blade's book perfectly, for it was a nose that pierced the thin crust of the English heart to its warm and pulpy core; a nose to take the thoughts of English manhood back to its schooldays, to the doughty-faced urchins on whom it had squandered its first affection, to memories of changing-room and chapel and battered straw boaters. Three English-men in five it is true, grow snobbish about these things in later life and prefer a nose that makes more show in public – but two in five is an average with which any girl of modest fortune may be reasonably content.

Hector kissed her reverently on the tip of this nose. As he did so, his senses reeled and in momentary delirium he saw the fading light of the November afternoon, the raw mist spreading over the playing-fields; overheated youth in the scrum; frigid youth at the touchline, shuffling on the duckboards, chafing their fingers and, when their mouths were emptied of biscuit crumbs, cheering their house team to further exertion.

'You will wait for me, won't you?' he said.

'Yes, darling.'

'And you will write?'

'Yes, darling,' she replied more doubtfully, 'sometimes . . . at least I'll try. Writing is not my best thing, you know.'

'I shall think of you all the time. Out There,' said Hector. 'It's going to be terrible – miles of impassable wagon track between me and the nearest white man, blinding sun, lions, mosquitoes, hostile natives, work from dawn until sunset singlehanded against the forces of Nature, fever, cholera. . . . But soon I shall be able to send for you to join me.'

'Yes, darling.'

'It's bound to be a success. I've discussed it all with Beck-thorpe – that's the chap who's selling me the farm. You see the crop has failed every year so far – first coffee, then sisal, then tobacco, that's all you can grow there, and the year Beckthorpe grew sisal, everyone else was making a packet in tobacco, but sisal was no good; then he grew tobacco, but by then it was coffee he ought to have grown, and so on. He stuck it for nine years. Well if you work it out mathematically, Beckthorpe says, in three years one's bound to strike the right crop. I can't quite explain why but it is like roulette and all that sort of thing, you see.'

'Yes, darling.'

Hector gazed at her little, shapeless, mobile button of a nose and was lost again. . . . 'Play up, play up,' and after the match the smell of crumpets being toasted over a gas-ring in his study. . . .

Later that evening he dined with Beckthorpe, and, as he dined, he grew more despondent.

'Tomorrow this time I shall be at sea,' he said, twiddling his empty port glass.

'Cheer up, old boy,' said Beckthorpe.

Hector filled his glass and gazed with growing distaste round the reeking dining-room of Beckthorpe's club. The last awful member had left the room and they were alone with the cold buffet.

'I say, you know, I've been trying to work it out. It *was* in three years you said the crop was bound to be right, wasn't it?'

'That's right, old boy.'

'Well, I've been through the sum and it seems to me that it may be eighty-one years before it comes right.'

'No, no, old boy, three or nine or at the most twenty-seven.'

'Are you sure?'

'Quite.'

'Good . . . you know it's awful leaving Milly behind. Suppose it *is* eighty-one years before the crop succeeds. It's the devil of a time to expect a girl to wait. Some other blighter might turn up, if you see what I mean.'

'In the Middle Ages they used to use girdles of chastity.'

'Yes, I know. I've been thinking of them. But they sound damnably uncomfortable. I doubt if Milly would wear one even if I knew where to find it.'

'Tell you what, old boy. You ought to give her something.'

'Hell, I'm always giving her things. She either breaks them or loses them or forgets where she got them.'

'You must give her something she will always have by her, something that will last.'

'Eighty-one years?'

'Well, say, twenty-seven. Something to remind her of you.'

'I could give her a photograph – but I might change a bit in twenty-seven years.'

'No, no, that would be most unsuitable. A photograph wouldn't do at all. I know what I'd give her. I'd give her a dog.'

'Dog?'

'A healthy puppy that was over distemper and looking like living a long time. She might even call it Hector.'

'Would that be a good thing, Beckthorpe?'

'Best possible, old boy.'

So next morning, before catching the boat train, Hector

hurried to one of the mammoth stores of London and was shown to the livestock department. 'I want a puppy.'

'Yes, sir, any particular sort?'

'One that will live a long time. Eighty-one years, or twenty-seven at the least.'

The man looked doubtful. 'We have some fine healthy puppies of course,' he admitted, 'but none of them carry a guarantee. Now if it was longevity you wanted, might I recommend a tortoise. They live to an extraordinary age and are very safe in traffic.'

'No, it must be a pup.'

'Or a parrot?'

'No, no, a pup. I would prefer one named Hector.'

They walked together past monkeys and kittens and cockatoos to the dog department which, even at this early hour, had attracted a small congregation of rapt worshippers. There were puppies of all varieties in wire fronted kennels, ears cocked, tails wagging, noisily soliciting attention. Rather wildly, Hector selected a poodle and, as the salesman disappeared to fetch him his change, he leant down for a moment's intense communion with the beast of his choice. He gazed deep into the sharp face, avoided a sudden snap and said with profound solemnity:

'You are to look after Milly, Hector. See that she doesn't marry anyone until I get back.'

And the pup Hector waved his plume of tail.

Millicent came to see him off, but, negligently, went to the wrong station; it could not have mattered, however, for she was twenty minutes late. Hector and the poodle hung about the barrier looking for her, and not until the train was already moving did he bundle the animal into Beckthorpe's arms with instructions to deliver him at Millicent's address. Luggage labelled for Mombassa, 'Wanted on the voyage', lay in the rack above him. He felt very much neglected.

That evening as the ship pitched and rolled past the Channel lighthouses, he received a radiogram: *Miserable to miss you went*

Paddington like idiot thank you thank you for sweet dog I love him father minds dreadfully longing to hear about farm dont fall for ship siren love Milly.

In the Red Sea he received another: *Beware sirens puppy bit man called Mike.*

After that Hector heard nothing of Millicent except for a Christmas card which arrived in the last days of February.

Generally speaking, Millicent's fancy for any particular young man was likely to last four months. It depended on how far he had got in that time whether the process of extinction was sudden or protracted. In the case of Hector her affection had been due to diminish at about the time she became engaged to him; it had been artificially prolonged during the succeeding three weeks, during which he made strenuous, infectiously earnest efforts to find employment in England; it came to an abrupt end with his departure for Kenya. Accordingly the duties of the puppy Hector began with his first days at home. He was young for the job and wholly inexperienced; it is impossible to blame him for his mistake in the matter of Mike Boswell.

This was a young man who had enjoyed a wholly unromantic friendship with Millicent since she first came out. He had seen her fair hair in all kinds of light, in and out of doors, crowned in hats in succeeding fashions, bound with ribbon, decorated with combs, jauntily stuck with flowers; he had seen her nose uplifted in all kinds of weather, had even, on occasions, playfully tweaked it with his finger and thumb, and had never for one moment felt remotely attracted by her.

But the pup Hector could hardly be expected to know this. All he knew was that two days after receiving his commission, he observed a tall and personable man of marriageable age who treated his hostess with the sort of familiarity which, among the kennel maids with whom he had been brought up, meant only one thing.

The two young people were having tea together. Hector watched for some time from his place on the sofa, barely stifling his growls. A climax was reached when, in the course of some barely intelligible backchat, Mike leant forward and patted Millicent on the knee.

It was not a serious bite, a mere snap, in fact; but Hector had small teeth as sharp as pins. It was the sudden, nervous speed with which Mike withdrew his hand which caused the damage; he swore, wrapped his hand in a handkerchief, and at Millicent's entreaty revealed three or four minute wounds. Millicent spoke harshly to Hector and tenderly to Mike, and hurried to her mother's medicine cupboard for a bottle of iodine.

Now no Englishman, however phlegmatic, can have his hand dabbed with iodine without momentarily at any rate, falling in love.

Mike had seen the nose countless times before, but that afternoon, as it was bowed over his scratched thumb, and as Millicent said, 'Am I hurting terribly?' as it was raised towards him, and as Millicent said, 'There. Now it will be all right,' Mike suddenly saw it transfigured as its devotees saw it and from that moment, until long after the three months of attention which she accorded him, he was Millicent's besotted suitor.

The pup Hector saw all this and realized his mistake. Never again, he decided, would he give Millicent the excuse to run for the iodine bottle.

He had on the whole an easy task, for Millicent's naturally capricious nature could, as a rule, be relied upon, unaided, to drive her lovers into extremes of irritation. Moreover, she had come to love the dog. She received very regular letters from Hector, written weekly and arriving in batches of three or four according to the mails. She always opened them; often she read them to the end, but their contents made little impression upon her mind and gradually their writer drifted into oblivion so that when people said to her 'How is darling Hector?' it came naturally to her to reply, 'He doesn't like the hot weather much I'm afraid, and his coat is in a very poor state. I'm thinking of having him plucked,' instead of 'He had a go of malaria and there is black worm in his tobacco crop.'

Playing upon this affection which had grown up for him, Hector achieved a technique for dealing with Millicent's young men. He no longer growled at them or soiled their trousers; that merely resulted in his being turned from the room; instead, he found it increasingly easy to usurp the conversation.

Tea was the most dangerous time of day, for then Millicent was permitted to entertain friends in her sitting-room; accordingly, though he had a constitutional preference for pungent, meaty dishes, Hector heroically simulated a love of lump sugar. Having made this apparent, at whatever cost to his digestion, it was easy to lead Millicent on to an interest in tricks; he would beg and 'trust', lie down as though dead, stand in the corner and raise a forepaw to his ear.

'What does SUGAR spell?' Millicent would ask and Hector would walk round the tea-table to the sugar-bowl and lay his nose against it, gazing earnestly and clouding the silver with his moist breath.

'He understands everything,' Millicent would say in triumph.

When tricks failed Hector would demand to be let out of the door. The young man would be obliged to interrupt himself to open it. Once on the other side Hector would scratch and whine for re-admission.

In moments of extreme anxiety Hector would affect to be sick – no difficult feat after the unwelcome diet of lump sugar; he would stretch out his neck, retching noisily, till Millicent snatched him up and carried him to the hall, where the floor, paved in marble, was less vulnerable – but by that time a tender atmosphere had been shattered and one wholly prejudicial to romance created to take its place.

This series of devices spaced out through the afternoon and tactfully obtruded whenever the guest showed signs of leading the conversation to a more intimate phase, distracted young man after young man and sent them finally away, baffled and despairing.

Every morning Hector lay on Millicent's bed while she took her breakfast and read the daily paper. This hour from ten to eleven was sacred to the telephone and it was then that the young men with whom she had danced overnight attempted to renew their friendship and make plans for the day. At first Hector sought, not unsuccessfully, to prevent these assignations by entangling himself in the wire, but soon a subtler and more insulting technique suggested itself. He pretended to telephone too. Thus, as soon as the bell rang, he would wag his tail and cock his head on one side in a way that he had learned was engaging. Millicent would begin her conversation and Hector would wriggle up under her arm and muzzle against the receiver.

'Listen,' she would say, '*someone* wants to talk to you. Isn't he an angel?' Then she would hold the receiver down to him and the young man at the other end would be dazed by a shattering series of yelps. This accomplishment appealed so much to Millicent that often she would not even bother to find out the name of the caller, but, instead, would take off the receiver and hold it directly to the black snout, so that some wretched young man half a mile away, feeling, perhaps, none too well in the early morning, found himself barked into silence before he had spoken a word.

At other times young men badly taken with the nose, would attempt to waylay Millicent in Hyde Park, when she was taking Hector for exercise. Here, at first, Hector would get lost, fight other dogs and bite small children to keep himself constantly in her attention, but soon he adopted a gentler course. He insisted upon carrying Millicent's bag for her. He would trot in front of the couple and whenever he thought an interruption desirable he would drop the bag; the young man was obliged to pick it up and restore it first to Millicent and then, at her request, to the dog. Few young men were sufficiently servile to submit to more than one walk in these degrading conditions.

In this way two years passed. Letters arrived constantly from Kenya, full of devotion, full of minor disasters – blight in the sisal, locusts in the coffee, labour troubles, drought, flood, the local government, the world market. Occasionally Millicent read the letters aloud to the dog, usually she left them unread on her breakfast tray. She and Hector moved together through the leisurely routine of English social life. Wherever she carried her nose, two in five marriageable men fell temporarily in love; wherever Hector followed their ardour changed to irritation, shame and disgust. Mothers began to remark complacently that it was curious how that fascinating Blade girl never got married.

At last in the third year of this régime a new problem presented itself in the person of Major Sir Alexander Dreadnought, Bart, MP, and Hector immediately realized that he was up against something altogether more formidable than he had hitherto tackled.

Sir Alexander was not a young man; he was forty-five and a widower. He was wealthy, popular and preternaturally patient; he was also mildly distinguished, being joint master of a Midland pack of hounds and a junior Minister; he bore a war record of conspicuous gallantry. Millie's father and others were delighted when they saw her nose was having its effect on him. Hector took against him from the first, exerted every art which his two and a half years' practice had perfected, and achieved nothing. Devices that had driven a dozen young men to frenzies of chagrin seemed only to accentuate Sir Alexander's tender solicitude. When he came to the house to fetch Millicent for the evening he was found to have filled the pockets of his evening clothes with lump sugar for Hector; when Hector was sick Sir Alexander was there first, on his knees with a page of *The Times*; Hector resorted to his early, violent manner and bit him frequently and hard, but Sir Alexander merely remarked, 'I believe I am making the little fellow jealous. A delightful trait.'

For the truth was that Sir Alexander had been persecuted long and bitterly from his earliest days – his parents, his sisters, his schoolfellows, his company-sergeant and his colonel, his colleagues in politics, his wife, his joint master, huntsman and hunt secretary, his election agent, his constituents and even his parliamentary private secretary had one and all pitched into Sir

Alexander, and he accepted this treatment as a matter of course. For him it was the most natural thing in the world to have his eardrums outraged by barks when he rang up the young woman of his affections; it was a high privilege to retrieve her handbag when Hector dropped it in the Park; the small wounds that Hector was able to inflict on his ankles and wrists were to him knightly scars. In his more ambitious moments he referred to Hector in Millicent's hearing as 'my little rival'. There could be no doubt whatever of his intentions and when he asked Millicent and her mama to visit him in the country, he added at the foot of the letter, 'Of course the invitation includes little Hector'.

The Saturday to Monday visit to Sir Alexander's was a nightmare to the poodle. He worked as he had never worked before; every artifice by which he could render his presence odious was attempted and attempted in vain. As far as his host was concerned, that is to say. The rest of the household responded well enough, and he received a vicious kick when, through his own bad management, he found himself alone with the second footman, whom he had succeeded in upsetting with a tray of cups at teatime.

Conduct that had driven Millicent in shame from half the stately homes of England was meekly accepted here. There were other dogs in the house – elderly, sober, well-behaved animals at whom Hector flew; they turned their heads sadly away from his yaps of defiance, he snapped at their ears. They lolloped sombrely out of reach and Sir Alexander had them shut away for the rest of the visit.

There was an exciting Aubusson carpet in the dining-room to which Hector was able to do irreparable damage; Sir Alexander seemed not to notice.

Hector found a carrion in the park and conscientiously rolled in it – although such a thing was obnoxious to his nature – and, returning, fouled every chair in the drawing-room; Sir Alexander himself helped Millicent wash him and brought some bath salts from his own bathroom for the operation.

Hector howled all night; he hid and had half the household

searching for him with lanterns; he killed some young phea-
sants and made a sporting attempt on a peacock. All to no purpose. He staved off an actual proposal, it is true – once in the
Dutch garden, once on the way to the stables and once while he
was being bathed – but when Monday morning arrived and he
heard Sir Alexander say, 'I hope Hector enjoyed his visit a
little. I hope I shall see him *very*, *very* often,' he knew that he
was defeated.

It was now only a matter of waiting. The evenings in London
were a time when it was impossible for him to keep Millicent
under observation. One of these days he would wake up to
hear Millicent telephoning to her girl-friends, breaking the
good news of her engagement.

Thus it was that after a long conflict of loyalties he came to a
desperate resolve. He had grown fond of his young mistress;
often and often when her face had been pressed down to his he
had felt sympathy with that long line of young men whom it
was his duty to persecute. But Hector was no kitchen-haunting
mongrel. By the code of well-born dogs it is money that counts.
It is the purchaser, not the mere feeder and fondler, to whom
ultimate loyalty is due. The hand which had once fumbled
with the fivers in the live-stock department of the mammoth
store, now tilled the unfertile soil of equatorial Africa, but the
sacred words of commission still rang in Hector's memory.
All through the Sunday night and the journey of Monday
morning, Hector wrestled with his problem; then he came to
the decision. *The nose must go*.

It was an easy business; one firm snap as she bent over his
basket and the work was accomplished. She went to a plastic
surgeon and emerged some weeks later without scar or stitch.
But it was a different nose; the surgeon in his way was an artist,
and as I have said above, Millicent's nose had no sculptural
qualities. Now she has a fine aristocratic beak, worthy of the
spinster she is about to become. Like all spinsters she watches
eagerly for the foreign mails and keeps carefully under lock and
key a casket full of depressing agricultural intelligence; like all
spinsters she is accompanied everywhere by an ageing lapdog.

THE BLIND ELEPHANT

by

C. T. STONEHAM

To ROGER the place looked like the Garden of Eden and always he thought of it as such.

It was 1914, he was hurrying back to join his regiment and had little time to spare, but he insisted they should camp for at least one night by the little stream which flowed down the heavenly valley.

Why such a place should be empty of men he could not imagine, but Van Niekerk told him it was full of tsetse and no domesticated beast could live there.

His draught oxen were well salted but he would feel happier when they got back on the trek. However, his client was a rich man and would pay for any replacements.

After dinner Roger left him to grease his wagons, picked up a shotgun, and started to wander about the place. Most of it was park savannah, with shady trees distributed as if by design, but near the crest of the surrounding hills lay forest, thick and wild as the breathless Congo.

There was game of every kind, from duiker to elephant. One could stand in the open and gaze upon a thousand animals, grazing or resting in the shade. It would seem the sound of a gun had not been heard here in years.

The young soldier was typical of the sportsman of his time, his main interest in wild animals lay in the killing of them.

But here he felt no inclination to kill. It would shatter a peace which would seem to endure for all time.

Near the forest line, behind a hummock, he came on a large cow elephant with a very small calf at foot. Roger recognized danger. He was too near to evade discovery and the gun was about as useful against this beast as a peashooter.

Elephant and man considered each other across forty yards

of turf. Elephants had not been persecuted here and this one was not hostile.

The calf was the trouble and he made certain of more trouble by ambling forward to make closer acquaintance. The cow grunted her alarm and surged into motion.

'Go back, Joey!' shouted the man, his gaze fixed on the mother, but Joey cared nothing for the human voice.

Roger remained cool and thought fast. If he could induce the calf to retreat, the cow would probably follow her precious charge at once. On impulse he fired both barrels of bird-shot into the calf's face.

The little animal squealed, turned and bolted for the protection of the trees, and his dam immediately followed.

Roger breathed deep and grinned as the preposterous toyshop beast disappeared. He flattered himself he had acted with commendable steadiness and foresight. Also there was no obligation to follow up and kill the quarry, for a charge of birdshot at that range could have done little harm.

In this he was mistaken. The pellets had destroyed both Joey's eyes.

Several days elapsed before his mother realized that Joey could not see. She applied mud poultices to his wounds to keep the flies off, but found she had to guide him and restrain him everywhere.

Otherwise he would have fallen over precipices and into swamps. She was devoted to her maternal duties and once having comprehended what was wrong she set herself to be guide and protector in every way.

They had no enemies to fear. Every beast made way for the elephants.

The years passed uneventfully in that little backwater and the little calf grew to be a huge bull, king of the forest he could not see.

His other senses were stimulated by the loss of sight. But he took no undue risks and never ventured beyond his familiar feeding-grounds.

After some years his mother obeyed the natural instinct and

G

went off to join a herd, but then Joey was capable of taking care of himself and did not need her.

On arrival at Headquarters Roger spared time to purchase the tract he had called Eden at a ridiculously low price. With his deed of purchase he sailed for England the same day, leaving Van Niekerk as his agent to guard his interests.

Meanwhile the scientists became convinced that the tsetse were nourished and spread by the game so the government decided to exterminate wild life over a wide area. Van Niekerk was one of the hunters and he chose for his field of operations the land which Roger had in a rash moment purchased.

Van Niekerk thought that all details of the transaction had been lost and forgotten by both parties and considered it foolish to mention the matter to officials who certainly would not believe him.

In a few weeks the place called Eden had become a shambles. Only one beast was spared: the hunters would not molest the blind elephant in the forest, for someone had spread a story that bad luck would follow the killer all his days.

Van Niekerk and his boys often saw Joey, and he was aware of them and found them no enemies.

At last the butchery was over and the hunters returned to their farms. But the fly was more numerous than before and continued to encroach. Entomologists declared that the monkeys and crocodiles were responsible, so those creatures went the way of the antelopes and zebra. The fly remained.

Then an investigator discovered that the fly flourished in a certain type of bush. This was destroyed, and with it the tsetse. Every one was content.

At the tail end of the war Roger, now a general and one of the most wounded officers on the active list, was standing in the drive at Meadowsweet, his country house, then a convalescent home for soldiers, waiting for his wife and daughter to join him.

They all heard the approaching aircraft but did not suppose it might be an enemy. The bomb exploded on the porch, killing Roger's wife and her daughter instantly and hurling the general into a flower bed.

When he recovered consciousness he was quite blind, one eye destroyed, the other damaged.

He was told the sight of the damaged eye would return in time but could not last very long.

With his loved ones and his good friends gone Roger found himself suddenly grown old: physically a wreck, an arm and a leg missing, almost blind.

He decided to withdraw from the world that knew him and remembered he owned a big piece of land in wild Africa, watched over by a steadfast Boer farmer.

He took ship with the intention of spending the rest of his days in the place he had called Eden.

Meanwhile the colonial government had expropriated a big acreage to make a game sanctuary. Van Niekerk had applied for employment as a ranger and had been accepted.

At Aden a wireless message informed Roger that old Van Niekerk had died suddenly of heart failure but that his son Jan had taken his place.

Roger bought a car and hired an African driver. When he arrived at the house the Warden had built to accommodate his head ranger he found it at the end of that wonderful valley where he had camped for a single night so long ago. It did not seem to have changed.

Jan and his young wife were pleased to see him but obviously embarrassed. He understood why when Jan told him the Warden was completely ignorant that this parcel of land was privately owned and could not be included within the sanctuary.

Roger was cynically amused at the perfidy of his old companion but declared his intention of establishing his rights.

This was a well-stocked hunting-ground, his friends would appreciate it when they came to stay.

Jan sighed regretfully at this decision but had no more to say. He was up and away to Headquarters at break of day.

After a good breakfast Roger got his car and drove out on a dirt road beside the stream. Near the forest-line he got out to walk a short way and sit on a fallen tree. It was a perfect day, and he groaned aloud at the thought that with his declining vision he would see few more such days.

He remembered this spot clearly: it was here he had been challenged by a wrathful cow elephant and saved himself by peppering her calf. He laughed at the thought of the comical little beast's dismay.

Then his smile froze, for out of the forest strode the biggest elephant he had ever seen: a noble beast with ears like windmill sails and long shining tusks. It paused for a moment and then came leisurely on.

Roger was shocked into stillness, for he could see the empty eye-sockets and had a dreadful premonition that this was the calf he had harmed long ago.

It had survived all these years without sight of the wonders around it, unable to enjoy the company of its kind, and he, Roger, was responsible.

It might be expected to exact summary vengeance. He could not run away from it; with fatalistic calm he sat still.

They said an elephant's memory was almost perfect: perhaps Joey would recognize the smell of that enemy who had sentenced him to walk all his life in darkness – a disablement whose grievousness Roger was soon about to measure.

He would have given much not to have fired that shot at the merry little calf.

The enormous beast came close with the utmost assurance and, towering above the seated man, ran its trunk lightly over his body.

Roger expected to be tusked or kicked into eternity at the creature's whim but Joey snorted softly and cautiously backed away, as if he had found a friend asleep and feared to wake him.

Roger opened his eyes and breathed again. The bull was going quietly back into the forest, his curiosity satisfied. Roger realized that he was not in the least afraid of men.

He walked back to his car and drove to the house. That afternoon he waylaid the young ranger, thrust a parchment into his hand and said in his terse manner: 'That is my title to this property: do what you like with it.'

Then seeing the look of delighted astonishment on Jan's honest face, he explained 'What use is it to me? I shall soon be as blind as that elephant. But I'd like to know there is one safe refuge for the unfortunate beasts.'

THE FINAL TEST

by

JOY ADAMSON

(from *Born Free*, by permission of Messrs Collins and Harvill Press.)

WE DROVE ten miles to another river, smaller but much deeper than the one we had left; here we intended to spend a week. Late in the afternoon George and I strolled along the bank; we walked quietly, our thoughts with Elsa. I realized acutely how much I had become dependent on her; how much I had for nearly three years lived the life of a lioness, shared her feelings, interests and reactions. We had lived so intimately together that being alone seemed unbearable. I felt desperately lonely with no Elsa walking at my side, rubbing her head against me and letting me feel her soft skin and warm body. There was of course the hope of seeing her again in one week's time. How much that meant to me.

Suddenly George stopped, pointing ahead, and we sank to the ground. A lesser kudu advanced towards us, nibbling gracefully at the young buds of the undergrowth. Then it stopped grazing, lifted its head and looked cautiously around, instinctively alert to every moving shadow or snapping twig. Although we were well hidden and on the right side of the wind, I wondered whether it had not sensed our presence? Or perhaps it was the natural inborn fear of danger which kept this beautiful animal so constantly on its guard? Its perfect proportions, its exquisite body-markings and white stripes and the magnificently shaped horns make this antelope one of nature's masterpieces. We watched the kudu with intense pleasure while it browsed slowly from bush to bush till it eventually disappeared.

Next we heard a noise by the river and advancing carefully saw a hippo-cow and her calf feeding in the lush vegetation, on the opposite bank. The sun was still too hot for them to leave the cool water, so they remained comfortably half-submerged while noiselessly crunching their dinner. We judged that, given the depth of the river, they must be standing on their hind legs as they plodded slowly sideways along the bank to the juicy leaves which hung over the water.

We watched this peaceful scene, but my heart was with Elsa. Then I noticed an elephant on the far bank, only separated from us by a few yards of water. He was the leader of a small herd which now approached the rapids opposite us as silently as ghosts. The gap in the rock bank was narrow and each elephant had to drink in turn, touching the water repeatedly with its trunk before it sucked it up in long draughts. When it had had its fill, each elephant carefully stepped back to make way for the next thirsty animal. . . . Meanwhile the herd huddled close together round two tiny calves, protecting them by their solid bodies from any danger that might lurk beyond.

The sun was sinking, and its warm light was reflected on the shiny fronds of the doum-palms, tinting their tops with a golden glow.

Again I thought of Elsa – what a beautiful world she had been born into. Whatever losing her might mean to me, we must now try our utmost to give her back to this life and save her from a captive existence, in which she would be deprived of all that nature intended for her. Although, up to now, there was no record of a hand-reared lion being successfully liberated, we still hoped that Elsa would be able to adapt herself to wild life, to a life to which she had always been so close.

At last, the week of anxiety ended and we went back to see how Elsa had stood up to the test.

When we arrived at our former camp we looked at once for her pugmarks; there was no sign of them. I began to call. Soon afterwards we heard her familiar 'hnk-hnk' and saw her coming from the river trotting as fast as she could. Her welcome showed us that she had missed us as much as we had missed her and her rubbings and miaowings touched us deeply. We had brought her a buck, but she hardly glanced at it and continued her greetings. As soon as the great rejoicings were over I looked at her stomach: it was full. She must have eaten recently; this took a great load off my mind for it meant that she was now safe. She had proved that she could fend for herself and be independent of us, at least so far as food was concerned.

While our tents were being pitched, I took her to the river and there we rested together. I was happy now and could relax, feeling that Elsa's future was assured. She must have felt the same, for she laid her big soft paw on me and dozed off. I was awakened by her raising her head and looking at a bush buck, whose reddish shape appeared through the foliage on the opposite bank. Elsa watched without interest while the antelope stepped slowly along, unaware of our presence. However happy Elsa might be at the moment I knew that her lack of interest in the buck was partly due to her full belly. What had she eaten? Some little vervet monkeys were watching us silently through the trees, but where were our noisy friends, the usually ever-present baboons? Later on my fears about her first kill were confirmed for we found tufts of baboon hair close to the drinking place, where they had so often teased Elsa.

Now that our minds were at ease regarding Elsa's future, we decided to enjoy her company for another short period and wait till an opportunity occurred of making the final break, in some way which would not be too painful. We took up our life where we had left it off. Although Elsa seldom let us out of her sight, we thought it a good omen that she continued to follow her hunting instinct and sometimes, when we were on our walks, deserted us for an hour.

The country had become very dry and often the sky was lit up by grass fires. The short rains were due in the next two or three weeks and the parched ground was thirsty for their life-giving food. Tsetse flies were very active and poor Elsa found them most irritating, particularly just after sunrise and again before sunset. She would rush frantically through the low bush to brush them off or would fling her itching body on to the ground, her normally sleek coat standing on end.

To make her more independent of our camp life, we took her

out for the whole day and after an early morning walk of two or three hours, settled down in a shady place along the river. We picnicked and I took out my sketch-book. Elsa soon dozed off and I often used her as a pillow when I read or slept. George spent most of the time fishing and usually produced our lunch straight out of the river. Elsa had to have the first fish, but after mouthing it for a short time she would pull a grimace of disgust and showed no further interest in the rest of George's catch. Nuru and the gun bearer proved to be excellent chefs and roasted our meal as soon as it had been caught.

Once we surprised a crocodile sunning itself on a rock; startled, it plunged into a narrow pool which was cut off by rapids at either end. The water was so clear and shallow that we could see the bottom, but we could see no sign of the 'croc' and we wondered where it could have got to. We settled down to our meal. Elsa relaxed on the water's edge and I leant against her. Soon George got up to go on with his fishing; but first, to make sure that the 'croc' was not still in the pool, he prodded along the bottom with a long stick; suddenly it was wrenched from his hand and a six-foot 'croc', which had been hiding in the sand, slithered over the rapids and disappeared into another pool. It had bitten off the end of the rough stick. As Elsa had not noticed this incident, and as we did not wish to encourage her to hunt crocodile, we moved away.

Shortly afterwards, a wart-hog came along for his noonday drink. Elsa stalked him carefully, then, helped by a bullet from George's rifle, seized the pig by the throat and suffocated it. The encounter took place at a little distance from the river and, as I thought it would be more comfortable for Elsa to guard her kill in the shade by the water, I pointed to the pig and then to the river, several times, saying, '*Maji*, Elsa, *maji*, Elsa.' She was familiar with the word *maji*, which I used when I wanted Nuru to fill her water-bowl. Now it seemed that she perfectly understood this Swahili word for water, for she dragged her pig to the river. She played with the carcass in the water for nearly two hours, splashing and diving with it, and thoroughly enjoying herself until she was quite exhausted. Finally she pulled the pig on to the opposite bank and disappeared with it into a thicket; there she guarded it until it was time for us to return to camp, then she seemed determined not to be left behind, for as soon as we got up to go, she dragged the kill back to our side. We cut it up before her and, having distributed the meat between Nuru and the gun bearer, set off with Elsa trotting good-naturedly behind us.

From then on, every time Elsa made a kill near the river, she went to great pains to drag it down to the water and repeated the game she had had with the wart-hog. We were at a loss to account for this strange behaviour: perhaps she had accepted ' Maji, Elsa' as a good rule and as part of her education.

These daily excursions brought all of us much closer together and even Nuru and the gun bearer felt so much at ease in Elsa's presence that they did not bother to get up when she strolled over to them for a nose-rubbing or sat on them, in her playful way. Nor did they mind sharing the back of the Land-Rover with her and when she dumped her 300 lb. between their bony legs, they only laughed and petted her, while she licked their knees with her rough tongue.

Once, when we were resting on the river bank with Elsa lying asleep between us, George noticed two black faces peering at us out of the undergrowth on the opposite bank. They were a couple of poachers armed with bows and poisoned arrows, who had chosen this spot to lie up and ambush game coming down to the water to drink.

Immediately he gave the alarm and dashed across the river closely followed by Nuru and the gun bearer; Elsa, suddenly alerted and always ready for a bit of fun, joined in the chase. The poachers made good their escape, but I would give a lot to hear the tale they had to tell when they got back to their village about how 'bwana game' (George's native name) was now employing lions to hunt poachers.

Early one morning when we were out on our pre-breakfast walk, Elsa took the lead and with great determination headed in a set direction, towards a point at which we had heard much trumpeting of elephant during the night.

Suddenly she stopped sniffing the wind and, with her head stretched out, went off at a fast trot, leaving us behind. A few moments later, in the far distance, we heard the faint call of a lion. She stayed away all that day. Late in the evening we heard her call a long way off mingled with that of another lion. During the night hyena were much in evidence and kept us awake with their inane laughter. At dawn, we followed Elsa's spoor and soon found it leading away from camp and mixed up with the pugmarks of the other lion. The next day we found her spoor alone; on the fourth day of her absence, we tracked her across the river. We searched for her all that day until we found ourselves unexpectedly in the middle of a herd of elephant; then there was nothing but to run for it. Early on the fifth morning Elsa returned very hungry and ate until her belly was near to bursting point. After that, she retired to my camp bed and made it clear that she was not to be disturbed. Later I noticed two deep bites and several smaller claw marks on the curve of her hind legs; these I dressed as best I could. She responded affectionately, sucking my thumbs and holding me close. In the afternoon, she did not want to go for a walk and sat on the roof of the Land-Rover until dark, then she disappeared into the night. Some two hours later we heard a lion's roar in the distance and Elsa's immediate reply. At first, the sound came from near the camp but gradually her voice faded away in the direction of the lion.

The following morning, we decided that this was an opportune moment to leave her alone for another few days and moved camp so as not to handicap her association with the wild lion, who might take exception to our presence. We knew now that she was quite capable of looking after herself, which made this parting less painful than the first one, but I was worried about her bites, which looked as though they might turn septic.

After a week we returned to our camping place and interrupted Elsa while she was stalking two waterbuck. It was early in the afternoon and very hot; poor thing, she must have been very hungry to be hunting so late in the day. She gave us a touching welcome and gorged herself on the meat we had brought her. I noticed a new bite on her elbow and her old wounds were badly in need of dressing. For the next three days she made up for her period of starvation.

By now, Elsa's fame had spread far and wide and a party of American sportsmen paid us a visit specially to film her. She entertained them royally and did everything she could to please them. She climbed a tree, played in the river, hugged me, joined us for tea and behaved in such a docile manner that none of our guests could believe that she was a full-grown lioness, who shortly before they arrived had been equally at ease in the company of wild lions.

That night, we heard a lion call and Elsa promptly vanished into the darkness and was away for two days. During this time she returned for one brief visit to George's tent. She was most affectionate and nearly broke his camp bed by sitting on top of him, as he lay asleep. After a short meal, she went off again. In the morning we followed her spoor which led us to a rocky ridge near the camp. After climbing to the top and looking un-successfully for her in all her favourite lying-up places, we nearly fell over her in a clump of thick bush. Obviously she had kept quiet in the hope that we should not see her. Yet, in spite of her obvious wish to be alone, she gave us her usual affectionate greeting and pretended to be very pleased to see us. We re-spected her feelings and tactfully left her alone. Late that evening we heard the roar of a lion and the howling of his retinue of hyena upriver. Soon Elsa's voice sounded close to camp. Perhaps by now she had learned to keep away from her lord and master while he was at his kill and was waiting until he had his fill before making a closer acquaintance with him. Later she returned to George's tent for a few moments, put her paw affectionately round him and moaned softly, as if to say to him: 'You know that I love you, but I have a friend outside to whom I simply *must* go; I hope you will understand,' then she was off again. Early next morning, we found the pugmarks of a big lion close to camp; obviously he had waited while Elsa went to George's tent to explain the situation. She kept away for three days, returning each evening for a few minutes just to show us her affection but going off again without touching the meat which was ready for her. When she returned after such escapades she always seemed more affectionate than ever, as though she wished to make up for having neglected us.

The rains had started and as usual they stimulated Elsa's energy and playfulness. She just had to ambush us from any suitable cover. As among our pride I was her favourite 'lioness' she honoured me with most of her attentions, and so I was the one who usually found myself on the ground with Elsa's soft, but heavy, body on top of me, holding me down until George released me. Although I knew it was only affection that singled me out for these privileges, I had to stop this practice as I was quite unable to get her off me without help. Soon she understood by the tone of my voice that the game was not popular and it was touching to see how she tried to control her pent-up energy so that, even when she was making a flying leap, she would control it at the last moment and reach me in a dignified manner.

After the first downpour of rain the dry, grey thornbush changed within a few days into a garden of Eden. Every grain of sand seemed to give way to a seed bursting up from beneath. We walked along tracks of luxuriant sap-green growth; each bush a giant bouquet of white, pink or yellow blossom. But, however pleasing this transformation was to our senses, it only added to the anxieties of our walks, for now visibility was reduced to a few feet. There were rain pools everywhere and each was a concentration of freshly marked game tracks. Elsa took full advantage of these bush newsreels and would often leave us to go hunting. Sometimes, we watched her stalking waterbuck, which she drove towards us, at others, followed her tracks while she was in pursuit of bush buck; when doing this she would cleverly cut in a straight line across their winding tracks. However, as in these days she was well fed and had a full stomach, she regarded such hunts more as a pastime than as serious work.

One morning, we were walking quietly along the river, intending to spend the day out; Elsa was with us, full of energy, and, judging by the twitching of her tail, was having a wonderful time. After walking for two hours we were looking for a place to have breakfast when, suddenly, I saw her stop abruptly, her ears cocked and her body tense with excitement. The next moment she was off, jumping noiselessly down the rocks which flank the river at this point; then she disappeared into the thick undergrowth below. Here the river is divided by several islets, each an impenetrable thicket of bush, fallen trees and debris. We had stopped to wait for the outcome of her stalk, when we heard, as I thought, the unmistakable sound of elephant trumpeting. Deep vibrations shook the air and I was convinced that there was more than one elephant in the thicket below. George disagreed, saying that the noise was made by a buffalo. I had heard countless buffalo making their various expressive bellows but none had ever made such a typical elephant sound. We waited for at least five minutes, hoping that Elsa would get bored with her big friends as after a short time, she usually did. Then came a deep rumbling sound and before I realized what was happening George leapt down the rocks, saying that Elsa was in trouble. I followed, as fast as I could, but was brought to a halt by a fresh outburst of violent bellowings just ahead. I felt most uneasy as I penetrated the thick bush, imagining that at any moment the massive shape of an enraged elephant would break through and squash everything in its path. Instinctively the men and myself stopped and called to George not to go on, but nothing would deter him and he disappeared behind the green walls of creepers and trees. Now we heard an ear-splitting scream followed by urgent shouts from George: 'Come, quick, quick!' My heart turned to lead – an accident must have happened. As I stumbled as fast as I could through the thicket, terrible scenes flashed through my mind. But soon, thank God, I saw George's sunburnt back through the foliage; he was standing upright, so all must be well.

Again he repeated his summons to hurry. When I finally broke through the bush to the river bank, what I saw was Elsa dripping wet, sitting on top of a bull buffalo in the middle of the rapids. I could not believe my eyes; here was a buffalo helplessly forced down with his head half-submerged, while Elsa tore away at its thick skin and attacked from every angle. We could only guess at what had happened since, ten minutes earlier, I first heard my 'elephant noise'. Elsa must have disturbed the buffalo, an old bull past his prime, as we later discovered, while he was resting close to the water, and chased him towards the river. Then in his attempt to cross, he must have fallen on the slippery rock of the rapids; and Elsa had taken advantage of his predicament, jumped on him and held his head under water until he was half-drowned and too exhausted to get up. After this she had attacked him at his most vulnerable spot, between the hind legs and was doing so when we arrived.

George waited until Elsa gave him a chance to end the unfortunate animal's agony with a merciful bullet. As soon as this *coup de grâce* had been delivered, we saw Nuru wade, waist deep, into the foaming rapids. He could not resist the chance of gorging himself on this mountain of meat, but, as he was a Mohammedan, he would not be able to eat the buffalo unless he had cut its throat before it died. There was no time to lose, so there he was venturing between the hidden, slippery rocks towards the kill. From her position on top of the buffalo Elsa watched his every movement with tense excitement. Although she had known Nuru since she was a tiny cub and had allowed him every sort of familiarity, she was now highly suspicious and, with flattened ears and threatening growls, defended her buffalo even against her nanny. She looked really dangerous; but Nuru, driven by gluttonous visions, paid no heed to her warnings. It was a ludicrous sight to see his fragile skinny figure staggering fearlessly towards the fiercely growling lioness, perched on the top of a dying and kicking buffalo; as he advanced he waved his first finger at her, calling out, 'No, no'.

Incredible as it may seem, Elsa obeyed him and, sitting quietly on top of the buffalo, allowed him to cut its throat.

The next problem was to get the dead beast out of the river. We had to drag it through the rapids between the slippery rocks. To achieve moving 1200 lb. in such circumstances with an excited lioness guarding it, was no easy task.

But Elsa, intelligent as she is, soon realized what was required, and by seizing him by the root of the tail, while three men pulled at the head and legs, literally helped to get the buffalo out. Combined with much laughter at Elsa's efforts, their joint strength succeeded in hauling out the carcass, which was then cut up. Here again, Elsa was most helpful. Each time one of the big, heavy legs was severed from the body, she at once dragged it into the shade of a bush, thus saving the boys the task of doing so later on. Luckily we were able to bring the Land-Rover to within a mile of the scene and managed to get most of the meat to camp.

Elsa was exhausted: she must have swallowed quantities of water during her battle with the great beast and she had spent at least two hours up to her neck in the fast current of the river. But, tired as she was, she would not leave her kill until she knew that it was safe and that all had been cut up; only when all was finished did she retire to the shade of a bush.

When I joined her a few moments later, she licked my arm, embraced me with her paw and hugged me to her wet body. We relaxed after the morning's excitement. I felt very touched by her gentleness and the care with which she treated my skin and avoided scratching me with claws that only a few minutes ago had been so deadly to the thick skin of a powerful buffalo.

Even for a wild lion, it would have been a remarkable achievement to kill a buffalo bull single-handed, let alone for Elsa, who had only recently learned the art of hunting from her very inferior foster-parents. Although the river had been a good ally to her, it had needed considerable intelligence on her part to take advantage of it and I felt very proud of her.

Late in the afternoon on our way back to camp, we came upon a giraffe drinking on the opposite bank of the river. Forgetting her weariness, Elsa stalked it; she crossed the river, most carefully, down wind and out of view of her quarry, and, avoiding making the least splash, she disappeared into the riverine bush. The giraffe, unaware of any danger, splayed its forelegs as far as possible, and bent its long neck down to the water to drink. We held our breath, expecting that at any moment Elsa would leap out of the bush and attack, but, to our great relief, the giraffe heard, or sensed, Elsa's presence in the nick of time and with a swift movement turned and galloped away. It was lucky for the giraffe that Elsa was so full of buffalo meat. Her adventures for the day were not yet at an end and as her motto seemed to be 'the bigger the better', it only remained for an elephant to appear, ambling slowly along the game path towards us. While we hurriedly retreated in order to make a detour round him, Elsa sat quietly in the middle of the path and waited until the mighty animal was nearly upon her, then sprang nimbly aside, causing him to turn and make off at high speed. After this she quietly followed us back to camp, flung herself down on George's bed and quickly went to sleep. Not a bad record for one day.

Not long afterwards we were walking together along the shady river bank when we noticed basin-shaped circular depressions of mud about three feet in diameter, in a shallow lagoon. George told me they were the breeding-places of *tilapia*, a fish we had not so far seen in the river. While we investigated these mud hollows Elsa sniffed with great interest at a bush and wrinkled up her nose, a thing she often did when scenting a lion. Now we saw fresh pugmarks nearby and Elsa, who was purring distinctly, followed the spoor and disappeared. She kept away all night and the following day. When, in the afternoon, we looked for her, we detected her through field-glasses outlined on her favourite rock. She must have seen us, for we heard her calling, but she made no attempt to move from her position. Thinking she might be near wild lions, we did not want to interfere, and returned home. After everyone had gone to bed, George heard the agonized cries of an animal in pain, and after a short time Elsa appeared in the tent and threw herself down next to his bed. She patted him several times with her paws as though she wanted to tell him something. Then after a few minutes she left again and was absent all night and the following day.

While we were having our dinner next evening, she walked into the tent, rubbed her head affectionately against me and then went out and spent the night away. In the morning we tracked her spoor over a long distance; it led far away. That evening she failed to come back; she had now kept away for three days, except for brief visits during which she had shown us her affection. Might this be her touching way of telling us that she had found her pride and, while she still loved us, was trying to loosen our ties?

During the night we were awakened by the most alarming lion growls mixed with the laughing of hyenas. We listened, expecting Elsa to come in at any moment, but morning dawned and she did not return. As soon as it became light, we went in the direction from which the growls had come, but stopped after a few hundred yards, startled by an unmistakable lion grunt coming from the river below us. At the same time we saw an antelope and some vervet monkeys racing in flight through the bush. Creeping cautiously through thick under-growth down to the river, we found the fresh pugmarks of at least two or three lions in the sand; they led across the river. Wading through, we followed the still-wet spoor up the oppo-site bank when I noticed, not fifty yards away, through the dense bush the shape of a lion. While I strained my eyes to see if it was Elsa, George called to her. She walked away from us. When George repeated his call she only trotted faster along the game path until we saw the black tuft on the end of her tail switch for the last time through the bush.

We looked at each other. Had she found her destiny? She must have heard us; by following the lions she had decided her future. Did this mean that our hopes for her to return to her natural life had been fulfilled? Had we succeeded in letting her part from us without hurting her?

We returned to camp alone, and very sad. Should we leave her now, and so close a very important chapter of our lives? George suggested that we should wait a few more days to make sure that Elsa had been accepted by the pride.

I went to my studio by the river and continued to write the

story of Elsa, who had been with us until this morning. I was sad to be alone, but tried to make myself happy by imagining that at this very moment Elsa was rubbing her soft skin against another lion's skin and resting with him in the shade, as she had often rested here with me.

GRUMPHIE

by

F. G. TURNBULL

(from *Kallee and Other Stories*, Sampson Low, Co.)

SINCE THE appearance of Grumphie at the last cattle show at Kirkbracken, pigs have acquired a new significance in that locality. No longer are they regarded merely as potential rashers, but also as creatures of unusual character and temperament.

This state of affairs, however, is due less to the illustrious pig itself than to the tremendous efforts of Tam and Wullie Donaldson, the boys who reared it. Tam and Wullie are the twin sons of the postman, who since the great event has viewed his progeny with mixed feelings of pride and uncertainty. The lads are twelve years old, red-polled, and magnificently freckled.

The affair began when the flooded Ericht brought Grumphie, then about the size of a rabbit, and sent him whirling half-drowned into a creek where the boys were paddling. Of course they salvaged the pig, and, when its owner could not be traced, claimed the booty.

Sandy Petrie, the farmer of Bannockbrae, offered to provide accommodation for the foundling – an offer which was gladly accepted. And the farmer gave things a send-off when he suggested facetiously that Tam and Wullie should send their pig to the cattle show, due to take place some months later.

Naturally enough, the boys decided that this was a whale of a notion, and they had their own ideas of how a pig should be reared and prepared for prize-winning. As Tam expressed it: 'It has tae be terrible clean an' awfu' fat.' And the fact that Sandy Petrie was to show a pig of his own introduced the competitive touch that inspired the pair to mighty, if unusual effort.

Operations commenced when the twins arrived at Bannock-brae one Saturday morning bearing a pail, scrubbing brush, and a piece of perfumed soap wherewith to wash their pig.

Little Grumphie squealed his protest at the first touch of the water; he squirmed and fought, but the twins persisted, although when smothered in suds the pig was as slippery as an eel. However, the victim quietened down quickly and inexplicably, submitting without further struggle to the novel treatment.

After the first application of the brush, Wullie turned to the pail for more water, then he searched about his feet for something.

'Where's the soap?' he asked.

His brother looked around, but the soap had vanished. Presently Tam's inquiring eye lit on Grumphie's face. The little creature was munching busily with a look of supreme bliss on his funny features. White froth dripped from his jaws. Tam crouched to sniff it.

'Great Pete!' he said. 'Lily o' the Valley! The wee beggar's eaten the soap!'

'Hevvins!' gasped Wullie, utterly appalled.

For several moments the twins stared in open-mouthed astonishment, marvelling at the appetite of their pet. Only a few minutes earlier he had had a meal of jawsticker toffee, carrots, potatoes and turnip. But their thoughts were rudely interrupted when Grumphie suddenly uttered a hoarse squeak of dismay and became violently sick.

Somewhat chastened by this experience, Grumphie had not the heart or energy to struggle as his toilet was completed. Then Tam began to collect the washing material. Once more he searched about his feet, then he asked abruptly: 'Where's the brush?'

Instantly Wullie's eyes turned in consternation on Grumphie.

'Hevvins!' he again exclaimed. 'Dinna tell me he's eaten *it*!

That's apple, spuds, carrots, turnip, jawsticker, soap, an' now a scrubbin' brush. Gosh! What a stummick!'

But to their intense relief the boys found the brush jammed in the underside of the pail.

As the weeks went by heaven on earth was Grumphie's lot. He was stuffed with foods of every description, and attention such as no pig had ever known before was lavished on him. Wullie attended to his feeding and the sty, while Tam attended to his toilet.

Tam's especial pride was Grumphie's peerless tail. It was an absolute gem, he thought – the curliest a pig ever wore. The tuft of pale yellow hair on the end of it was washed, brushed, and combed regularly, and, encouraged by such solicitude, it lengthened considerably. But the soap had to be chosen with discretion. The perfumed variety was hopeless, it possessed such a fascination for the pig. So eager was he to eat it, the twins dared not put it down within his reach. As a substitute they tried carbolic, and Grumphie's interest in the soap immediately waned.

Later, as his weight and strength increased, the pig began to assert his independence. He accepted his mighty meals as his birthright, but he began to take exception to the washing. Whereupon he developed a fraction of his lazy brain to deal with the situation, and he kicked the water pail over whenever he saw it. When the lads countered this move by placing the pail on the low sty roof, Grumphie refused to stand still; he raced screeching round the sty with the twins and the brush in pursuit.

'Och, this'll no'dae!' panted Wullie one morning after a strenuous and vain pursuit. 'We'll have to tie him up.'

Tam agreed. 'I'll tell ye,' he said. 'Let's shove his tail through yon wee hole in that board an' tie a knot on the other side.'

After a herculean struggle the twins managed to poke Grumphie's tail through the hole, but found that the thing would not tie in a knot. So a piece of thin rope was attached to it by a cunning hitch, and a stone on the other end of the rope anchored the rebellious porker securely to the sty wall. He uttered blood-curdling shrieks and pulled with all his might, but the rope would not break, nor would his tail tear out at the roots.

The washing proceeded, and when the pig received his final wipe down the rope was removed. With a surly grunt of relief Grumphie waddled towards his food trough, and as he did so a look of horror overspread the faces of the twins. They stared as though hypnotized at the stern of their pig.

In his struggle to escape he had straightened his tail. Gone was the curl that had delighted the hearts of his owners. The appendage stuck out and upwards, stiff as a poker, whilst the drooping pennant of hair at the end accentuated its oddity. Tam was on the verge of tears.

'Look,' he said. 'After a' my brushin' an' combin', we've gone an' took the spring oot o' it.'

'Ay,' added Wullie, gloomily, 'an' a pig withoot a curly tail is as much use at a show as a hedgehog is in your bed. That's done it noo.'

But, having gone so far with the preparation of their pet, the lads could not let a straightened tail baulk them of a possible prize. Presuming that the sinews were strained, they borrowed some embrocation from Sandy Petrie and proceeded to anoint Grumphie's rudder. They rubbed and rubbed, letting the tail go now and then to see whether it would assume its earlier curl. But no. It remained as stiff as ever, without the least suspicion of a twist.

The treatment was repeated at intervals for a week, without success. In desperation Tam suggested that they thread the tail through a coiled length of lead gas pipe. The pipe was obtained and the stubborn tail pulled it with a string, then the whole spectacular arrangement was firmly fastened to Grumphie's rear.

Three days later, with bated breath, the boys removed the pipe, screwing it off carefully so that a possible new curl might not be disturbed. But the confounded thing seemed straighter than ever. It was then coiled round and round a thin stick and tightly bound with string. This device also failed in its object, and the heartbroken twins concluded that the glory had departed for ever from the plumpest end of Grumphie.

While they sat and stared despondently at the pig a large blue fly whizzed round and round, then lit on Grumphie's back. Wullie flicked it away and scratched the spot where it had landed. And to the unbounded delight and astonishment of the boys, the obstinate tail slowly but surely assumed its normal curl.

For a long, breathless moment Tam and Wullie gazed pop-eyed at the miracle, then, throwing himself on his knees beside the pig, Tam looked with moist affection into Grumphie's bleary eyes and said:

'Weel, noo; there's a real, clever auld beast. Ye deserve a –' His voice trailed away in dismay. That brute of a tail had gone and straightened out again.

Wullie wondered if the scratching, which Grumphie had always enjoyed, had anything to do with it. Again he rubbed his fingers along the rough hide, and in immediate response the tail curled up once more. He ceased rubbing, and the tail poked out again. This was terrific. The next five minutes were spent in intermittent scratchings and hilarious laughter as the remarkable tail popped out and in.

'By gosh, this is something like a pig!' said Tam with enthusiasm. 'All we have tae do tae mak' him curl his tail at the show is just tae scratch his back. Hooray, we'll get a prize wi' him yet!'

The evening before the show was one of awful experience for Grumphie. He was scrubbed and scoured until he was almost skinned. Then to ease his hurt feelings he was given the mightiest meal of all. Here was consolation. Life, he felt, still had its points.

While he devoured his food, Tam seated himself in the rear to devote his attention to the hair on the porker's tail. He teased it out, brushed it tenderly, then applied brilliantine and screwed it up in a curling pin. The captivating odour of the dressing wafted to Grumphie's nose. He sniffed, and traced it to its

source, but was much too fat to bend far in the middle, and so
was denied the privilege of a chew at his own tail. Life lost a
point.

While the pig cleaned the corners of his trough, his proud
owners wondered if there was anything further they could do
to enhance his appearance. Tam studied the toe of his boot
while considering, and there he found inspiration.

'Wullie!' he exclaimed. 'What about blackenin' his trotters
wi' boot polish. They'd show up a lot better than they dae noo.'

'Great idea,' agreed Wullie. 'We'll just dae that. An' Mr
Petrie says we can get a cart specially for him in the mornin',
so we'll tie him up in paper tae keep him clean on the road.'

*

The twins arrived at the show next day in a downpour of rain.
The judges had decided that in view of the weather all those
animals that could walk should be brought into the ring under
cover for judging. So the twins left Grumphie in the cart with a
cover to keep him dry until it was his turn to appear, and they
went inside to witness the parade of animals.

The ring where the judging took place was surrounded by
tiers of seats where farmers and their friends sat discussing and
criticizing the entries. With them sat Tam and Wullie, until it
was announced that the pigs would now come in. They waited
near the door to hear their number called. It was 23 – the last on
the list. In the interval Sandy Petrie had spoken to the judges,
warning them that the final exhibit was something of a novelty,
and he related its history.

When the second last number was reached the twins dashed
out and unwrapped their pet. Wullie brushed his bristles until
they shone, and Tam removed the curling pin from his tail.
They were polishing his blackened feet with their handkerchiefs
when a raucous voice bawled: 'Number Twenty-Three.'

'Come on; oot wi' ye!' urged the lads excitedly. With a
grunt of relief the pig leapt heavily from the cart, and, guiding
him carefully, the twins drove him towards the ring. At every
other step they glanced at his tail. It was tightly curled. There

was a toffee apple in his mouth. Then into the ring marched the postman's sons and their pig.

A murmur of surprise and amusement arose from the assembled farmers as the trio came in. This was followed by a ripple of laughter when the black trotters were noticed, and the beautifully waved tail. The boys blushed furiously.

'Umph!'

Grumphie uttered a grunt of disapproval. Apparently he disliked noisy crowds, and to express his feelings he unwound his tail and stuck it straight out. A gale of laughter greeted this feat, but it was nothing to the roar of approval that arose when Tam, with a look of desperation, seized the offending object and tried to curl it up again.

With the pig in his present humour it was like trying to put a curl in rubber. The thing sprang out straight immediately the boy released it. At this the audience was convulsed with mirth.

Seeing the state of affairs, Wullie began to scratch the pig's thick neck energetically with one hand and to stroke the underside of his fat tummy with the other. Rummaging frantically in his pocket, Tam produced another toffee apple and rammed it into the sulky porker's mouth.

By a storm of hand-clapping the farmers showed their appreciation of this cunning move. But Grumphie refused to respond. He wanted to get out of here, and no amount of scratching or toffee would make him curl his rudder if he didn't want to.

Meanwhile Tam wrought manfully. Now and again when he had pushed it in, the tail would remain coiled for an instant. And, watching it like a hawk, he knelt with upheld hands ready to push it in again should the infernal thing shoot out.

The judges leaned against the railings and howled. Never in all their lives had they seen anything like this. The pig was almost hidden from sight by the boys who tried so desperately to make it happy. The farmers roared with delight; tears of joy streamed down their weather-beaten faces. They hadn't enjoyed anything so much since the day when a stallion bit the judge's ear off.

The officials held a quick consultation, then the leading judge stifled his laughter and addressed the boys.

'If only your pig had a permanent curl in his tail,' he said, 'he would have got a prize. He's a magnificent specimen except for that one flaw.'

The twins looked at each other in despair. Then, suddenly, Tam bawled:

'Wullie; bolt oot an' get a cake o' scented soap.'

A tremendous yell from the audience followed this extraordinary command, and a loud cheer accompanied Wullie's exit.

'If yer honours'll wait just one wee minnit,' said Tam, pleadingly to the judges, 'we'll put a better curl in Grumphie's tail than ye ever saw before.'

Hearing Tam's plea, the judges looked inquiringly at one another and nodded.

Three minutes later, Wullie dashed into the ring, tearing the wrappings from a tablet of highly perfumed soap. He flopped down on his knees in front of the disgruntled animal and held out the offering.

'Here; eat it, ye stubborn brute,' he growled savagely.

'Now, then, Grumphie,' wheedled Tam, 'ye're a fine pig. Will ye no' curl your bonny tail up? I'll feed ye on jawsticker and scented soap as lang as ye live if ye dae.'

Grumphie sniffed the Lily of the Valley, then with a grunt of pleasure he opened his mouth and engulfed the titbit. And now the show, prizes, competition and everything else were forgotten as every eye focused on Grumphie's tail. Slowly it began to bend, then with a gay whirl it assumed the tightest curl that ever adorned the blunt end of a pig.

The result was pandemonium. Cheer upon cheer rang out, and wild, insistent cries of 'Special! Special! Special!' And in response to the general demand the judges decided to award the twins a special prize for their remarkable pig. A fresh burst of cheering greeted the announcement, and with freckled, beaming faces the boys looked up to the audience.

The leading judge called to his clerk for a 'special' ticket, and the gaily coloured card was handed to him. In honour of the occasion the official determined to add a longer length of string and hang the card round Grumphie's neck himself. Down he crouched before the pig and reached out his hands to fasten the string round the fat neck.

Suddenly Grumphie emitted a queer, gurgling sound: 'Uuuumph, grumph, aaaouwp!' Tam and Wullie danced on their toes, yelling frantically.

'Look oot, yer honour; *he's goin' tae be sick!*'

The next instant Grumphie proved it, and in a mighty bound the judge hurled himself to the railings out of the way. Twenty seconds later, helpless with mirth, the audience saw Grumphie pick up his prize card and devour it with every sign of satisfaction. And in a resounding thunder of applause, Tam and Wullie drove Grumphie out of the ring.

MY LAST HOME

by

ANNA SEWELL

(from *Black Beauty*)

AT THIS sale of course I found myself in company with the old broken-down horses – some lame, some broken-winded, some old, and some that I am sure it would have been merciful to shoot.

The buyers and sellers, too, many of them, looked not much better than the poor beasts for which they were bargaining. There were poor old men trying to get a horse or pony for a few pounds to drag about some little wood or coal cart. There were poor men trying to sell a worn-out beast for two or three pounds, rather than have the greater loss of killing him.

Some of them looked as if poverty and hard times had hardened them all over; but there were others for whom I would willingly have used the last of my strength – poor and shabby, but kind and human, with voices that I could trust. There was one tottering old man that took a great fancy to me, and I to him, but I was not strong enough – it was an anxious time!

Coming from the better part of the fair, I noticed a man who looked like a gentleman farmer, with a young boy by his side. He had a broad back and round shoulders, a kind, ruddy face, and he wore a broad-brimmed hat. When he came up to me and my companions, he stood still and gave a pitiful look round upon us. I saw his eye rest on me; I had still a good mane and tail, which did something for my appearance. I pricked my ears and looked at him.

'There's a horse, Willie, that has known better days.'

'Poor old fellow!' said the boy. 'Do you think, grandpapa, he was ever a carriage horse?'

'Oh, yes, my boy,' said the farmer, coming closer, 'he might have been anything when he was young. Look at his nostrils and his ears, and the shape of his neck and shoulders; there's a deal of breeding about that horse.' He put out his hand and gave me a kind pat on the neck. I put out my nose in answer to his kindness, and the boy stroked my face.

'Poor old fellow! See, grandpapa, how well he understands kindness. Could you not buy him and make him young again, as you did Ladybird?'

'My dear boy, I can't make all old horses young. Besides, Ladybird was not so old as she was run down and badly used.'

'Well, grandpapa, I don't believe that this one is old; look at his mane and tail. I wish you would look into his mouth, and then you could tell. Though he is so very thin, his eyes are not sunken like some old horses'.'

The old gentleman laughed. 'Bless the boy! he is as horsy as his old grandfather.'

'But do look at his mouth, grandpapa, and ask the price; I am sure he would grow young in our meadows.'

The man who had brought me for sale now put in his word.

'The young gentleman's a real knowing one, sir. Now the fact is, this 'ere hoss is just pulled down with overwork in the cabs. He's not an old one, and I heerd as how the vet should say that a six months' run off would set him right up, being as how his wind was not broken. I've had the tending of him these ten days past, and a gratefuller, pleasanter animal I never met. 'Twould be worth a gentleman's while to give a five-pound note for him and let him have a chance. I'll be bound he'd be worth twenty pounds next spring.'

The old gentleman laughed, and the little boy looked up eagerly.

'Oh! grandpapa, did you not say the colt sold for five pounds more than you expected? You would not be poorer if you did buy this one.'

The farmer slowly felt my legs, which were much swollen and strained; then he looked at my mouth – 'Thirteen or four-teen, I should say. Just trot him out, will you?'

I arched my poor thin neck, raised my tail a little, and threw out my legs as well as I could, for they were very stiff.

'What is the lowest you will take for him?' said the farmer as I came back.

'Five pounds, sir; that was the lowest price my master set.'

''Tis a speculation,' said the old gentleman, shaking his head, but at the same time slowly drawing out his purse – 'quite a speculation! Have you any more business here?' he said, counting the sovereigns into the man's hand.

'No, sir, I can take him for you to the inn if you please.'

'Do so; I am now going there.'

They walked forward, and I was led behind. The boy could hardly control his delight, and the old gentleman seemed to enjoy his pleasure. I had a good feed at the inn, and was then gently ridden home by a servant of my new master and turned into a large meadow with a shed in one corner of it.

Mr Thoroughgood, for that was the name of my benefactor, gave orders that I should have hay and oats every night and morning, and the run of the meadow during the day. 'You, Willie,' said he, 'must take the oversight of him; I give him into your charge.'

The boy was proud of his charge, and undertook it in all seriousness. There was not a day when he did not pay me a visit, picking me out from among the other horses to give me a bit of carrot or some other good thing, or sometimes to stand by me whilst I ate my oats. He always came with kind words and caresses, and of course I grew very fond of him. He called me Old Crony, as I used to come to him in the field and follow him about. Sometimes he brought his grandfather, who always looked closely at my legs.

'That is our point, Willie,' he would say; 'but he is improving so steadily that I think we shall see a change for the better in the spring.'

The perfect rest, the good food, the soft turf, and gentle exercise soon began to tell on my condition and my spirits. I had a good constitution from my mother, and I was never strained when I was young, so that I had a better chance than many horses who have been worked before they came to their full strength.

During the winter my legs improved so much that I began to feel quite young again. The spring came round, and one day in March Mr Thoroughgood determined that he would try me in the phaeton. I was well pleased, and he and Willie drove me a few miles. My legs were not stiff now and I did the work with perfect ease.

'He's growing young, Willie; we must give him a little gentle work now, and by midsummer he will be as good as Ladybird; he has a beautiful mouth and good paces; they can't be better.'

'Oh, grandpapa, how glad I am you bought him!'

'So am I, my boy, but he has to thank you more than me. We must now be looking out for a quiet, gentle place for him where he will be valued.'

One day during this summer the groom cleaned and dressed me with such extraordinary care that I thought some new change must be at hand. He trimmed my fetlocks and legs, passed the tar-brush over my hoofs, and even parted my fore-lock. I think the harness also had an extra polish. Willie seemed half anxious, half merry, as he got into the chaise with his grandfather.

'If the ladies take to him,' said the old gentleman, 'they'll be suited, and he'll be suited: we can but try.'

At the distance of a mile or two from the village we came to a pretty, low house with a lawn and shrubbery at the front and a drive up to the door. Willie rang the bell, and asked if Miss Blomefield or Miss Ellen was at home. Yes, they both were. So whilst Willie stayed with me, Mr Thoroughgood went into the house.

In about ten minutes he returned, followed by three ladies. One tall, pale lady, wrapped in a white shawl, leaned on a younger lady with dark eyes and a merry face; the third, a very stately-looking person, was Miss Blomefield. They all came to look at me and ask questions. The younger lady – that was Miss Ellen – took to me very much; she said she was sure she should like me, for I had such a good face. The tall, pale lady said that she should always be nervous in riding behind a horse that had once been down, as I might come down again; and if I did, she should never get over the fright.

'You see, ladies,' said Mr Thoroughgood, 'many first-rate horses have had their knees broken through the carelessness of their drivers, without any fault of their own; and from what I see of this horse, I should say that is his case: but of course I do not wish to influence you. If you wish, you can have him on trial, and then your coachman will see what he thinks of him.

'You have always been such a good adviser to us about our horses,' said the stately lady, 'that your recommendation would go a long way with me, and if my sister Lavinia sees no objection, we will accept your offer of a trial with thanks.'

It was then arranged that I should be sent for the next day.

In the morning a smart-looking young man came for me. At first he looked pleased, but when he saw my knees, he said in a disappointed voice: 'I didn't think, sir, you would have recommended my ladies a blemished horse like this.'

'Handsome is that handsome does,' said my master. 'You are only taking him on trial, and I am sure you will do fairly by him, young man: and if he is not as safe as any horse you ever drove, send him back.'

I was led home, placed in a comfortable stable, fed, and left to myself. The next day, when my groom was cleaning my face, he said: 'That is just like the star that Black Beauty had, and he is much the same height, too; I wonder where he is now.'

A little farther on he came to the place in my neck where I was bled, and where a little knot was left in the skin. He almost started, and began to look me over carefully, talking to himself.

'White star in the forehead, one white foot on the off side, this little knot just in that place'; then, looking at the middle of my back – 'and as I am alive, there is that little patch of white hair that John used to call "Beauty's threepenny-bit". It *must* be Black Beauty! Why, Beauty! Beauty! do you know me, little Joe Green that almost killed you?' And he began patting and patting me as if he was quite overjoyed.

I could not say that I remembered him, for now he was a

H

fine grown young fellow with black whiskers and a man's voice, but I was sure he knew me, and that he was Joe Green; so I was very glad. I put my nose up to him, and tried to say that we were friends. I never saw a man so pleased.

'Give you a fair trial! I should think so indeed! I wonder who the rascal was that broke your knees, my old Beauty! You must have been badly served out somewhere. Well, well, it won't be my fault if you haven't good times of it now. I wish John Manly were here to see you.'

In the afternoon I was put into a low park chair and brought to the door. Miss Ellen was going to try me, and Green went with her. I soon found that she was a good driver, and she seemed pleased with my paces. I heard Joe telling her about me, and that he was sure I was Squire Gordon's old Black Beauty.

When we returned, the other sisters came out to hear how I had behaved myself. She told them what she had just heard, and said, 'I shall certainly write to Mrs Gordon to tell her that her favourite horse has come to us. How pleased she will be!'

After this I was driven every day for a week or so, and as I appeared to be quite safe, Miss Lavinia at last ventured out in the small close carriage. After this, it was quite decided to keep me and to call me by my old name of 'Black Beauty'.

I have now lived in this happy place a whole year. Joe is the best and kindest of grooms. My work is easy and pleasant, and I feel my strength and spirits all coming back again. Mr Thoroughgood said to Joe the other day, 'In your place he will last till he is twenty years old – perhaps more.'

Willie always speaks to me when he can, and treats me as his special friend. My ladies have promised that I shall never be sold, and so I have nothing to fear; and here my story ends. My troubles are all over and I am at home; and often before I am quite awake, I fancy I am still in the orchard at Birtwick, standing with my old friends under the apple-trees.

THE ANIMAL CATCHERS

by

Colin Willock

(André Deutsch Ltd.)

The lion was lying in a clump of dried grass and he was beginning to be dissatisfied with the situation. His belly was full. The sun had climbed high into the sky and there wasn't enough shade for comfort. Several times he had considered moving, but this would have meant a long lope down to the shelter of the nearest thorn tree. For the moment, desire to sleep overcame discomfort. The smoky lamp in his eyes flickered and went out. He dozed, head on paws. A few minutes later, his head was up again and he was awake, but without panic. His ears had heard something beyond the hissing sound barrier set up by the cicadas; his stomach had felt something strange tremble in the ground.

Soon, he saw them. At first they were just a far-off cloud. Then they became three separate dots, each one trailing its own plume of choking red dust. The lion watched them advance, twisting and weaving their way between boulders and anthills, each vehicle a little to the side of its nearest companion in an attempt to escape its asphyxiating wash. The lion relaxed now that he had placed the intruders in his limited scheme of things. He had seen these creatures before, and, since he had never been hunted by them, knew no reason for fear. If he stayed still they would almost certainly pass by. Then would be as good a time as any to make the effort and seek the shade.

But the three trucks came straight on. The lion heard the first one give a curious growl as it approached the base of the little hill on whose crest he lay. He flicked a speculative ear. Was this growl, perhaps, an offer of aggression? He flattened his belly to the grass. He had no way of knowing that the noise came from the gearbox of one of the most maltreated vehicles in the entire history of locomotion.

The first truck ground its way straight up the little rise and stopped not twenty yards from where the lion was lying. Its motor beat painfully under its battered bonnet like a labouring heart. The truck was an exceptional specimen of ex-WD fifteen hundredweight. It had been shipped out to North Africa too late to take part in the eviction of Rommel. Thereafter, by some freak of maladministration, it had lain in vehicle pool after vehicle pool unwanted, undriven and slowly deteriorating. Its early post-war career had not been much more exciting. Its movement then had been like that of a human derelict well on the slide. It had journeyed wearily from dump to dump, each dump more tired and tatty than the last. Always there was the faint chance of redemption and reprieve but all the time ultimate decay and dissolution only drew nearer. The turning point came unexpectedly in a sale of Government surplus material in Northern Rhodesia. A man bought the truck. He didn't buy it for its tyres: they had collapsed long ago. He certainly wasn't swayed by its accessories: its battery had corroded to green dust and its hood was a shred or two of canvas on a rusted frame. Nor did he fancy it for its engine. This was in pretty poor shape, too, though he knew that a good mechanic could soon make sense of what lay under the bonnet. He bought it because he saw that it had a remarkably low centre of gravity and because its metal flanks had sufficient freeboard to enable him to bolt two stout tree trunks vertically to each side. And these things, for him, were what counted.

Whatever the truck had missed in the way of glory during the war years, it had more than made up for it in the hands of its present owner. It had been with him now only two years and yet it bore wounds that few of its brothers could have sustained in the service without being pensioned off. From radiator to tailboard it looked as though it had been shot up by small arms fire. Every few feet, something heavier had hit it and left its mark. The edges of its front wings were folded back on themselves like the cauliflowered lobes of a boxer's ears. The near-side cab door had been torn from its hinges. At intervals along its flanks something like armour-piercing cannon shells had punched large holes. Of the two tree trunks bolted to its starboard side, one had been torn loose at its upper fixings and swayed with every irregularity of the ground. The petrol tank showed a series of weld marks which untidily made good the damage caused by something sharp going violently in at the bottom and coming almost as violently out of the top. As the vehicle panted on to the top of the hill its radiator boiled.

The face of the man at the wheel was almost as marked as the truck he drove. The face was not so much scarred as eroded: by wind, weather and, most of all, by sun. The driver was, in fact, just the right side of fifty, yet he had features that were hard to place in the age scale. They resembled much of the countryside in which he lived and worked – on the surface downright inhospitable and yet in certain tricks of light and mood capable of becoming softer and friendlier. There were certain purely physical resemblances to the African countryside as well. The ridges and wrinkles of this face closely matched the fantastic weather patterning of the sandstone gullies of a thousand dried-up watercourses. The lines round the eyes were caused by screwing up the face against the sun, and by sheer hard looking in a blinding light for something that could make itself featureless in a featureless landscape. The man had been so much exposed to brilliant sunlight that both the troughs and the crests of the wrinkles that covered his face were the same even shade of sepia.

He climbed down from the driver's seat and held up his hand for the two vehicles following him to stop. His body beneath the faded khaki shirt and the clean but anciently spotted khaki slacks also gave the impression of extreme weatherbeatenness. He wasn't exactly thin; he was spare. The arm he raised was muscled yet skinny, like a limb of old driftwood rubbed bare of every bit of soft tissue by the sea. He might have been a plainsman from the early West of America. The fair hair, thinning on top but growing thick and wavy down the neck, heightened the impression as did the red sweat rag knotted inside the neck of his shirt.

He dropped his hand, took a pair of battered binoculars from behind the driver's seat and slammed the door of the truck. On its dented panelling was shakily painted:

TED MAXWELL
BIG GAME TRAPPER
KENYA

Maxwell walked round the front of the truck and lifted the bonnet, taking care to stand back from the cloud of steam that gushed out at him. He nodded to one of the Africans sitting huddled in the open body of the truck and the boy leapt down with a five-gallon oil drum filled with water. Maxwell ordered him in Swahili to wait before he poured the water into the boiling radiator. This African, a Kikuyu, had topped up the water level on at least a hundred previous occasions but Maxwell knew that unless he told him this time, and every time, that he must wait for the engine to cool down he would surely pour the water in at once. Maxwell no longer felt any particular rancour about this situation: it was just something you lived with like mosquitoes at night or dust by day. Equally, if the African had poured the water in straight away he would have had no compunction in abandoning him to walk home. Home was six hundred miles away, but then that was the way Maxwell operated.

He watched for a second to see that the message had been received and understood. Only when he saw the boy drop the can, sit down on it and relapse almost immediately into an attitude of semi-coma did he start towards an outcrop of rock that stood some fifty feet higher than the point at which the vehicle rested.

His path took him within thirty yards of the lion. The slight breeze blew steadily from lion to man, so the lion remained wary but comparatively unalarmed. Flattened like a hearth rug, he watched Maxwell climb to the top of the rise and scramble up on the rocks.

As Maxwell made his first stride on to the sloping surface of the outcrop the heat came out to meet him like a leaping antagonist. Used as he was to the sun, the force of it all but knocked him off balance. By his second stride he had forgotten the sensation and stood on top of the highest rock.

Maxwell looked first with his eyes because, on the whole, he trusted them more than binoculars. The plain beneath him danced and sang with the heat of the day. Yellow as the skin of the lion, it stretched away into the distance and far beyond. Just as the lion's skin rippled with the tensed muscles beneath it, so the plain rippled with the sheer muscular power of the sun. The only relief to its yellowness was an occasional rock or bush that looked like a large animal and in some instances was just that. Maxwell searched the horizon and at last seemed to have found what he was after, for he finally put the binoculars to his eyes. Somewhere in that punishing heat haze he had detected a hint of green and the glasses now confirmed this for him.

Still holding the binoculars in his hand, he leapt down from the rock. This time the path he took down the outcrop set him on a different course towards the vehicles. He was upwind of the lion and heading almost straight for it.

As he approached, the lion flattened itself even more, only the tip of its tail moving. Though it was invisible to Maxwell, he stopped dead still ten yards from it and stared at the tall grass ahead of him.

The smell of man was now overpoweringly terrifying to the lion. It did not wish to attack and yet it knew that it would be forced to do something. The lion raised himself slightly on his pads the better to spring – or fly. Maxwell saw this movement and, for the first time, saw the lion. He knew instantly that the lion had been forced into an intolerable situation and one which, in a second, would be resolved by attack or flight. There was no question now of his backing away. Any movement might trigger the lion off. There had, however, to be movement to break the deadlock. Without being aware of making the decision, Maxwell raised his hand and hurled his binoculars full at the lion's head. The lion saw the whirling black shape coming and turned his head so that the glasses struck him on the shoulder. But the movement of the head had started a train of action and he followed it blindly. Once turning, he kept turning. He flashed past the stationary trucks and away down the hill towards the thorn trees. Maxwell stood watching him. Then he picked up his binoculars, tried the adjusting screw and examined the lenses. Miraculously, they seemed undamaged. He walked slowly down towards the vehicles. For the first time since they had stopped he spoke to the grey-haired woman who shared the front of the fifteen hundredweight with him.

'See that bloody lion?' he said.

'Yes. But you didn't.'

He ignored the implied criticism. 'Big bastard,' he said almost admiringly. 'Big black-maned bastard.'

The woman, who had a strong, pained face, asked, 'See anything else up there?'

'Yes. We're spot on. The river's about fifteen mile up ahead. I told you we were right.'

'Time something was,' said the woman.

Maxwell called out, 'Here, Mgulu, you lazy good-for-nothing bastard. Fill that damn radiator.'

The Kikuyu grinned and got off his water drum.

Very shortly afterwards the little column started off again, kicking up its red cloud behind it.

It took them two hours to reach the river. Once they were down the hill, the plain became tussocky, furrowed by soil erosion and runnelled with game tracks. The going was not nearly as flat as it had looked from up top. Maxwell kept the fifteen hundredweight moving at a steady rate, bouncing it from rut-top to rut-top and seldom hitting the troughs. As in a sea-going convoy in which some ships wear the weather better than others, so there was a wide difference in performance between the three units of this party.

Second in line came a jeep. Even though it was weighted down with gear and the two cook boys, the jeep bucked like an impala. Its proper pace in the bush was flat out on good going. On this rough stuff it skittered and jumped as though trying to twist its frame apart at the welds. The girl who drove the jeep was used to this kind of thing but she had her work cut out to hold the wheel.

Behind the jeep, a Mercedes five-tonner wallowed and rolled like a fat old freighter in a North Atlantic gale. She was over-loaded and top heavy with it. Roped on her long, flat, open back were two wooden crates big enough to hold a rhino or a young elephant. They had done both in their time and would do so again if they didn't jolt to pieces first. Packed round the crates on top of the safari gear were the remaining eight Africans who made up the outfit. The young man driving the Mercedes was not troubled by the conditions. Driving was something he did as if in his sleep; sometimes he had actually done it in his sleep. His job was to maintain the vehicles and keep them going. At the wheel he regarded himself as another working part that could expect no better treatment than wheels or springs. He was aware that he might have had a more com-fortable ride by increasing the speed a bit, but he felt too much sympathy with his vehicle to do so. So he kept the revs down.

The fifteen hundredweight gained consistently on its two companions but, since it boiled twice more and had to stop to refill each time, the convoy arrived more or less together at the greener land that announced the river.

Here the leaves were surprisingly vivid. The going became easier, but the vegetation was more lush and there was more need to change course to avoid bushes and trees.

Once they disturbed three giraffe busy lassoing the tops of acacia thorn trees with their long tongues and dragging the merciless barbs down into their velvet mouths. Maxwell, who had seen this a thousand times, screwed up his eyes in wonder and laughed aloud. 'How the hell they do it beats me,' he said. The woman didn't answer him but looked at him sideways and for a moment her face, too, relaxed. The giraffe took off in fright, accelerating quickly through the trees in a gallop that appeared almost to be done in slow motion. Maxwell gave the fifteen hundredweight some throttle and chased the animals for fifty yards but they were soon doing twenty miles an hour and this was more than he could manage, heavily loaded and in such close country.

The fifteen hundredweight's burst of speed was surprising. In third gear she snarled away with a throaty crackle. This was due to the work of the young man driving the Mercedes lorry. She might boil but he saw to it that when called upon she could certainly go.

As Maxwell slowed down again, the woman beside him said, '*Do* you mind?'

Maxwell didn't answer.

As they approached a thick belt of scrub Maxwell changed down and set the nose of the truck at the nearest thorn tree. It collapsed without resistance and disappeared under their wheels. In this way they began to cut their way steadily forward. Suddenly one of the boys up top called out '*Tembo*.'

Through the screen Maxwell could only see the foliage jammed against the bonnet. Without anger he said quite quietly, '*Where*, you silly bastard?'

The boy answered by banging on the metal roof of the cab. Then the black hand darted down through the roof hatch on the passenger's side, its palm extended to the right. At the thump Maxwell eased his foot off the accelerator, keeping up just enough speed to deal with the bush which the truck was, at that moment, trampling flat. When the hand appeared he swung the wheel in the opposite direction to the pointing fingers. The code of thump and point had been devised to deal with the thunder and chaos of a full-throttle chase. Very often when driving flat out through tall grass in pursuit of a running animal it was impossible for the driver to see a rhino wallow or anthill five yards ahead of him. Thump meant stop at once if you can; the pointing hand indicated an urgent change of course; or, as now, the direction in which imminent peril lay. For all his experience Maxwell had no wish to bump the rear end of an elephant in country that left no room for a speedy exit. Elephants were the one animal for whom he had great respect. They could gang up on you. They were brave and intelligent. Moreover, they had a weapon that could be more

terrible than their sheer bulk or thrusting tusks. They had a
trunk that could tap a man on the top of his skull and drive his
head down into his shoulders. This trunk could also pluck a
man off the truck. This had happened to Maxwell's head roper,
Nguru, on a previous catching expedition. The man had escaped by quick thinking. While the elephant still held him the
African had whipped off his bush shirt and stuffed it into the
elephant's mouth. The beast had been surprised into dropping
him and Nguru had managed to crawl back under the wheels of
the stationary truck. Others whom Maxwell had seen caught by
elephants had not been so quick or so lucky. Twice he had
watched an elephant pick up a man, toss him four or five times
and then kneel on him just to make sure.

It was Nguru who had given the alarm now. Maxwell knew
this, knew his head boy's dread of elephants, but knew, too,
that he would not have dared to call for a sudden stop unless
there was good reason.

The truck emerged from the bushes into a small clearing to
find itself faced by a large cow elephant flapping its ears, fling-
ing its trunk about and squealing with fury. Beyond her the
foliage bobbed and thrashed with life.

'Totos,' Maxwell said. 'They've got babies around.'

A second later six adult elephants came out at the run. As
they turned their trunks towards the truck, Maxwell marvelled
at the speed and silence with which they moved. Beside them,
and often beneath them ran, a party of small calves dodging
the huge legs and feet and squealing like children in delighted
terror. The big cow who had made a couple of false charges
now offered a more determined threat, bashing the front of the
truck with one tusk and whipping her trunk about over the
bonnet. Maxwell shouted to the boys up top 'Scream at her.'
At the same time he pressed the horn button. The elephant
checked. Above, Nguru thrust a long thick bamboo lassoing
pole at her. The elephant caught it and flung it far over her
shoulder. By now the herd of adults and totos had run a
hundred yards into open country. They paused in their own
dust cloud and looked back towards the truck.

With a final trumpet, the big cow turned. As she did so her flank caught the front of the truck and lifted its front wheels off the ground. Then, ears still flapping, tail erect, trunk waving, she retreated at a dignified trot to join the herd. Maxwell let out his breath. Tensions gone, the boys were roaring with laughter and banging the sides of the truck.

Maxwell turned to the woman beside him who seemed unmoved by the encounter. 'You've got to hand it to 'em,' he said. 'They've got bags of guts.'

It didn't even occur to the woman that he might have been referring to the Africans who had driven the elephant off with their shouting. She had been married to Maxwell for eighteen years.

AFTER THE BATTLE

by the

EMPEROR NAPOLEON

SUDDENLY I saw a dog coming out from under the clothes of a corpse. He rushed forward towards us and then returned to his retreat uttering mournful cries. He licked the face of his master and darted towards us again; it seemed as if he was seeking aid and vengeance at the same time. Whether it was my state of mind, or the peace, the time, the weather, the act itself, or I know not what, never has anything, on all my fields of battle, made such an impression upon me. I stopped involuntarily to contemplate the spectacle; that man, I said to myself, perhaps has friends, perhaps he has them in the camp, in his company, and yet he lies here abandoned by all except his dog. What is man! and what the mystery of his impressions! I had ordered battles without emotion, battles which were to decide the fate of the army; I had seen, dry-eyed, movements executed which brought about the loss of a great number of our soldiers; here I was moved to tears. What is certain is that at the moment I must have been more favourably disposed towards a suppliant enemy; I better understood Achilles surrendering Hector's body to Priam's tears.

GIVEN YOUR HEART TO A DOG TO TEAR

by

ALEC WAUGH

A Man Discovers First Love Comes only Once

AT THE top of his morning's mail was an envelope in his sister's handwriting. He noted its presence there with irritation. Long experience had taught Hugh Osborne that Phyllis never wrote unless she wanted something.

'I look on you as a kind of uncle, you're so much older,' she would say.

Which he was; by sixteen years; and which had been well enough when the gap of half a generation had been set in the relationship of twenty-six and ten, and avuncular generosity had been tested by expeditions to the zoo and supplications to intercede with parental discipline on such problems as concerned the frequency of theatre tickets. It was a very different situation now, when their respective ages were twenty-one and thirty-seven; and he was expected to act as an intermediary on such very much less clement issues as concerned latchkeys, allowances and unchaperoned acquaintance.

What on earth did she want now, he wondered.

'Hugh Darling, I'm going to be a nuisance – a ghastly nuisance,' the letter started. 'But I'm in trouble, real trouble and you're the one person who can help me. It's about John.'

John? Osborne paused, his memory searching the lengthy gallery of young men who had disturbed over the last four years his sister's peace of mind; John? No, he could not place him. He resumed his reading. 'We're crazy about each other; really crazy,' he read on. 'We want to be married right away. At least John does; and I would, desperately; if only I could be certain it was fair to him. But I can't, not quite, it's the money part. We've enough to live on, just. But it would mean desperately hard work, not spending one unnecessary farthing; no travel, no entertaining, nothing, and is that fair to John? Oughtn't he at this stage of his career, to get about, see people? An architect after all –'

An architect, so that was who it was. He recalled a tall, untidy youth, with one of those thin, hard-boned faces that often develop in later life a look of real distinction; an uncomfortable young man, who did not smoke, who kept fidgeting with his tie and pulling at his hair, yet had managed, nevertheless, to give Osborne the impression that one day he might amount to something. So that was who John was.

And it was in order that everything should be made easy for this John, that John might be able, in Hollywood parlance, 'to go places and to do things' that Phyllis was proposing to her uncle-brother that her marriage, for the first few years, should be endowed to an annual extent of two hundred pounds.

No, no, really, he thought, this was the limit; this time she had gone too far.

Only one thing about the letter pleased him: Nowhere was the word 'loan' mentioned. The Danegeld was demanded as a gift.

From his wife's room next door came the tinkle of a breakfast tray. He pushed the letter into his pocket, examined his reflection in the glass, satisfied himself that the knot of his dark blue seven-fold silk-tie was correctly centred in his stiff white collar, then tapped upon her door.

In his hand he carried a small sealed packet. At the sight of it she clapped her hands.

'If you aren't the most thoughtful husband.'

He had written on the card accompanying the clip, 'On the anniversary of my happiest day, to thank you for my six happiest years.'

'Darling,' the eyes that looked up at him were tender.

'That is true, that really is?'

'Did you need reminding?'

She smiled, fondly.

'Six years, it's a long time, you know. That other time, that first time, after all . . .'

'*That was another kind of thing.*'

'*Was it? I suppose it was. But you were in love, to begin with anyhow. That used to worry me so, once. If that first marriage of yours could be shipwrecked so completely within three years, what was there to stop . . .*'

But he laid his hand across her mouth, stopping this flow of nonsense at its source. Voices on the stairs heralded the children's visit.

There were two of them, a boy and girl, five years old and three. It was with shouts and bounds that they had chased across the landing but outside the door they paused to recover breath, entering finally with the staid gait to which their weekly dancing classes had accustomed them.

'I say do you know?' It was the girl's invariable prelude. She would stand, her eyes very wide, an expression of the most solemn earnestness upon her face. 'I say do you know when Putsi and Truddy tore the rug and Ada said . . .' you would imagine that she was about to announce the fall of the Guelph dynasty as she embarked on the trailing anacoluthon of an utterly pointless saga about their two dachshunds and the parlour maid.

Her brother at her side listened with the condescendingly approving attention of a schoolmaster who hears a favourite pupil recite a lesson; prompting with an occasional 'No, when Putzi jumped up what Ada said . . .'

It was a pantomime with which Osborne was familiar. Without detaching his attention, he picked up the pile of letters that lay by his wife's breakfast tray. Two of them were still unopened.

'Here's one from Doreen. It feels like an invitation.'

'Open it and see.'

It was to a cocktail party for the Wednesday of the following week.

'Isn't that the day we're dining with the Marchants?'

'It's on our way. We could go there changed.'

'If we accept, we ought to ask them to our box at Lord's.'

'And they don't like the Williams.'

'That's what I was thinking.'

'Why ask the Williams then? We don't owe them anything.'

'We could work them into something else sometime.'

'Anything, any time.'

In thirty seconds, in the interval of being good parents to two exactingly possessive infants, the problem had been settled. How easily they had arranged it too. How easily they arranged everything, for that matter. Whereas once . . .

He smiled, remembering how many discussions, how much acrimony would have been involved twelve years ago, in that other marriage before any solution to so simple a problem could have been reached and then unsatisfactorily with a feeling of grievance on one side if not on both. Suave mari magno . . . He could afford to smile from this safe habour.

Was there a single issue of domestic life on which he and Molly had not contrived to quarrel? They had been so young. Twenty and twenty-four. How could one help quarrelling at that age. One had not learned forbearance, patience, tolerance. How could one hope to make a success of marriage? Twenty and twenty-four.

And how old was this John of Phyllis's? Twenty-four, twenty-five? Only a few months older than he, himself, had been. It was absurd. Of course it was. Why on earth should he pay out money that he could ill afford so that Phyllis could make for herself the same ultimate atmosphere of friction that he had created for himself thirteen years ago. Why should he, why, in heaven's name?

'I'm sorry, very sorry, my dear Phyllis,' his letter started.

The moment he had finished the dictation of his morning's mail, he set himself to his uncongenial task, with instructions that he was not to be disturbed for twenty minutes.

'You must know that no one is more anxious than I am to see you happy, but under the particular conditions . . .' he paused. The words came laboriously. He had progressed no further than the second paragraph when the sharp summons of the telephone shattered his concentration.

'Didn't I say I wasn't to be disturbed,' he snapped.

'I know, sir, but it's Mrs Burnham. I thought you would want to speak to her.'

'Oh . . . well . . . yes . . . put her through . . .'

Embarrassed, confused, bewildered, he listened for the voice that once had so enchanted him, that later had so ripped his nerves.

He waited anxiously. It was six years since he had heard her voice, since the announcement of her remarriage had lifted from his conscience the burden of a moral responsibility and from his scale of living the very fettering obligation of mounting alimony. At the news that she was on the line his spirits sank. Had this second marriage of hers broken? Was she back on his hands again?

But no, it was not that.

'You mustn't think me silly. I'm sorry to be worrying you. I know how busy you are. But I thought you'd want to know. It's about old Woolley. He's getting old, thirteen is old even for a poodle. He's very rheumatic. He must be in pain half the time. It isn't kind keeping him alive. The vet's coming round this morning. I thought you'd like to know. I wondered – you were so fond of him, perhaps you might want to say goodbye to him.'

She spoke in that quick, breathless, staccato fashion that had been one of her first attractions for him, that later had been one of the traits in her that had exasperated him the most. 'Will you never come to the point?' he had thought as she had rushed sentence after sentence against the circumference of her subject. Even now after all these years, he felt his impatience rise as the short sentences rattled one upon the other:

'The vet won't be coming round till twelve. I live quite close. University Mansions. Just off the Edgware Road. It wouldn't take you twenty minutes.'

The sentences clattered on. But he was scarcely listening. Woolley, the absurd black ball that they had bought on the afternoon of their engagement, that they had named after the Kent cricketer because that morning Woolley had made a century at Lord's. Woolley, the squiggling puppy that had welcomed him on his return each evening from his office. Woolley the proud, hand-

some dog that had bounded ahead of their walks over the heath. He had not seen Woolley for seven years, he had pictured him still as the proud high-stepping dog. Woolley, old and rheumatic, at his tether's end. It was like the sudden opening of a porthole on a windy day. 'I'll be round at once,' he said.

University Mansions was designated in the postal records as W.1. A large red brick block of flats, it had been described as 'the acme of modern comfort' when its gables of Edwardian gothic rose over the Praed Street reaches of the Edgware Road. Before the war it had enjoyed a brief season of fashionable patronage, but now in an age of air-conditioning and central heating, it was clearly about to qualify for the status of a tenement.

Osborne had not seen Molly for seven years. What, he wondered, did she look like now. It was with a certain trepidation that he wondered that. Would the Molly of today bear to the Molly that he had married, the same relation that this deteriorating block of flats bore to the trim Victorian cottage on the edge of the heath beyond the Vale of Health where they had begun thirteen years ago the honeymoon of their first year of marriage? She had been little and dark and plump with ragamuffin ways. Had she grown blowsy, fat, ill-kept?

He was afraid of that, but he need not have been. In a long holland smock, with white cuffs and collar and small bow tie, she had on this hot June morning the unexpectedly dewy freshness of ripe blackberries in a country lane. As she took his hand, her scent, a blend of tuberose, that had once thrilled him so, and later he had condemned as 'Oriental' struck upon his senses like a phrase of dance music.

'It is nice of you. I'm afraid he'll be a shock to you. He's got so fat. But he will be pleased. Woolley,' she called out, 'look who's come to see us. Twoodie.'

The use of that old pet name, so familiar once, long buried now among the memories rarely recalled of that courtship period, would have struck vibrations from a chord of nostalgic sentiment, had not another chord quivered more insistently.

*At the name 'Twoodie', a quiver had shaken the thick mass
upon the carpet; a bark had come from it; a grotesque object
struggled to its feet, shuffled across the carpet, a back leg trailing,
trying to wriggle its hind quarters to wag its tail. The hair that fell
over the eyes was grey and straggly; the centre of the back was
bald. There was no line of waist. Nothing remained of the dog that
he remembered except a trick of lifting the upper lip over the teeth,
in a kind of laugh. Nothing but that remained, the laugh and the
quiver of recollection that had shaken the mass of flesh at the
sound of his old master's name.*

'Woolley, my poor Woolley.' There was a pouffe beside the
fireplace. Seated there he drew the dog's head upon his knees,
drawing his hands slowly over the heavy head, unable to trust
himself to speak, as Molly's voice rushed on.

'A dog never forgets, at least a poodle doesn't. He'd always
go back to his first master: no matter how long after. You saw
how he looked up when I said "Twoodie". Do you remember
my telling you about my brother Robert and his dachshund?'

She was started on an anecdote with which he was long
familiar, breaking the story in midcurrent and beginning on
another in the way that had so charmed him when he had
thought of her inconsequent ramblings as 'pretty chatter'
and had so infuriated him later when he had labelled it 'silly
gabble'!

'It's so strange to see him old. Do you remember that day at
Hendon when we thought we'd lost him?'

It was in the first autumn of their marriage, in the days before
snubnosed Morris Cowleys had ruined Hendon as a picnic
centre. They had taken a bus from the war memorial at
Golder's Green. It was before the tube had come out to
Colindale, it was the Hampstead tube then, not the Edgware
line. In those days the tops of buses were uncovered. They had
sat in the front seat with Woolley lying over their feet like a hot
water bottle.

They had picnicked in the shadow of a hedge (long since cut
down by speculative builders) that had looked out over the
Welsh Harp. The sun had been warm upon their faces. He had

dozed as her voice ran on from this anecdote to that, dozed till he had been roused by the cry, 'Woolley. Where is he? I can't see him.' Over twelve years ago, but would he ever forget the agonized anxiety of that long search, the shouting till his voice was hoarse, with Molly whimpering at his side, 'If only we'd had his name put upon the collar.' Would he ever forget that, or the relief when at the very moment when they had started to abandon hope, Woolley had emerged wet and dusty, reeking of the filth in which he had rolled luxuriantly. 'And I only bathed him yesterday,' had been her plaint.

'He was so full of life, too. Do you remember how he pestered us that day at Chagford?'

That, too, was a vivid memory. It was in the second year. The early part of it. They had gone to Devonshire, for a golfing holiday. They had breakfast in bed. It was wet and they had idled there, the gas fire lit, when suddenly with the unexpectedness that can make a happy marriage a more spontaneous adventure than the most intense intrigue, they had found themselves in love. At that very moment Woolley had decided on a display of filial devotion, had jumped on the bed, pranced on the pillows, snuggled his nose between their heads, trying to lick both their faces simultaneously. Would Osborne ever forget the noisy romp that had been their lovemaking; of how laughing and breathless she had said, 'One really has to be in love to laugh like this.'

'And do you remember how upset he got that day we quarrelled about Janet's invitation?'

It hadn't been their first quarrel, not by many weeks. But one of their most typical. She had been away, visiting for a couple of days. There had been a letter addressed to her in Janet's script. It bore a penny stamp. The flap was turned over a post card. Clearly it was an invitation. To fix the date, to arrange his own diary, he had opened it.

'By the way,' he had said on her return, 'I accepted for a party of Janet's on Friday night.' It had been the signal for one of their fiercest rows; as absurd as it had been symptomatic. 'You open my letters? What do you mean by opening my letters?' That was how it had begun. 'You knew it was an invitation? Yes, I dare say you did. But why should you accept it in my name? How did you know that I would want to go?'

That was how it had gone on. Finally, a point of recrimination had been reached when their whole social life had become a corpse under the dissecting knife. 'You're always complaining that I don't like people till I've got to know them. That's why you accepted that invitation on your own; to force me into a position where I couldn't possibly refuse.' On and on the flood of recrimination streamed, and all the time the poodle realizing that they were quarrelling had barked between them with an insistence that had forced them finally to abandon or rather postpone the issue; to declare an armistice.

'He always knew when we were quarrelling; as some dogs know when thunder's coming, he could only be happy when we were happy. Do you remember when we went for walks and there were four of us, and you and the other man walked on ahead, how he'd run backwards and forwards trying to join us up? Do you remember when . . .?'

The stream of recollection rushed on jerkily. He knew now why she had rung him up. Not so that he should say goodbye to Woolley, but that she might relieve her grief by talking over the dog's life with the person who had shared its early half with her. For thirteen years this dog had been her friend; she was absorbed by sorrow. That was what his presence in this hour meant to Molly.

But for himself who had not seen Woolley for seven years, the hour had a different meaning.

For him the past had been suddenly recreated. With the heavy head pressed against his knee, with the tangled curls rough beneath his hand, there passed in a stream of pictures before his mind those days of youth when they had loved and quarrelled, when they had quarrelled because they were too young, because they were too in love, the carefree, improvident days when they had done madcap things, of those days of which Woolley so limp and helpless now, was the final symbol, days that were as distant for her as they were for him.

More distant probably. He lifted his eyes, looked around him. The room in which they sat was a sure index to what her life was now. It was a bright and cheerful room with light, gay chintz curtains and chair covers; with Turner reproductions on the walls, with a large bowl of roses in the window. There was nothing expensive in her room. But it had a well-cared-for look.

He had fancied, remembering the ragamuffin she had been, that he would find in a dreary locality like University Mansions a slovenly background suitable to someone who had gone to seed. He had not though. Just as she herself had stayed fresh and pretty so was her home neat and bright. She had made of her life in her different way very much the same kind of thing that he had made of his.

On a table against the window a child's books and drawing materials were stacked in a tidy pile : an exemplary child, no doubt, who would appear at breakfast with clean hands and well brushed hair. On the mantelpiece were a couple of invitation cards. Molly was ready enough now for the mild amusement of an occasional cocktail party ; the days when each invitation was the signal for disagreement were as much a thing of the past as his sick and tired poodle, Woolley, the last reminder, the last link with the old days.

The sun was shining with promise of a long day's heat when he walked out into the noisy garishness of the Edgware Road. He had a heavy commitment of work ahead of him. He had hoped to get away from his office early, to watch an hour or so of the Essex match at Lord's. But he did not turn northward to the tube station. He turned westward down Praed St., taking the same side turning he had taken thirteen years before.

He paused; and something under his heart went round and over. Yes, there it stood, the same dark shop where, in a distant summer a bundle of black wool, squiggling against a window pane had laid its spell upon two young hearts. And there standing before the window the reincarnation of himself and Molly; young love personified; were two young people.

Her hand lay upon his arm; upon her finger was an engagement ring. Her eyes were bright. Her voice was pleading. "Darling, he's a pet; we must, we really must." Her voice was glowing.

He smiled wryly as they pushed through the door into the shop. What had Kipling written. 'You've given your heart to a dog to tear.' Did they realize as they pushed open the shop door that they were not only buying themselves a dog, they were buying pain for themselves, twelve or fourteen years from now, such pain as at this moment was tearing Molly's heart.

Did they realize that? Probably. But who at such moments looked ahead, fingering out the cost? They realized that, but did they realize that that knowledge was only half the truth? It was not only a dog that would be dying in fourteen years; something else would have died, many summers before that; the youth in their hearts, the capacity to do wild things, to quarrel over nothings. They might be together still, that couple.

When that puppy grown into old age lay for the last time between them, its head heavy upon their knees, they might be bound by a deep devotion, by mutual sympathy, by trust and confidence. The death of this dog that they were buying now might be a shared sorrow; one of those shared things that constitute the sum of marriage. It might; or it might not. That lay on the gods' knees. One thing alone was certain. Youth would have left their hearts.

In his pocket was his sister's letter. That morning he had shrugged impatient shoulders. But at home he had been surrounded by his 'family man', his 'middle-aged' responsibilities. At his office desk he had started an admonitory letter. But at his office he had been surrounded by filing cabinets, typewriters, sales charts; the testimonies to a planned prosperity. In a home such as his, in an office such as his, it was by a standard of prudently planned future that one assessed importance. But here, standing in front of a dog shop window, with the picture of the past before his eyes, with the sound in his ears of a voice that glowed, it was less easy to be sure of what was and what was not important.

Was it really wisdom to plan the future, to figure out the

cost? Was one deterred from the purchase of a dog by the knowledge that one was buying one's sorrow ten or fifteen years ahead? Did the knowledge that love, or at least one side of love, was transitory hold one back from love? Did youth's improvidence ask counsel of the cooled blood of middle-age?

His office was in Holborn, but it was to the Charing Cross Tube Station that he booked a ticket. His bank was in Whitehall.

'My ledger, please,' he said.

His account was substantially in the black. Three hours earlier prudence would have warned him to weigh the various dangers of the moment, the wavering nature of the world's markets in view of the world's unrest. But now, in the light of memory, the present was more insistent than the future – whatever the next years might hold there was that long black entry now.

What was it in the last analysis that his sister had really asked of him? What else but the chance to enjoy to its fullest, the reckless improvidence of youth. She had not known what she was asking for. But he, in his experience, did. The chance to savour first love at its highest, in its fullest measure was his for giving.

How much was it that she had asked him for, two hundred? Yes, but one always underestimated one's expenses. Things always cost more than one expected.

He was in no mood to figure out the cost. He could manage three. Let her have those few years at their best and freshest, without worries, uncomplicated. He signed the banker's order. Whatever else in life came twice, that did not come. Whatever happened Phyllis would have unspoiled the memory of these next years. The gods themselves could not recall their gifts.

THE INQUISITIVE MONGOOSE

by

CHERRY KEARTON

(from *My Animal Friendships*)

IT TAKES two to make a friendship, just as much as a quarrel; and this is true of friendships between men and animals as well as of those between human beings. If you take the trouble to understand an animal, you will find that you are not only learning natural history, but you are also achieving a wider understanding and a better state of feeling towards life in general; for is not understanding and love of *all* your fellow-creatures the basis of Christianity, of ethics, of all that makes life worth while? 'Go to the ant . . .' There is a great deal that animals can teach you.

It is because of that that I am hopeful that I shall induce some people to enlarge their outlook on the keeping of animals. There is no better friend than a dog, and most homes are made more homely by the presence of a cat. But why should one's relations with animals stop there? If your surroundings – and your neighbours! – permit, keep a baby bear, a chimpanzee, a small monkey, or a squirrel.

The number of such animals kept in English gardens is daily increasing, although many people who have no proper reason for such an idea still imagine that the keeping of a pet of that kind would involve far too much trouble.

Well, if you want to keep and study an interesting wild animal, and yet run no real risk of being overwhelmed with trouble and work, keep a mongoose. There are few creatures that make such good companions and yet are so easy to keep, for the mongoose has few fads in the matter of food (and indeed could support himself if necessary on what he would find in an average garden), is not too particular where he sleeps, and is very easily made happy, provided that he has a fair amount of ground to run about in. And once you have shown that you mean well by him, he will soon settle down as one of your family.

The mongoose that I kept for some years I originally called 'Parker', because of his unbridled curiosity. He always wanted to explore, and as my garden was full of bushes and boulders, little valleys and trees, he had plenty of scope for his hobby. But we didn't always call him Parker, because when we felt particularly affectionate towards him (as indeed we often did) that, being a surname, seemed a trifle formal; and then we added a Christian name and called him Robin. Most of our animals have more than one name: Tommy, the fox-terrier, has two others in fairly general use. But our friend Robin Parker is known to readers of one of my other books, who may also be reading this one; and therefore, to avoid confusion, he will here be called by his Christian name alone.

When he first arrived, we put him down in the large studio which stands by itself just in front of the house, and which was the home of Mary the chimpanzee, Tommy, and, from time to time, various other animals. In one corner of the studio was standing a heavy pile of wooden poles and planks; and the mongoose, being rather uncertain for the moment of his new surroundings, at once ran there for shelter.

He was very shy and rather frightened, and although at first I could see his little nose and his beady eyes in the space between two of the poles, he retreated as I approached, and finally he appeared to decide that it was safest to stay in his second line of defence, somewhere right at the back of the wood-stack. I called to him, clicked my fingers enticingly, and at last set down a tempting plate of food. But nothing would induce him to come into the open.

To have pulled down the stack of planks would have been a good deal more than one man's work, and eventually, after a day of ineffectual efforts, I had to leave him. But before I went I placed a meal a foot beyond the foremost plank. I was hopeful that he would get over his shyness in the night, so that I might find him playing in the studio when I returned.

But in the morning, although the plate was empty, there was still no sign of the shy mongoose.

He did not appear all that day, and when, the next morning, I again found an empty plate, I began to wonder whether the food I had so carefully prepared was nourishing only the rats and mice, while the mongoose had crept away through some hole under the wall and then had escaped through the garden into open country.

However, on the fourth morning I got to the studio rather earlier than usual, and to my delight I surprised the mongoose in the act of clearing the last crumb of his breakfast. I stopped at once, so as not to startle or frighten him, and as he was at heart a very friendly little fellow, he did not run away but stood quietly watching me.

That moment, I knew, would be the turning-point between friendship and continued shyness. If he was convinced that he had nothing to fear, we should get on well together. So, resisting the temptation to go closer, I sat down on the floor and returned his stare.

After a while I began to make little friendly noises and to scratch on the floor with my finger-nail. He did not seem disturbed. Indeed, after ten minutes he looked down at his plate, noticed a spot on it that was not licked clean and, in front of me, set to work on it.

Then I knew that he had accepted me, and was prepared to make friends.

To cement the bond I took from my pocket my pipe, which I had been in the act of filling when I entered the studio, and put it on the ground in front of me. He looked at it and up at me. Then his curiosity got the better of him, and, creeping up to the pipe, he began to pull the tobacco out of the bowl.

Robin never could resist the temptation to empty things. Once he found the gardener's coat; in a very few minutes he had pulled everything out of the pockets and all the tobacco out of the pouch. Curiosity was always his weakness and, as I shall shortly relate, it led him into a great deal of trouble, although it certainly also brought him much enjoyment.

He won his name 'Parker' directly he left the studio. As soon as we felt that he had grasped that my wife and I were his friends, and that he had come to a new and not objectionable home, we opened the door of the studio and let him run out to see the delights of the garden. He ran to the doorway, stopped and looked out. Quite a lot of exciting things were within his view: a thrilling bed of Michaelmas daisies, a heap of stones where slugs would lurk for a certainty, and in the distance another flower-bed and a stretch of lawn – just the place for a rat-hunt. So off he went on what was no doubt intended as a voyage of exploration, although it wasn't that for long. Exploring the distance could wait: there was so much to do near at hand.

The very first stone attracted his attention, and he walked all round it, sniffing excitedly. Then he put his little paw into a crevice and drew out a slug.

That early success, of course, put an end for that day to the craze for exploring: what mongoose would trouble about exploration when there were obvious chances of successful hunting? He had just finished a very good dinner, but that didn't matter. It was the chase he loved, and off he went to the daisies, alert for possible rats or mice.

Fond as he was of putting his little nose into places where it had no business to go, there was nothing that ever appealed to him so much as hunting. However much food I might provide, he always preferred what he had caught. Slugs were his principal quarry, but he hunted rats and mice whenever he got a chance and he was extremely partial to frogs – or rather to the heads of frogs.

Rats and mice didn't often escape when he started on their trail; but he was beaten every time when he stalked a water-rat. There were many of these, living in the banks of the lake, and they would often sit on the bank to nibble at blades of grass, see Robin in the distance and be seen by him, and then turn and dive for home.

I could almost hear Robin saying then: 'Ah ha! A rat!' and off he would go, full of confidence every time, at top speed; and then the rat, which he had thought to be like any other rat, an easy victim, would disappear into the lake, leaving Robin unable to follow, absolutely dumbfounded, and not a little annoyed. This sort of thing would happen two or three times every week, but after a year of it Robin was just as much surprised and just as much put out as he was the first time. 'Hang it all,' he seemed to be saying, 'a rat is a rat, and it ought to behave like one!'

Sometimes he would try to catch butterflies – another difficult prey, though not so impossible as the water-rats. That was usually in the sloping field adjoining my garden, where the grass grew long enough to cover his body. The grass rather confused him, for he couldn't see where he was going, and every few feet he had to make a little jump into the air for a hasty look forward before he came to ground again. Then, having seen a butterfly hovering some yards in front, he would creep in that direction till he thought he was near enough for a spring, when up he went, striking out at where he imagined the butterfly would be with his paw, in the rather fruitless hope of crippling it. Of course, the butterfly by that time had generally moved on to a tempting poppy some yards distant; but even if it hadn't, its chances of escaping from Robin's blind jump and thrust would have been considerable – and of that I was glad, for though as a gardener I rejoiced in the successful onslaught on slugs, I could not so happily spare the butterflies, which make the country joyous.

Strange to say, the sparrows never interested Robin. He would lie down on the wooden veranda, where the sparrows and a tame robin came to feed, and he would snooze quietly within six feet of them. Nor did he bother about the moorhens, who used to swim to the bank and cluck at him cheekily, as if daring him to come and see if they were not even more difficult to catch than water-rats. He was not with me in the days of Mr Penguin, and perhaps that was as well, for he had the freedom of the garden, and it would have been impossible to stop him from raiding Mr Penguin's apartment if he had wanted to do so.

His lack of interest in the sparrows and his namesake the robin always surprised me, for the mongoose in his wild state lives partly on small birds as well as on snakes, mice and rats. Perhaps he thought them too easy a prey to be worth bothering about; or perhaps he couldn't bring himself to take advantage of their innocence, and so destroy their faith in him.

Fortunately, too, he did not raid the chicken-runs of my neighbours. Once he was accused of this, but it was so much against his general habits that I daringly put him into the run with three chickens to prove my point; and he bore me out by leaving them to their own devices while he paid attention to a rat-hole. And yet, of all the delicacies which we gave him and which he found for himself, there was nothing that pleased him so much as the raw neck-bones of a chicken!

Robin's daily round, of course, was by no means all work and hunting. On getting up in the morning, my first duty was to go across the garden to the studio to take breakfast to Mary the chimpanzee. She was ready enough for it, and so was Tommy the terrier for his, and for the run that followed; but Robin was never in any hurry, because this was one of the times when he was allowed to share in our family life.

As soon as I opened the studio door, he would give my hand a little sniff by way of greeting and then run out, across the lawn, up the steps to the veranda, into the house (I used to leave the door open specially for him), up the stairs and into the bedroom. There, like a child greeting his mother in the morning, he would climb into my wife's bed and snuggle under the bedclothes.

There he would stay, very warm and comfortable and happy, till I returned. Then I would say: 'Now then, Robin, come along,' and turn him out.

Every morning, when this happened, he would sit up on the bed and swear at me; and then he would go obediently down to the dining-room. Half an hour later we would find him there, sitting before the fire in the winter or under the grand piano in

summer, and he would look up at me and seem to be saying:
'Oh, yes, you can turn me out of the bed because you are
bigger than I am; but I don't care. I've found a much better
place down here.'

Robin loved to sit in front of the fire in winter, especially
when he had got wet in the rain outside. Then he would come
in and take the central position on the hearth-rug, sitting
upright with his two little paws outstretched sideways, till the
front of him was dry and comfortable, and then turning round
in the same attitude to dry his back, propping himself up with
his long bushy tail.

Coming as he did from Africa, he very much appreciated
warmth, and when he was cold and there wasn't a fire he would
nose his way under an old coat or a rug. But of all nestling
places, the one he preferred was inside my wife's coat while she
was wearing it. He would climb in at the front and work his
way round till he could lie across the small of her back, with his
head on one hip and his hind toes on the other, and his long tail
somewhere in front.

His tail, as his photographs show, was normally long and
narrow; but when he became excited, hunting or playing, it
would spread out till it was about four inches in diameter.

When we sat down to breakfast he would climb on to my
knee. We would give him a saucer of milk or a bowl of bread-
and-milk, sometimes an egg – he preferred them raw – and on
very special occasions the chicken-neck which I have already
mentioned. He was good at breakfast-time, as a rule, and also
when, together with Mary, he would join us at tea; but when
his appetite got the better of his manners, his sin was usually
stealing other people's eggs or helping himself to butter. Often
he would sit so quietly that we almost forgot he was present;
and then, if no one seemed to be looking, a little arm would
come tentatively forward towards the butter dish, and, if still
no notice was taken, a greasy paw would go up, a minute later,
to be licked. (Of course, this was very, very wrong; but on
more than one occasion my wife caught my eye, signalled what
was happening, and then, by mutual agreement, we fussed

over coffee-pots and bacon dishes till the crime was finished and the traces of it properly cleared away.)

After breakfast Robin would want a game. Sometimes it would be hide-and-seek, either in the house or in the garden: he would run to the flower-beds and hide behind a clump of Michaelmas daisies, peeping out from time to time to make sure that we were coming to look for him. Then, when we got near, he would wait till the thrill became unbearable, and at last spring away to the next clump and wait for us to follow.

He loved, too, to be tickled, lying on his back like a cat, with paws in the air, and enjoying himself to the full. Often he wanted games when no one was free to play with him. There was a great deal of work for us to do in the garden, the house and the studio, apart from my ordinary tasks, and sometimes it wasn't possible to pay Robin all the attention he desired. Then he would become insistent. If my wife was tying up the chrysanthemums, he would suddenly appear beside her, make a funny little grunting noise, run round the bush, jump into the air and try to strike her arm: then he would stand back and look up, as much as to say: 'Come on, it's your turn now,' and run round the bush again, looking back to see if she were following him.

It was tempting, of course, to leave one's work on those occasions, and sometimes we did; but not always. When we were obdurate Robin would run away, and a little later we would find him playing with Mary.

He was very fond of Mary. A native in East Africa, as I have related, couldn't understand the games of Chuey and Toto. I, in my turn, was surprised at the extraordinary affection between a mongoose, a chimpanzee and an English fox-terrier in my garden. Yet there it was. Those three played together, exactly like children, except when Mary took the role of mother, which she did when Robin showed that he was feeling particularly lonesome. Then she would pick him up in her arms, hold him very nearly in the way that a mother holds a baby, and pet him till, nestling in the warmth of her fur, he was happy again.

I

Then, at last, he would wriggle out of her arms and run off: and Mary would watch him affectionately, getting more and more interested, until at last she couldn't stand being a mother any longer and would run and join him like a child again.

When Robin first came to me, before the days of Tommy, I used to have an old sheep-dog, and it was with him that Robin first learnt to play. A little later, when the sheep-dog was replaced by Tommy, then very puppyish and energetic, the games became friskier. Mary would discover an old rag and run off with it, then Tommy would catch the trailing end of the rag, and the stage would be set for a grand tug-of-war. Or else Robin and Tommy would start a playful fight, and Mary would come into the middle of it and grapple either or both of the others, catching an arm or a leg or a tail or a head, whatever was nearest, so that the duel turned into a general scrimmage.

One day when the three animals were playing in the garden, Tommy wandered off by himself, nosing about the flower-bed until by chance he discovered a wasps' nest in the ground. Of course, the sight of the wasps constantly going in and out attracted the dog's attention, with the result that his nose went too close and got stung. His yelps attracted Mary's attention, and she came running across the lawn to see what was the matter. Tommy looked up for a moment from rubbing his nose to tell her, and then she couldn't resist trying to prove his tale. The proof was forthcoming, in the shape of a sting on the end of her finger, and Mary joined Tommy in the search for cooling grass.

Meanwhile, Robin was left alone, deserted by both his playmates, and, of course, he very soon guessed that there was something worth inquiring about. He in his turn appeared on the scene, learnt the sad story, and, undismayed but full of curiosity, went to have a look for himself, and started scratching to make the hole bigger.

This third attack was a little too much for the wasps, and they (I suppose) sounded the alarm with the result that a whole army came out of the nest. By all the laws of justice Tommy, as the originator of the raid, ought to have borne the brunt of the attack; but by this time he had retired to a safe place by the bank of the lake. Failing him, Mary, as the second attacker, perhaps deserved punishment; but she had gone back to the studio to work with the aid of an old hairpin, on what she apparently thought was a splinter in her finger. Consequently the comparatively innocent Robin was left alone on the field of battle, and the sortie took full advantage of his lack of support. The wasps settled down on to his ears and head and gave him punishment.

Poor Robin, heavily outnumbered as he was, made no serious attempt at a fight, but quickly beat a retreat across the lawn, running on his hind legs while he tried to fight a desperate rear-guard action with his little front paws.

Alas! It was three saddened little animals that I put to bed that night!

But this sort of incident was soon forgotten, and its lessons were never learnt. It couldn't cure Robin of his fatal curiosity, and anything new had always to be explored. Coat-sleeves, for instance, always attracted him and, wondering what could be at the farther end of those long dark tunnels, he would set to work to find out. If the sleeve were big enough, he would crawl half-way up it, and then, losing his nerve, he would try the safer method of pushing up one of his little arms.

Another thing that absolutely fascinated him was the ink-pot. He soon learnt its mysteries and discovered that this curious dark water, though not good to drink, was excellent for making pretty patterns on carpets. If no one was about, he would clamber first on to a chair, up to the writing-desk, then push the lid off the ink-well, and dip in his paw.

After this had happened three or four time we made a rule of always leaving a nice white sheet of paper invitingly on the desk, in the hope of saving the carpet; and sometimes the ruse succeeded, with the result that we would come in half an hour later to find Robin, like a small child with a new and messy game, entirely absorbed in making his paw-prints.

Once I received an urgent request on the telephone to come

and remove Robin from a neighbouring house. The message clearly implied that this was a matter of life and death, but whether for Robin or for my neighbour I did not know till I arrived and was greeted by an indignant gentleman who had spent a hectic morning over financial calculations (I should think from his fury that they must have been connected with an income tax return), and then after leaving the room for dinner had returned to find his careful work entirely obliterated by Robin's inky fingerprints!

That was the direful result of one of Robin's expeditions outside the garden fence. He often trespassed abroad, and as he grew older he went farther and farther afield, until it grew to be a not infrequent thing for him to stay away from home for two or three nights at a time. At first this caused us a great deal of uneasiness, and once or twice we even sat up for him till the early hours of the morning. But after a while we decided that he was able to take care of himself, although in that subsequent events proved us to be wrong.

The trouble was that the mongoose, creeping along in the dusk, was more than once mistaken for a fox, the sworn enemy of farmers in my part of the country as in all others. Robin had several hair-raising adventures through this mistake, and one in particular.

He had gone out by himself one day on a rat-hunt, and our last view of him was when he was jumping in the long grass of an adjacent field, in his efforts to see something worth chasing.

Neither that night nor the next morning did he return, and then the baker casually informed us that a fox had been seen half a mile away in the early hours of the morning, and that, as foxes had been particularly mischievous in the local chicken runs for some time past, an S O S had been circulated, with the result that some forty men and boys had turned out in pursuit.

We wondered at the time whether the 'fox' could possibly be Robin, and felt a certain amount of anxiety. However, the hunt was unsuccessful, and the next news that reached us was that a small but mysterious animal, believed to bear some resemblance to our mongoose, was at bay under the shelter at the tram terminus.

We hurried, of course, to see and if need be to rescue. We found a considerable crowd of spectators just dispersing, and learnt that some enterprising sportsman had brought his dog to the tram shelter just before our arrival, and that the dog had at once shown a lot of excitement and had set to work scraping away the earth on one side, so as to be able to squeeze into the narrow space between the wooden foundations of the shelter and the ground. The crowd, naturally, at once went round to that side to enjoy the fun, and the unknown animal very wisely took the providential chance of safety, slipped under the edge of the shelter on the opposite side from the dog, and disappeared into the adjoining cabbage patch.

As to the animal – well, it might have been a ferret or it might have been a weasel, but Bill James swore it was an otter and two telegraph boys (delaying after the manner of telegraph boys) were certain it was a fox; but, nevertheless, as soon as I mentioned that Robin was missing from his home everyone present (including Bill James and both the telegraph boys) was certain that it was a mongoose.

Feeling by now rather seriously alarmed, we searched the cabbage patch and satisfied ourselves that Robin – if it really was Robin – was well away into the comparative safety of the fields. Then, as there was nothing more to be done at the moment, we went home, hoping against hope that our mongoose would have sought the only shelter that was really safe for him. But he wasn't there, and there was nothing for it but to sit as patiently as we could and await further news.

This came before very long. A friend, who had heard of the disappearance, telephoned to say that she was certain that Robin was hiding under her potting-shed: or if it wasn't Robin it was some other animal whom we, as notorious animal lovers, ought to rescue immediately, as she was having difficulty in restraining her dogs.

As may be imagined, we lost no time in getting to our friend's house. By the time we arrived, one of the dogs had broken loose and was already half-way under the shed. This time the sheltering animal would have had no back-door exit, for the potting-shed was enclosed on three sides by a brick wall. The dog, to his grievous disappointment, was chivvied off, and in case of accidents I made sure that he and his brother were securely tied up.

Then I lay flat on the ground, in front of the hole which the dog had conveniently enlarged, and tried to peer under the shed. It was too dark to see anything but a form that moved and might have been that of Robin, but might equally well have belonged to almost any other small creature. So I called for a spade and started to finish the dog's work; and three minutes later poor Robin was lying in my wife's arms, utterly exhausted and with his heart still beating furiously from sheer terror.

He lay still in her arms, looking from one to the other in his joy at finding us. But it was some hours before he completely recovered from his fright, and that night, for the only time in his life, we let him sleep, rolled in an eiderdown, beside our bed.

ONE MAN AND HIS DOG

by

RUPERT CROFT-COOKE

(from *A Football for the Brigadier*, by permission of
A. D. Peters)

IN OUR village of Charden there is one ghost story, and I'm not
going to tell it. At least, I'll tell you the story without the ghost,
because I think the ghost such as he is, to be a natural conse-
quence of the story. I mean I'm not interested in the people
who believe they have seen and heard things, but I am interested in the events which have made them believe that the
things were there.

Some years ago a man named Albert Bartram confided in his
friends at The Ploughboys that he had had enough of his wife's
nagging, and on the following day walked out of his cottage and
took to the road.

There had, of course, and as usual, been faults on both sides.
Bartram drank too much and was free with his fists; his wife
had a particularly violent and indefatigable tongue. It was
generally felt that she was well rid of Albert, but there was also
some sympathy expressed for the wanderer. The woman had a
little money in the savings bank and became housekeeper at
The Moat, our biggest house, where she made life difficult for
the girls who worked under her but ran her department with
efficiency.

When next Albert appeared in Charden it was as a confirmed
gentleman of the road, a milestone inspector as we called them
thereabouts, who did his alternate day's work in the spike (the
workhouse), and his day's march to the next, year in and year
out, and had no intention of ever doing otherwise. Whether he
was happy or not no one could say before or after his visit to the
village, for it was not a point on which he himself could give any

opinion. He was invited to The Ploughboys and so well treated that he was refused admission that night to our workhouse and had to sleep in a barn. He had grown into a heavy, silent man, grudging of speech even when he had drunk enough of our excellent Mild to make him talkative. He told us, however, that he should never change the life now, that he couldn't settle down again to live in a house, and that life on the road wasn't as bad as it was made out to be.

Mr Kenny, our Workhouse Master, told us afterwards that Albert Bartram was typical of most of his visitors. It seemed – though it was incomprehensible both to him and to us – that once having grown accustomed to the routine, the eternal march from place to place, the arrival at the spike, the compulsory bath, the hot cocoa, bread and cheese, the warm bed, the day's work and the onward march again, few men could be induced to leave it.

'I've known cases,' he said, 'where their families have begged them to come back and they've been offered good jobs, and still they won't come off the roads. Funny isn't it?'

Funny was not the adjective I should have used, but I nodded.

Perhaps once a year, perhaps once in two years, Albert Bartram used to come through Charden and no one paid much attention to his calls. He must have been in his fifties when we had to tell him on one visit that his wife had died of pneumonia during the previous winter. We suggested to him that since he had only left us in the first place in order, as he had said, to get away from her, he should now settle down again. One of the farmers offered him a job and the Vicar had a long talk with him in which he pointed out that Bartram was wasting his life and that he owed it to Society to take his place as a productive worker and not merely continue this useless endless perambulation.

But it was no good. Albert didn't argue. He just said to everyone who asked him that he had 'got used to it' and 'shouldn't change now'. And next morning he sloped out of the village with that steady, stooping, tireless walk which all tramps seem to have learnt.

Another ten years must have passed before he was recalled to our minds again, and then by a very startling piece of news. A brother of his who had owned a small newsagent-and-tobacconist business in a London suburb had died intestate, and our Albert Bartram had inherited nearly a thousand pounds. Efforts were being made to trace him, but since it was impossible to guess in what part of the British Isles he might be, and since he was unlikely to read newspapers, it was supposed that not until he called again at Charden would he hear his good news.

This was so. He trudged in on one June evening and was taken to The Ploughboys and told that he was a – comparatively – rich man. The business side of the thing had been left with an Ashford firm of solicitors and a clerk came over that evening with five pound notes for him, documents for him to sign, and a request for his instructions about the money.

Albert dealt with all this unemotionally.

'I'll have a hundred in notes,' he said, 'and the rest's to go into the Post Office. I shan't need it.'

Without fuss he bought drinks for everyone present. Then he went back into his normal habit of silence.

We tried to rally him.

'Going to buy a pub, Bert?'

He shook his head.

'A cottage, then?'

'No.'

'What are you going to do with it?'

'You heard. Put it in the Savings.'

'And what'll *you* do?'

'I shan't change.'

'What's that?'

'I shan't change. I'm used to the life. I don't see any reason to change it.'

And believe it or not he didn't. He put that money into a Post Office Savings Account and went off with a hundred, all in

pound notes, stuck up in an envelope. And when he came back
to the village after that he used to show us that envelope still
sealed up. He said he didn't need any money. He'd got used to
doing without. He didn't even seem to have his old taste for
drinking. As they said in The Ploughboys, with *that* money he
could have gone on the booze every night. But the daily round
of the mumper seemed to have claimed him for the rest of his
days.

It happened that on one of his visits to Charden, about three
years after he had inherited his fortune, he walked up the
village street at the time when Miss Cuff was exercising her
dogs. Miss Cuff breeds spaniels and retrievers and looks rather
as though that might be her occupation. She wears tweeds and
a collar and tie, or sometimes jodhpurs, and her face is freckled
and tanned. She comes to The Ploughboys sometimes and
makes a point of choosing the public bar, drinking from a pint
glass and having a game of darts with the fellows, although her
own Pedigree is as long as that of her prize dogs.

On that evening she was whistling, and she could whistle
like a milkman on his rounds. She was not whistling a tune,
though, she was calling to a spaniel puppy of hers which was
missing. And presently old Bartram comes down the road
looking bedraggled and unshaven and like a tramp in a comic
drawing.

'Was this what you were looking for?' he asked her, and
showed her the pup inside his torn greatcoat.

'Yes. Thanks,' said Miss Cuff holding out her hand for it.

'Seemed to take to me,' said old Bartram thoughtfully, to
which Miss Cuff made no reply.

'I suppose you wouldn't part with this dog?' he asked.

'Part with it? Certainly not. Ten pounds wouldn't buy that
dog.'

She had said ten pounds because it was the first figure that
had come into her head and because any sum of money seemed
so completely out of the compass of the tatterdemalion in front
of her that the actual figure did not matter. In point of fact the
puppy was worth considerably more.

To her astonishment old Bartram delved down into his clothes, pulled out a greasy envelope, extracted his money, counted out ten notes and pushed them into her hand.

'But . . . but I said ten pounds *wouldn't* buy him,' said the dumbfounded woman.

'Well, it has,' said Bartram curtly and walked on. Miss Cuff said afterwards that she was so flummoxed that she let him go.

The workhouse master has often told us what happened that evening since it had such notable consequences. Old Bartram shuffled in as usual and it was not until ten minutes later that the puppy was seen.

'Now, Bartram, you know very well that no dogs are allowed in here,' said Mr Kenny.

'Oh?' said Bartram, and never a word more. He got up, pulled on his old black overcoat, and left the Institution.

That night he slept in a barn and next morning he called on Mr Spruce, our grocer, who had a tumble-down cottage empty on the outskirts of the village. In as few words as possible he indicated that he was the grocer's future tenant and paid three months' rent in advance. He bought a chair, a table and a few cooking-pots from Spruce and before noon had settled in.

Thereafter we saw him daily, and never without his dog which he called for some reason never explained, 'Nelson'. Miss Cuff pointed out that the name was most unsuitable for a high-born creature whose father was Pride of Exmoor and mother Glory of the Guns. But Bartram paid no heed. He led Nelson about on a leather strap when he was in the main street because there is a good deal of through traffic in Charden, but when he left the village he let him run free.

Clearly the puppy became attached to his master, as was inevitable. But old Bartram felt not only love but pride. After a week or two we noticed that he had purchased from somewhere a decent suit of clothes, and it was said that he had done so only to look fit to walk out with his dog. He shaved, not regularly but at respectable intervals. He even bought a new pair of boots.

But it must not be supposed that Albert Bartram was in any sense a reformed character. If the Vicar had hoped, many years before, that by persuading him to settle down he could turn the old ruffian into a useful member of society he was gravely mistaken. Bartram did no regular work; only at times of extra wages when the farms needed labour enough to pay disproportionately for it, did he offer himself for employment. Hop-picking, hay-making, fruit-picking, such choice and profitable labour he condescended to undertake, but never a regular job. He was an inveterate poacher. A field of mushrooms or a wall of peaches would disappear in the small hours and no one but Bartram could be suspected. Several times a week he drank, it was said, more than was good for him, denying angrily that there existed such a quantity. Indeed it was soon seen, and freely commented on, that Albert Bartram had led a more virtuous life as a tramp than as a householder.

He was never without his dog, and the spaniel seemed wretched away from his feet. Even Miss Cuff had to admit that no dog bred by her received more attention, for all the modern kennels and scientific dieting in the homes to which they went. He had changed his whole life for the sake of Nelson, and for Nelson, I honestly believe, the old man would have given the rest of his time on earth. At least when the Vicar pointed out tactfully that he was risking eternal damnation by not coming to church he explained adequately that he could not take the dog in.

He had aged a good deal now, both in appearance and in fact. He must have been approaching seventy and he looked even older. He had grown more silent than ever, rarely even bidding us good evening. But it was said that in his cottage he had been heard talking to his dog. And if he ever had occasion to call Nelson he did so with a peculiar whistle, a succession of three quick blasts on one note. If you passed his cottage at night you sometimes heard it in the darkness – 'Whee! Whee! Whee!' and then silence, for he never needed to call more than once.

Age did not improve him. There was a copse up the road

from where he lived – it's become the Eaglemont Building Estate now – and Bartram was reputed to visit it frequently in the small hours in search of small game. He had taught Nelson a few poacher's tricks, we supposed; at any rate he took the spaniel with him. And it was a fact that the private car of an unscrupulous poulterer used to call at intervals at Bartram's cottage and never before dark.

This might have gone on for years until Nelson was old and blind and kept alive by Bartram's care. But it was cut short rather shockingly. Seven years after Bartram had settled amongst us his dog was killed in the main street of Charden by a speeding motor car. Nelson was only six feet away from Bartram at the time, crossing the road to join him. The car drove on. Bartram turned, stooped over his dog and examined him, saw that the car had passed right over his neck and that Nelson was stone dead, then walked straight home. He never even picked the animal up, and Tom Richards who lived opposite had to carry him in and bury him.

After that Bartram's behaviour was described as queer. He did not often leave his cottage but could be heard talking, presumably to himself. When he came to The Ploughboys he walked in as though a dog was at his feet, and seemed to look down as he had done when Nelson was with him. It was said, and I do not know with how much truth, that he would purchase a packet of biscuits every evening and scatter them on the floor as he had done for his spaniel.

Certainly he often whistled as he used to do. We heard that 'Whee! Whee! Whee!' coming sharply across the dusk, once no more, as though it was still unnecessary to repeat it to bring the dog to heel. It seemed that the incident of the motor car was unreal to him, that Nelson had never left his feet.

But it is not the ghost of the dog about which there is talk in Charden. Old Bartram was found dead in the copse one morning of thick frost, as stiff a corpse as anyone had seen. And by those who return through the little wood to the lights of the village it is sworn that a shrill – 'Whee! Whee! Whee!' once and no more breaks the silence. They say that Bartram is still calling Nelson in. Even now, when rows of hire-purchase houses and neat gardens cover the place, the residents say that while they are putting the cat out at night, or locking up the hen-run, they hear it in the night-breeze. But, as I say, it is probable that the story made the ghost.

TOBERMORY

by

SAKI

(H. H. Munro)

IT WAS a chill, rain-washed afternoon of a late August day, that indefinite season when partridges are still in security or cold storage, and there is nothing to hunt – unless one is bounded on the north by the Bristol Channel, in which case one may lawfully gallop after fat red stags. Lady Blemley's house-party was not bounded on the north by the Bristol Channel, hence there was a full gathering of her guests round the tea-table on this particular afternoon. And, in spite of the blankness of the season and the triteness of the occasion, there was no trace in the company of that fatigued restlessness which means a dread of the pianola and a subdued hankering for auction bridge. The undisguised open-mouthed attention of the entire party was fixed on the homely negative personality of Mr Cornelius Appin. Of all her guests, he was the one who had come to Lady Blemley with the vaguest reputation. Someone had said he was 'clever', and he had got his invitation in the moderate expectation, on the part of his hostess, that some portion at least of his cleverness would be contributed to the general entertainment. Until teatime that day she had been unable to discover in what direction, if any, his cleverness lay. He was neither a wit nor a croquet champion, a hypnotic force nor a begetter of amateur theatricals. Neither did his exterior suggest the sort of man in whom women are willing to pardon a generous measure of mental deficiency. He had subsided into mere Mr Appin, and the Cornelius seemed a piece of transparent baptismal bluff. And now he was claiming to have launched on the world a discovery beside which the invention of gunpowder, of the printing-press, and of steam locomotion were inconsiderable trifles. Science had made bewildering strides in many directions during recent decades, but this thing seemed to belong to the domain of miracle rather than to scientific achievement.

'And do you really ask us to believe,' Sir Wilfrid was saying, 'that you have discovered a means of instructing animals in the art of human speech, and that dear old Tobermory has proved your first successful pupil?'

'It is a problem at which I have worked for the last seventeen years,' said Mr Appin, 'but only during the last eight or nine months have I been rewarded with glimmerings of success. Of course I have experimented with thousands of animals, but latterly only with cats, those wonderful creatures which have assimilated themselves so marvellously with our civilization while retaining all their highly developed feral instincts. Here and there among cats one comes across an outstanding superior intellect, just as one does among the ruck of human beings, and when I made the acquaintance of Tobermory a week ago I saw at once that I was in contact with a 'Beyond-cat' of extraordinary intelligence. I had gone far along the road to success in recent experiments; with Tobermory, as you call him, I have reached the goal.'

Mr Appin concluded his remarkable statement in a voice which he strove to divest of a triumphant inflection. No one said 'Rats', though Clovis's lips moved in a monosyllabic contortion, which probably invoked those rodents of disbelief.

'And do you mean to say,' asked Miss Resker, after a slight pause, 'that you have taught Tobermory to say and understand easy sentences of one syllable?'

'My dear Miss Resker,' said the wonder-worker patiently, 'one teaches little children and savages and backward adults in that piecemeal fashion; when one has once solved the problem of making a beginning with an animal of highly developed intelligence one has no need for those halting methods. Tobermory can speak our language with perfect correctness.'

This time Clovis very distinctly said, 'Beyond-rats!' Sir Wilfrid was more polite, but equally sceptical.

'Hadn't we better have the cat in and judge for ourselves?' suggested Lady Blemley.

Sir Wilfrid went in search of the animal, and the company settled themselves down to the languid expectation of witnessing some more or less adroit drawing-room ventriloquism.

In a minute Sir Wilfrid was back in the room, his face white beneath its tan and his eyes dilated with excitement.

'By Gad, it's true!'

His agitation was unmistakably genuine, and his hearers started forward in a thrill of awakened interest.

Collapsing into an armchair he continued breathlessly: 'I found him dozing in the smoking-room, and called out to him to come for his tea. He blinked at me in his usual way, and I said, "Come on, Toby; don't keep us waiting"; and, by Gad! he drawled out in a most horribly natural voice that he'd come when he dashed well pleased! I nearly jumped out of my skin!'

Appin had preached to absolutely incredulous hearers; Sir Wilfrid's statement carried instant conviction. A Babel-like chorus of startled exclamation arose, amid which the scientist sat mutely enjoying the first fruit of his stupendous discovery.

In the midst of the clamour Tobermory entered the room and made his way with velvet tread and studied unconcern across to the group seated round the tea-table.

A sudden hush of awkwardness and constraint fell on the company. Somehow there seemed an element of embarrassment in addressing on equal terms a domestic cat of acknowledged dental ability.

'Will you have some milk, Tobermory?' asked Lady Blemley in a rather strained voice.

'I don't mind if I do,' was the response, couched in a tone of even indifference. A shiver of suppressed excitement went through the listeners, and Lady Blemley might be excused for pouring out the saucerful of milk rather unsteadily.

'I'm afraid I've spilt a good deal of it,' she said apologetically.

'After all, it's not my Axminster,' was Tobermory's rejoinder.

Another silence fell on the group, and then Miss Resker, in

her best district-visitor manner, asked if the human language had been difficult to learn. Tobermory looked squarely at her for a moment and then fixed his gaze serenely on the middle distance. It was obvious that boring questions lay outside his scheme of life.

'What do you think of human intelligence?' asked Mavis Pellington lamely.

'Of whose intelligence in particular?' asked Tobermory coldly.

'Oh, well, mine for instance,' said Mavis, with a feeble laugh.

'You put me in an embarrassing position,' said Tobermory, whose tone and attitude certainly did not suggest a shred of embarrassment. 'When your inclusion in this house-party was suggested Sir Wilfrid protested that you were the most brainless woman of his acquaintance, and that there was a wide distinction between hospitality and the care of the feeble-minded. Lady Blemley replied that your lack of brain-power was the precise quality which had earned you your invitation, as you were the only person she could think of who might be idiotic enough to buy their old car. You know, the one they call "The Envy of Sisyphus," because it goes quite nicely uphill if you push it.'

Lady Blemley's protestations would have had greater effect if she had not casually suggested to Mavis only that morning that the car in question would be just the thing for her down at her Devonshire home.

Major Barfield plunged in heavily to effect a diversion.

'How about your carryings-on with the tortoise-shell puss up at the stables, eh?'

The moment he had said it everyone realized the blunder.

'One does not usually discuss these matters in public,' said Tobermory frigidly. 'From a slight observation of your ways since you've been in this house I should imagine you'd find it inconvenient if I were to shift the conversation on to your own little affairs.'

The panic which ensued was not confined to the Major.

'Would you like to go and see if cook has got your dinner ready?' suggested Lady Blemley hurriedly, affecting to ignore the fact that it wanted at least two hours to Tobermory's dinner-time.

'Thanks,' said Tobermory, 'not quite so soon after my tea. I don't want to die of indigestion.'

'Cats have nine lives, you know,' said Sir Wilfrid heartily.

'Possibly,' answered Tobermory; 'but only one liver.'

'Adelaide!' said Mrs Cornett, 'do you mean to encourage that cat to go out and gossip about us in the servants' hall?'

The panic had indeed become general. A narrow ornamental balustrade ran in front of most of the bedroom windows at the Towers, and it was recalled with dismay that this had formed a favourite promenade for Tobermory at all hours, whence he could watch the pigeons – and heaven knew what else besides. If he intended to become reminiscent in his present outspoken strain the effect would be something more than disconcerting. Mrs Cornett, who spent much time at her toilet table, and whose complexion was reputed to be of a nomadic though punctual disposition, looked as ill at ease as the Major. Miss Scrawen, who wrote fiercely sensuous poetry and led a blameless life, merely displayed irritation; if you are methodical and virtuous in private you don't necessarily want every one to know it. Bertie van Tahn, who was so depraved at seventeen that he had long ago given up trying to be any worse, turned a dull shade of gardenia white, but he did not commit the error of dashing out of the room like Odo Finsberry, a young gentleman who was understood to be reading for the Church and who was possibly disturbed at the thought of scandals he might hear concerning other people. Clovis had the presence of mind to maintain a composed exterior; privately he was calculating how long it would take to procure a box of fancy mice through the agency of the *Exchange and Mart* as a species of hush-money.

Even in a delicate situation like the present, Agnes Resker could not endure to remain too long in the background.

'Why did I ever come down here?' she asked dramatically.

Tobermory immediately accepted the opening.

'Judging by what you said to Mrs Cornett on the croquet-lawn yesterday, you were out for food. You described the Blemleys as the dullest people to stay with that you knew, but said they were clever enough to employ a first-rate cook; otherwise they'd find it difficult to get anyone to come down a second time.'

'There's not a word of truth in it! I appeal to Mrs Cornett –' exclaimed the discomfited Agnes.

'Mrs Cornett repeated your remark afterwards to Bertie van Tahn,' continued Tobermory, 'and said, "That woman is a regular Hunger Marcher; she'd go anywhere for four square meals a day," and Bertie van Tahn said –'

At this point the chronicle mercifully ceased. Tobermory had caught a glimpse of the big yellow Tom from the Rectory working his way through the shrubbery towards the stable wing. In a flash he had vanished through the open french window.

With the disappearance of his too brilliant pupil Cornelius Appin found himself beset by a hurricane of bitter upbraiding, anxious inquiry, and frightened entreaty. The responsibility for the situation lay with him, and he must prevent matters from becoming worse. Could Tobermory impart his dangerous gift to other cats? was the first question he had to answer. It was possible, he replied, that he might have initiated his intimate friend the stable puss into his new accomplishment, but it was unlikely that his teaching could have taken a wider range as yet.

'Then,' said Mrs Cornett, 'Tobermory may be a valuable cat and a great pet; but I'm sure you'll agree, Adelaide, that both he and the stable cat must be done away with without delay.'

'You don't suppose I've enjoyed the last quarter of an hour, do you?' said Lady Blemley bitterly. 'My husband and I are very fond of Tobermory – at least, we were before this horrible accomplishment was infused into him; but now, of course, the only thing is to have him destroyed as soon as possible.'

'We can put some strychnine in the scraps he always gets at dinner-time,' said Sir Wilfrid, 'and I will go and drown the stable cat myself. The coachman will be very sore at losing his pet, but I'll say a very catching form of mange has broken out in both cats and we're afraid of it spreading to the kennels.'

'But my great discovery!' expostulated Mr Appin; 'after all my years of research and experiment –'

'You can go and experiment on the short-horns at the farm, who are under proper control,' said Mrs Cornett, 'or the elephants at the Zoological Gardens. They're said to be highly intelligent, and they have this recommendation, that they don't come creeping about our bedrooms and under chairs, and so forth.'

An archangel ecstatically proclaiming the Millennium, and then finding that it clashed unpardonably with Henley and would have to be indefinitely postponed, could hardly have felt more crestfallen than Cornelius Appin at the reception of his wonderful achievement. Public opinion, however, was against him – in fact, had the general voice been consulted on the subject it is probable that a strong minority vote would have been in favour of including him in the strychnine diet.

Defective train arrangements and a nervous desire to see matters brought to a finish prevented an immediate dispersal of the party, but dinner that evening was not a social success. Sir Wilfred had had rather a trying time with the stable cat and subsequently with the coachman. Agnes Resker ostentatiously limited her repast to a morsel of dry toast, which she bit as though it were a personal enemy; while Mavis Pellington maintained a vindictive silence throughout the meal. Lady Blemley kept up a flow of what she hoped was conversation, but her attention was fixed on the doorway. A plateful of carefully dosed fish scraps was in readiness on the sideboard, but sweets and savoury dessert went their way, and no Tobermory appeared either in the dining-room or kitchen.

The sepulchral dinner was cheerful compared with the subsequent vigil in the smoking-room. Eating and drinking had at

least supplied a distraction and cloak to the prevailing embarrassment. Bridge was out of the question in the general tension
of nerves and tempers, and after Odo Finsberry had given a
lugubrious rendering of 'Mélisande in the Wood' to a frigid
audience, music was tacitly avoided. At eleven the servants
went to bed, announcing that the small window in the pantry
had been left open as usual for Tobermory's private use. The
guests read steadily through the current batch of magazines,
and fell back gradually on the 'Badminton Library' and bound
volumes of *Punch*. Lady Blemley made periodic visits to the
pantry, returning each time with an expression of listless depression which forestalled questioning.

At two o'clock Clovis broke the dominating silence.

'He won't turn up tonight. He's probably in the local newspaper office at the present moment, dictating the first instal-
ment of his reminiscences. Lady What's-her-name's book
won't be in it. It will be the event of the day.'

Having made this contribution to the general cheerfulness,
Clovis went to bed. At long intervals the various members of
the house-party followed his example.

The servants taking round the early tea made a uniform
announcement in reply to a uniform question. Tobermory had
not returned.

Breakfast was, if anything, a more unpleasant function than
dinner had been, but before its conclusion the situation was relieved. Tobermory's corpse was brought in from the shrubbery,
where a gardener had just discovered it. From the bites on his
throat and the yellow fur which coated his claws it was evident
that he had fallen in unequal combat with the big Tom from
the Rectory.

By midday most of the guests had quitted the Towers, and
after lunch Lady Blemley had sufficiently recovered her spirits
to write an extremely nasty letter to the Rectory about the loss
of her valuable pet.

Tobermory had been Appin's one successful pupil, and he
was destined to have no successor. A few weeks later an elephant in the Dresden Zoological Garden, which had shown no

previous signs of irritability, broke loose and killed an Englishman who had apparently been teasing it. The victim's name
was variously reported in the papers as Oppin and Eppelin, but
his front name was faithfully rendered Cornelius.

'If he was trying German irregular verbs on the poor beast,'
said Clovis, 'he deserved all he got.'

LIVING WITH MIJBIL

by

GAVIN MAXWELL

(from *Ring of Bright Water*)

TWO DAYS before the date of our rendezvous I returned to the Consulate-General late in the afternoon, after several hours' absence, to find that my mail had arrived. I carried it to my bedroom to read, and there squatting on the floor were two Marsh Arabs; beside them lay a sack that squirmed from time to time.

They handed me a note from Thesiger. 'Here is your otter, a male and weaned. I feel you may want to take it to London – it would be a handful in the *tarada*. It is the one I originally heard of, but the sheikhs were after it, so they said it was dead. Give Ajram a letter to me saying it has arrived safely – he has taken Kathia's place. . . .'

With the opening of that sack began a phase of my life that in the essential sense has not yet ended, and may, for all I know, not end before I do. It is, in effect, a thraldom to otters, an otter fixation, that I have since found to be shared by most other people who have ever owned one.

The creature that emerged, not greatly disconcerted, from this sack on to the spacious tiled floor of the Consulate bedroom did not at that moment resemble anything so much as a very small medievally-conceived dragon. From the head to the tip of the tail he was coated with symmetrical pointed scales of mud armour, between whose tips was visible a soft velvet fur like that of a chocolate-brown mole. He shook himself, and I half expected this aggressive camouflage to disintegrate into a cloud of dust, but it remained unaffected by his manoeuvre, and in fact it was not for another month that I contrived to remove the last of it and see him, as it were, in his true colours

Yet even on that first day I recognized that he was an otter of a species that I had never seen in the flesh, resembling only a curious otter skin that I had bought from the Arabs in one of the marsh villages. Mijbil, as I called the new otter, after a sheikh with whom we had recently been staying and whose name had intrigued me with a conjured picture of platypus-like creature, was, in fact, of a race previously unknown to science, and was at length christened by zoologists, from examination of the skin and of himself, *Lutrogale perspicillata maxwelli*, or Maxwell's otter. This circumstance, perhaps, influenced on my side the intensity of the emotional relationship between us, for I became, during a year of his constant and violently affectionate companionship, fonder of him than of almost any human being, and to write of him in the past tense makes me feel as desolate as one who has lost an only child. For a year and five days he was about my bed and my bath spying out all my ways, and though I now have another otter no whit less friendly and fascinating, there will never be another Mijbil.

For the first twenty-four hours Mijbil was neither hostile nor friendly; he was simply aloof and indifferent, choosing to sleep on the floor as far from my bed as possible, and to accept food and water as though they were things that had appeared before him without human assistance. The food presented a problem, for it did not immediately occur to me that the Marsh Arabs had almost certainly fed him on rice scraps only supplemented by such portions of fish as are inedible to humans. The Consul-General sent out a servant to buy fish, but this servant's return coincided with a visit from Robert Angorly, a British-educated Christian Iraqi who was the Crown Prince's game warden and entertained a passionate interest in natural history. Angorly told me that none of the fishes that had been bought was safe for an animal, for they had been poisoned with digitalis, which, though harmless to a human in this quantity, he felt certain would be dangerous to a young otter. He offered to obtain me a daily supply of fish that had been taken with nets, and thereafter he brought every day half a dozen or so small reddish fish from the Tigris. These Mijbil consumed with gusto, holding them upright between his forepaws, tail end uppermost, and eating them like a stick of Edinburgh rock, always with five crunches of the left-hand side of the jaw alternating with five crunches on the right.

The otter and I enjoyed the Consul-General's long-suffering hospitality for a fortnight. The second night Mijbil came on to my bed in the small hours and remained asleep in the crook of my knees until the servant brought tea in the morning, and during that day he began to lose his apathy and take a keen, much too keen, interest in his surroundings. I fashioned a collar, or rather a body-belt, for him, and took him on a lead to the bathroom, where for half an hour he went wild with joy in the water, plunging and rolling in it, shooting up and down the length of the bath underwater, and making enough slosh and splash for a hippo. This, I was to learn, is a characteristic of otters; every drop of water must be, so to speak, extended and spread about the place; a bowl must at once be overturned, or, if it will not be overturned, be sat in and sploshed in until it overflows. Water must be kept on the move and made to do things; when static it is as wasted and provoking as a buried talent.

It was only two days later that he escaped from my bedroom as I entered it, and I turned to see his tail disappearing round the bend of the corridor that led to the bathroom. By the time I had caught up with him he was up on the end of the bath and fumbling at the chromium taps with his paws. I watched, amazed by this early exhibition of an intelligence I had not yet guessed; in less than a minute he had turned the tap far enough to produce a dribble of water, and, after a moment or two of distraction at his success, achieved the full flow. (He had, in fact, been fortunate to turn the tap the right way; on subsequent occasions he would as often as not try with great violence to screw it up still tighter, chittering with irritation and disappointment at its failure to cooperate.)

The Consulate had a big walled garden in which I exercised

him, and, within it, a high-netted tennis court. In this enclosure I established after a few days that he would follow me
without a lead and come to me when I called his name. By the
end of a week he had accepted me in a relationship of de-
pendence, and with this security established he began to display the principal otter characteristic of perpetual play. Very
few species of animal habitually play after they are adult; they
are concerned with eating, sleeping, or procreating, or with the
means to one or other of these ends. But otters are one of the
few exceptions to this rule; right through their lives they spend
much of their time in play that does not even require a partner.
In the wild state they will play alone for hours with any convenient floating object in the water, pulling it down to let it bob
up again, or throwing it with a jerk of the head so that it lands
with a splash and becomes a quarry to be pursued. No doubt in
their holts they lie on their backs and play, too, as my otters
have, with small objects that they can roll between their paws
and pass from palm to palm, for at Camusfeàrna, in northern
Scotland, all the sea holts contain a profusion of small
shells and round stones that can only have been carried in for
toys.

Mij would spend hours shuffling a rubber ball round the
room like a four-footed soccer player using all four feet to
dribble the ball, and he could also throw it, with a powerful
flick of the neck, to a surprising height and distance. These
games he would play either by himself or with me, but the
really steady play of an otter, the time-filling play born of a
sense of well-being and a full stomach, seems to me to be when
the otter lies on its back and juggles with small objects between
its paws. This they do with an extraordinarily concentrated
absorption and dexterity, as though a conjuror were trying to
perfect some trick, as though in this play there were some goal
that the human observer could not guess. Later, marbles became Mij's favourite toys for this pastime – for pastime it is,
without any anthropomorphizing – and he would lie on his
back rolling two or more of them up and down his wide, flat
belly without ever dropping one to the floor, or, with forepaws

upstretched, rolling them between his palms for minutes on end.

Even during that first fortnight in Basra I learnt a lot of Mij's language, a language largely shared, I have discovered, by many other races of otter, though with curious variations in usage. The sounds are widely different in range. The simplest is the call note, which has been much the same in all the otters I have come across; it is a short, anxious, penetrating, though not loud, mixture between a whistle and a chirp. There is also a query, used at closer quarters; Mij would enter a room, for instance, and ask whether there was anyone in it by the word 'Ha!' uttered in a loud, harsh whisper. If he saw preparations being made to take him out or to the bath, he would stand at the door making a musical bubbling sound interspersed with chirps; but it was the chirp, in all its permutations and combinations of high and low, from the single querulous note to a continuous flow of chitter, that was Mij's main means of vocal communication. He had one other note unlike any of these, a high, snarling caterwaul, a sort of screaming wail, that meant unequivocally that he was very angry, and if provoked further would bite. He bit, in anger as opposed to nips in excitable play, four times during the year that I had him. Each of these occasions was memorable in the highest degree, though I was only once at the receiving end.

An otter's jaws are, of course, enormously powerful – indeed the whole animal is of strength almost unbelievable in a creature of its size – and those jaws are equipped with teeth to crunch into instant pulp fish heads that seem as hard as stone. Like a puppy that nibbles and gnaws one's hands because he has so few other outlets for his feelings, otters seem to find the use of their mouths the most natural outlet for expression; knowing as I do their enormous crushing power I can appreciate what efforts my otters have made to be gentle in play, but their playful nips are gauged, perhaps, to the sensitivity of an otter's, rather than a human, skin. Mij used to look hurt and surprised when scolded for what must have seemed to him the most meticulous gentleness, and though after a time he learned to be as soft mouthed as a sucking dove with me he remained all his life somewhat over-excitably good-humoured and hail-fellow-well-bit with strangers.

The days passed peacefully at Basra, but I dreaded dismally the unpostponable prospect of transporting Mij to England, and to his ultimate destination, Camusfeàrna. BOAC would not fly livestock at all, and there was then no other line to London. Finally I booked a Trans-World flight to Paris, with a doubtful Air France booking on the same evening to London. Trans-World insisted that Mij should be packed into a box of not more than eighteen inches square, and that this box must be personal luggage, to be carried on the floor at my feet.

Mij's body was at that time perhaps a little over a foot long and his tail another foot; the designing of this box employed many anxious hours for myself and the ever-helpful Robert Angorly, and finally he had the container constructed by crafts-men of his acquaintance. The box was delivered on the after-noon before my departure on a 9.15 pm flight. It was zinclined, and divided into two compartments, one for sleeping and one for the relief of nature, and it appeared to my inexperi-enced eye as nearly ideal as could be contrived.

Dinner was at eight, and I thought that it would be as well to put Mij into the box an hour before we left, so that he would become accustomed to it before the jolting of the journey began to upset him. I manœuvred him into it, not without difficulty, and he seemed peaceful when I left him in the dark for a hurried meal.

But when I returned, with only barely time for the Consulate car to reach the airport for the flight, I was confronted with an appalling spectacle. There was complete silence from inside the box, but from its airholes and the chinks around the hinged lid, blood had trickled and dried on the white wood. I whipped off the padlock and tore open the lid, and Mij, exhausted and blood-spattered, whimpered and tried to climb up my leg. He had torn the zinc lining to shreds, scratching his mouth, his nose and his paws, and had left it jutting in spiky ribbons all around the walls and the floor of the box. When I had removed the last of it, so that there were no cutting edges left, it was just ten minutes until the time of the flight, and the airport was five miles distant. It was hard to bring myself to put the miserable Mij back into that box, that now represented to him a torture chamber, but I forced myself to do it, slamming the lid down on my fingers as I closed it before he could make his escape. Then began a journey the like of which I hope I shall never know again.

I sat in the back of the car with the box beside me as the Arab driver tore through the streets of Basra like a ricocheting bullet. Donkeys reared, bicycles swerved wildly, out in the suburbs goats stampeded and poultry found unguessed powers of flight. Mij cried unceasingly in the box, and both of us were hurled to and fro and up and down like drinks in a cocktail shaker. Exactly as we drew to a screeching stop before the airport entrance I heard a splintering sound from the box beside me, and saw Mij's nose force up the lid. He had summoned all the strength in his small body and torn one of the hinges clean out of the wood.

The aircraft was waiting to take off; as I was rushed through the customs by infuriated officials I was trying all the time to hold down the lid of the box with one hand, and with the other, using a screwdriver purloined from the driver, to force back the screws into the splintered wood. But I knew that it could be no more than a temporary measure at best, and my imagination boggled at the thought of the next twenty-four hours.

It was perhaps my only stroke of fortune that the seat booked for me was at the extreme front of the aircraft, so that I had a bulkhead before me instead of another seat. The other passengers, a remarkable cross-section of the Orient and Occident, stared curiously as the dishevelled late arrival struggled up the gangway with a horrifyingly vocal Charles Addams-like box, and knowing for just what a short time it could remain closed I was on tenterhooks to see what manner of passenger would be my immediate neighbour. I had a moment of real dismay when I saw her to be an elegantly dressed and *soignée* American woman in early middle age. Such a one, I thought, would have little sympathy or tolerance for the draggled and dirty otter cub that would so soon and so inevitably be in her midst. For the moment the lid held, and as I sat down and fastened my safety-belt there seemed to be a temporary silence from within.

The port engines roared, and then the starboard, and the aircraft trembled and teetered against the tug of her propellers, and then we were taxiing out to take off, and I reflected that whatever was to happen now there could be no escape from it, for the next stop was Cairo. Ten minutes later we were flying westwards over the great marshes that had been Mij's home, and peering downward into the dark I could see the glint of their waters beneath the moon.

I had brought a briefcase full of old newspapers and a parcel of fish, and with these scant resources I prepared myself to withstand a siege. I arranged newspapers to cover all the floor around my feet, rang for the air hostess, and asked her to keep the fish in a cool place. I have retained the most profound admiration for that air hostess, and in subsequent sieges and skirmishes with otters in public places I have found my thoughts turning towards her as a man's mind turns to water in desert wastes. She was the very queen of her kind. I took her into my confidence; the events of the last half-hour together with the prospect of the next twenty-four had shaken my equilibrium a little, and I daresay I was not too coherent, but she took it all in her graceful sheer nylon stride, and she received the ill-wrapped fish into her shapely hands as though I were travelling royalty depositing a jewel case with her for safe keeping. Then she turned and spoke with her countrywoman on my left. Would I not prefer, she then inquired, to have my pet on my knee? The animal would surely feel happier there, and my neighbour had no objection. I could have kissed her hand in the depth of my gratitude. But, not knowing otters, I was quite unprepared for what followed.

I unlocked the padlock and opened the lid, and Mij was out like a flash. He dodged my fumbling hands with an eel-like wriggle and disappeared at high speed down the fuselage of the aircraft. As I tried to get into the gangway I could follow his progress among the passengers by a wave of disturbance amongst them not unlike that caused by the passage of a stoat through a hen run. There were squawks and shrieks and a flapping of travelling-coats, and half-way down the fuselage a woman stood up on her seat screaming out, 'A rat! A rat!' Then the air hostess reached her, and within a matter of seconds she was seated again and smiling benignly. That goddess, I believe, could have controlled a panic-stricken crowd single-handed.

By now I was in the gangway myself, and, catching sight of Mij's tail disappearing beneath the legs of a portly white-turbaned Indian, I tried a flying tackle, landing flat on my face. I missed Mij's tail, but found myself grasping the sandalled foot of the Indian's female companion; furthermore my face was inexplicably covered in curry. I staggered up babbling inarticulate apology, and the Indian gave me a long silent stare, so utterly expressionless that even in my hyper-sensitive mood I could deduce from it no meaning whatsoever. I was, how-ever, glad to observe that something, possibly the curry, had won over the bulk of my fellow-passengers, and that they were regarding me now as a harmless clown rather than as a dan-gerous lunatic. The air hostess stepped into the breach once more.

'Perhaps,' she said with the most charming smile, 'it would be better if you resumed your seat, and I will find the animal and bring it to you.' She would probably have said the same had Mij been an escaped rogue elephant. I explained that Mij, being lost and frightened, might bite a stranger, but she did not think so. I returned to my seat.

I heard the ripple of flight and pursuit passing up and down the body of the aircraft behind me, but I could see little. I was craning my neck back over the seat trying to follow the hunt when suddenly I heard from my feet a distressed chitter of recognition and welcome, and Mij bounded on to my knee and began to nuzzle my face and neck. In all the strange world of the aircraft I was the only familiar thing to be found, and in that first spontaneous return was sown the seed of the absolute trust that he accorded me for the rest of his life.

For the next hour or two he slept in my lap, descending from time to time for copious evacuations upon the newspaper at my feet, and each time I had, with an unrehearsed legerdemain, to spirit this out of sight and replace it with fresh newspaper. Whenever he appeared restless I rang for fish and water, for I had a feeling that, like the storyteller of the Arabian Nights, if I failed to keep him entertained retribution would fall upon me.

Otters are extremely bad at doing nothing. That is to say that they cannot, as a dog does, lie still and awake; they are either asleep or entirely absorbed in play or other activity. If there is no acceptable toy, or if they are in a mood of frustration, they will, apparently with the utmost good humour, set about laying the land waste. There is, I am convinced, something positively provoking to an otter about order and tidiness in any form, and the greater the state of confusion that they can create about them the more contented they feel. A room is not properly habitable to them until they have turned everything upside-down; cushions must be thrown to the floor from sofas and armchairs, books pulled out of bookcases, wastepaper baskets overturned and the rubbish spread as widely as possible, drawers opened and contents shovelled out and scattered. The appearance of such a room where an otter has been given free rein resembles nothing so much as the aftermath of a burglar's hurried search for some minute and valuable object that he has believed to be hidden. I had never really appreciated the meaning of the word ransacked until I saw what an otter could do in this way.

This aspect of an otter's behaviour is certainly due in part to an intense inquisitiveness that belongs traditionally to a mongoose, but which would put any mongoose to shame. An otter must find out everything and have a hand in everything; but most of all he must know what lies inside any man-made container or beyond any man-made obstruction. This, combined with an uncanny mechanical sense of how to get things open – a sense, indeed, of statics and dynamics in general – makes it

K

much safer to remove valuables altogether rather than to challenge the otter's ingenuity by inventive obstructions. But in those days I had all this to learn.

We had been flying for perhaps five hours, and must, I thought, be nearing Cairo, when one of these moods descended upon Mijbil. It opened comparatively innocuously, with an assault upon the newspapers spread carefully round my feet, and in a minute or two the place looked like a street upon which royalty has been given a ticker-tape welcome. Then he turned his attentions to the box, where his sleeping compartment was filled with fine wood-shavings. First he put his head and shoulders in and began to throw these out backwards at enormous speed; then he got in bodily and lay on his back, using all four feet in a pedalling motion to hoist out the remainder. I was doing my best to cope with the litter, but it was like a ship's pumps working against a leak too great for them, and I was hopelessly behind in the race when he turned his attention to my neighbour's canvas Trans-World travel bag on the floor beside him. The zipper gave him pause for no more than seconds; by chance, in all likelihood, he yanked it back and was in head first, throwing out magazines, handkerchiefs, gloves, bottles of pills, tins of ear-plugs and all the personal paraphernalia of long-distance air travel. By the grace of God my neighbour was sleeping profoundly; I managed, unobserved, to haul Mij out by the tail and cram the things back somewhat. I hoped that she might leave the aircraft at Cairo, before the outrage was discovered, and to my infinite relief she did so. I was still grappling with Mij when the instruction lights came on as we circled the city, and then we were down on the tarmac with forty minutes to wait.

I think it was at Cairo that I realized what a complex and – to me at that time – unpredictable creature I had acquired. I left the aircraft last, and during all the time that we were grounded he was no more trouble than a well-behaved Pekingese dog. I put the lead on him and exercised him round the edge of the airfield; there were jet aircraft landing and taking off with an appalling din all around us, but he gave no sign of noticing them at all. He trotted along at my side, stopping as a dog does to investigate small smells in the grass, and when I went into the refreshment room for a drink he sat down at my feet as if this were the only life to which he was accustomed.

On our way back to the aircraft an Egyptian official hazarded the first of the many guesses as to his identity that I was to hear during the subsequent months. 'What you got there?' he asked. 'An ermine?'

My troubles really began at Paris, an interminable time later. Mij had slept from time to time, but I had not closed an eye, and it was by now more than thirty-six hours since I had even dozed. I had to change airports, and, since I knew that Mij could slip his body strap with the least struggle, there was no alternative to putting him back into his box. In its present form, however, the box was useless, for one hinge was dangling unattached from the lid.

Half an hour out from Paris I rang for the last time for fish and water, and explained my predicament to the air hostess. She went forward to the crew's quarters, and returned after a few minutes saying that one of the crew would come and nail down the box and rope it for me. She warned me at the same time that Air France's regulations differed from those of Trans-World, and that from Paris onward the box would have to travel freight and not in the passenger portion of the aircraft.

Mij was sleeping on his back inside my jacket, and I had to steel myself to betray his trust, to force him back into that hateful prison and listen to his pathetic cries as he was nailed up in what had become to me suddenly reminiscent of a coffin. There is a little-understood factor that is responsible for the deaths of many wild animals in shipment; it is generally known as 'travel shock', and the exact causes have yet to be determined. Personally I do not question that it is closely akin to the 'voluntary dying' of which Africans have long been reputed to be capable; life has become no longer tolerable, and the animal *chooses*, quite unconsciously no doubt, to die. It was travel shock that I was afraid might kill Mijbil inside that box, which to him represented a circumstance more terrible than any he had experienced, and I would be unable even to give him the reassuring smell of my hand through the breathing-holes.

We disembarked in torrential rain that formed puddles and lakes all over the tarmac and had reduced my thin, semitropical suit to a sodden pulp before even I had entered the bus that was to take me and the three other London-bound passengers across Paris to Orly Airport. I clung to the unwieldy box all this time, in the hope of reducing Mij's unavoidable period of despair after I became separated from it; together with the personal impedimenta that I could not well lose sight of it rendered movement almost impossible, and I felt near to voluntary death myself.

After an hour's wait at Orly, during which Mij's cries had given place to a terrifying silence, I and my three companions were hustled into an aircraft. Mij was wrested from me and disappeared into the darkness on a luggage transporter.

When we arrived at Amsterdam instead of London the company was profusely apologetic. There was no flight to London for a further fifty-five minutes.

I had lost sight of Mij's box altogether and no one seemed to have a very clear idea of what had happened to any of the luggage, belonging to the four London-bound passengers. A helpful official suggested that it might still be in Paris, as it must be clearly labelled London and not Amsterdam.

I went to the Air France office and let the tattered shreds of my self-control fly to the winds. In my soaking and dishevelled condition I cannot have cut a very impressive figure, but my anger soared above these handicaps like an eagle on the wind. I said that I was transporting to London a live animal worth many thousands of pounds, that unless it was traced immediately it would die, and I would sue the Company and broadcast their inefficiency throughout the world. The official was under crossfire, for at my elbow an American businessman was also threatening legal action. When the shindy was at its height another official arrived and said calmly that our luggage was now aboard a BEA plane due for take-off in seven minutes, and would we kindly take our seats in the bus.

We deflated slowly. Muttering, 'I guess I'm going to cast my personal eyes on that baggage before I get air-borne again. They can't make a displaced person out of me,' my American companion spoke for all of us waifs. So we cast our personal eyes into the freight compartment, and there was Mij's box, quite silent in a corner.

It was the small hours of the morning when we reached London Airport. I had cabled London from Amsterdam, and there was a hired car to meet me, but there was one more con-tretemps before I reached the haven of my flat. In all my travels I have never, but for that once, been required by the British Customs to open a single bag or to do more than state that I carried no goods liable to duty. It was, of course, my fault; the extreme fatigue and nervous tension of the journey had de-stroyed my diplomacy. I was, for whichever reason, so tired that I could hardly stand, and to the proffered *pro forma* and the question, 'Have you read this?' I replied, with extreme testiness and foolishness, 'Yes – hundreds of times.'

'And you have nothing to declare?'

'Nothing.'

'How long have you been out of this country?'

'About three months.'

'And during that time you have acquired nothing?'

'Nothing but what is on the list I have given you.' (This comprised my few purchases in Iraq; two uncured otter skins, a Marsh Arab's dagger, three cushion covers woven by the Beni Lam tribe, and one live otter.)

He seemed momentarily at a loss, but then began to search my luggage. No corner was left unexplored; Mijbil himself could not have done better, and when he had finished none of the cases would close. Then he turned to the last item on my list, one live otter. He pondered this in silence for perhaps a minute. Then, 'You have with you a live otter?' I said that I very much doubted whether it was still alive, but that it had been when at Paris.

'If the animal is dead there will be no duty payable on the uncured skin; if it is alive it is, of course, subject to the quarantine regulations.'

I had taken the trouble to check this point before leaving Iraq, and at last I was on firm ground. I told him that I knew there to be no quarantine regulations, and that since he had now cleared my luggage I proposed to leave with the otter; if he tried to detain me I would hold him legally responsible for the death of a valuable animal.

Just how long this battle would have lasted I do not know, for at that moment he was relieved by an official who was as helpful as he had been hostile, as benign as he had been bellicose. Within three minutes the box and all my luggage had been loaded on to the waiting car and we were on the last lap of the journey. What meant still more to me was that from the box there now came a faint inquiring chitter and a rustle of wood shavings.

Mijbil had in fact displayed a characteristic shared, I believe, by many animals; an apparent step, as it were, on the road to travel-shock death, but in fact a powerful buffer against it. Many animals seem to me to be able to go into a deep sleep, a coma, almost, as a voluntary act independent of exhaustion; it is an escape mechanism that comes into operation when the animal's inventiveness in the face of adversity has failed to ameliorate its circumstances. I have seen it very occasionally in trapped animals; an arctic fox in Finmark, captive by the leg for no more than an hour, a badger in a Surrey wood, a common house mouse in a box trap. It is, of course, almost a norm, too, of animals kept in too cramped quarters in zoos and in pet stores. I came to recognize it later in Mij when he travelled in cars, a thing he hated; after a few minutes of frenzy he would curl himself into a tight ball and banish entirely the distasteful world about him.

On that first day that he arrived in England he had, I think, been in just such a barricaded state ever since the lid of the box was nailed down before reaching Paris, back, for all one may know, among the familiar scenes of his Tigris swamps, or perhaps in a negative, imageless world where the medulla had taken over respiration and the forebrain rested in a state bordering upon catalepsy.

He was wide awake once more by the time we reached my flat, and when I had the driver paid off and the door closed behind me I felt a moment of deep emotional satisfaction, almost of triumph, that I had after all brought back a live otter cub from Iraq to London, and that Camusfeàrna was less than six hundred miles distant from me.

I pried open the lid of the box, and Mijbil clambered out into my arms to greet me with a frenzy of affection that I felt I had hardly merited.

THE DOG THAT BIT PEOPLE

by

JAMES THURBER

(from *The Thurber Carnival*, by permission of Hamish, Hamilton Ltd.)

PROBABLY NO one man should have as many dogs in his life as I have had, but there was more pleasure than distress in them for me except in the case of an Airedale named Muggs. He gave me more trouble than all the other fifty-four or -five put together, although my moment of keenest embarrassment was the time a Scottish terrier named Jeannie, who had just had six puppies in the clothes closet on a fourth floor apartment in New York, had the unexpected seventh and last at the corner of Eleventh Street and Fifth Avenue during a walk she had insisted on taking. Then, too, there was the prizewinning French poodle, a great big black poodle – none of your little, untroublesome white miniatures – who got sick riding in the rumble seat of a car with me on her way to the Greenwich Dog Show. She had a red rubber bib tucked around her throat and, since a rain storm came up when we were half-way through the Bronx, I had to hold over her a small green umbrella, really more of a parasol. The rain beat down fearfully and suddenly the driver of the car drove into a big garage, filled with mechanics. It happened so quickly that I forgot to put the umbrella down and I will always remember, with sickening distress, the look of incredulity mixed with hatred that came over the face of the particular hardened garage man that came over to see what we wanted, when he took a look at me and the poodle. All garage men, and people of that intolerant stripe, hate poodles with their curious haircut, especially the pompoms that you got to leave on their hips if you expect the dogs to win a prize.

But the Airedale, as I have said, was the worst of all my dogs. He really wasn't my dog, as a matter of fact: I came home from a vacation one summer to find that my brother Roy had bought him while I was away. A big, burly, choleric dog, he always acted as if he thought I wasn't one of the family. There was a slight advantage in being one of the family, for he didn't bite the family as often as he bit strangers. Still, in the years that we had him he bit everybody but mother, and he made a pass at her once but missed. That was during the month when we suddenly had mice, and Muggs refused to do anything about them. Nobody ever had mice exactly like the mice we had that month. They acted like pet mice, almost like mice somebody had trained. They were so friendly that one night when mother entertained at dinner the Friraliras, a club she and my father had belonged to for twenty years, she put down a lot of little dishes with food in them on the pantry floor so that the mice would be satisfied with that and wouldn't come into the dining-room. Muggs stayed out in the pantry with the mice, lying on the floor, growling to himself – not at the mice, but about all the people in the next room that he would have liked to get at. Mother slipped out into the pantry once to see how everything was going. Everything was going fine. It made her so mad to see Muggs lying there, oblivious of the mice – they came running up to her – that she slapped him and he slashed at her, but didn't make it. He was sorry immediately, mother said. He was always sorry, she said, after he bit someone, but we could not understand how she figured this out. He didn't act sorry.

Mother used to send a box of candy every Christmas to the people the Airedale bit. The list finally contained forty or more names. Nobody could understand why we didn't get rid of the dog. I didn't understand it very well myself, but we didn't get rid of him. I think that one or two people tried to poison Muggs – he acted poisoned once in a while – and old Major Moberly fired at him once with his service revolver near the Seneca Hotel in East Broad Street – but Muggs lived to be almost eleven years old and even when he could hardly get around he bit a Congressman who had called to see my father on business. My mother had never liked the Congressman – she said the signs of his horoscope showed he couldn't be trusted (he was Saturn with the moon in Virgo) – but she sent him a box of candy that Christmas. He sent it right back, probably because he suspected it was trick candy. Mother persuaded herself it was all for the best that the dog had bitten him, even though father lost an important business association because of it. 'I wouldn't be associated with such a man,' mother said, 'Muggs could read him like a book.'

We used to take turns feeding Muggs to be on his good side, but that didn't always work. He was never in a very good humour, even after a meal. Nobody knew exactly what was the matter with him, but whatever it was it made him irascible, especially in the mornings. Roy never felt very well in the morning, either, especially before breakfast, and once when he came downstairs and found that Muggs had moodily chewed up the morning paper he hit him in the face with a grapefruit and then jumped up on the dining-room table, scattering dishes and silverware and spilling the coffee. Muggs's first free leap carried him all the way across the table and into a brass fire screen in front of the gas grate but he was back on his feet in a moment and in the end he got Roy and gave him a pretty vicious bite in the leg. Then he was all over it; he never bit anyone more than once at a time. Mother always mentioned that as an argument in his favour; she said he had a quick temper but that he didn't hold a grudge. She was for ever defending him. I think she liked him because he wasn't well. 'He's not strong,' she would say, pityingly, but that was inaccurate; he may not have been well but he was terribly strong.

One time my mother went to the Chittenden Hotel to call on a woman mental healer who was lecturing in Columbus on the subject of 'Harmonious Vibrations'. She wanted to find out if it was possible to get harmonious vibrations into a dog. 'He's a large tan-coloured Airedale,' mother explained. The woman said that she had never treated a dog but she advised my mother to hold the thought that he did not bite and would not bite. Mother was holding the thought the very next morning when Muggs got the iceman but she blamed that slip-up on the iceman. 'If you didn't think he would bite you, he wouldn't,' mother told him. He stomped out of the house in a terrible jangle of vibrations.

One morning when Muggs bit me slightly, more or less in passing, I reached down and grabbed his short stumpy tail and hoisted him into the air. It was a foolhardy thing to do and the last time I saw my mother, about six months ago, she said she didn't know what possessed me. I don't either, except that I was pretty mad. As long as I held the dog off the floor by his tail he couldn't get at me, but he twisted and jerked so, snarling all the time, that I realized I couldn't hold him that way very long. I carried him to the kitchen and flung him on to the floor and shut the door on him just as he crashed against it. But I forgot about the backstairs. Muggs went up the backstairs and down the frontstairs and had me cornered in the living-room. I managed to get up on to the mantelpiece above the fireplace, but it gave way and came down with a tremendous crash, throwing a large marble clock, several vases, and myself heavily to the floor. Muggs was so alarmed by the racket that when I picked myself up he had disappeared. We couldn't find him anywhere, although we whistled and shouted, until old Mrs Detweiler called after dinner that night. Muggs had bitten her once, in the leg, and she came into the living-room only after we assured her that Muggs had run away. She had just seated herself when, with a great growling and scratching of claws, Muggs emerged from under a davenport where he had been quietly hiding all the time, and bit her again. Mother examined the bite and put arnica on it and told Mrs Detweiler that it was only a bruise. 'He just bumped you,' she said. But Mrs Detweiler left the house in a nasty state of mind.

Lots of people reported our Airedale to the police but my father held a municipal office at the time and was on friendly terms with the police. Even so, the cops had been out a couple of times – once when Muggs bit Mrs Rufus Sturtevant and again when he bit Lieutenant-Governor Malloy – but mother told them that it hadn't been Muggs's fault but the fault of the people who were bitten. 'When he starts for them, they scream,' she explained, 'and that excites him.' The cops suggested that it might be a good idea to tie the dog up, but mother said that it mortified him to be tied up and that he wouldn't eat when he was tied up.

Muggs at his meals was an unusual sight. Because of the fact that if you reached towards the floor he would bite you, we usually put his food plate on top of an old kitchen table with a bench alongside the table. Muggs would stand on the bench and eat. I remember that my mother's Uncle Horatio, who boasted that he was the third man up Missionary Ridge, was splutteringly indignant when he found out that we fed the dog on a table because we were afraid to put his plate on the floor. He said he wasn't afraid of any dog that ever lived and that he would put the dog's plate on the floor if we would give it to him. Roy said that if Uncle Horatio had fed Muggs on the ground just before the battle he would have been the first man up Missionary Ridge. Uncle Horatio was furious. 'Bring him in! Bring him in now!' he shouted. 'I'll feed the — on the floor!' Roy was all for giving him a chance, but my father wouldn't hear of it. He said that Muggs had already been fed. 'I'll feed him again!' bawled Uncle Horatio. We had quite a time quieting him.

In his last year Muggs used to spend practically all of his time outdoors. He didn't like to stay in the house for some reason or other – perhaps it held too many unpleasant memories for him. Anyway, it was hard to get him to come in and as a result the garbage man, the iceman, and the laundryman wouldn't come near the house. We had to haul the garbage down to the corner, take the laundry out and bring it back, and meet the iceman a block from home. After this had gone on for some time we hit on an ingenious arrangement for getting the dog in the house so that we could lock him up while the gas meter was read, and so on. Muggs was afraid of only one thing, an electrical storm. Thunder and lightning frightened him out of his senses (I think he thought a storm had broken the day the mantelpiece fell). He would rush into the house and hide under a bed or in a clothes closet. So we fixed up a thunder machine out of a long narrow piece of sheet iron with a wooden handle on one end. Mother would shake this vigorously when she wanted to get Muggs into the house. It made an excellent imitation of thunder, but I suppose it was the most roundabout system for running a household that was ever devised. It took a lot out of mother.

A few months before Muggs died, he got to 'seeing things'. He would rise slowly from the floor, growling low, and stalk stiff-legged and menacing towards nothing at all. Sometimes the Thing would be just a little to the right or left of a visitor. Once a Fuller Brush salesman got hysterics. Muggs came wandering into the room like Hamlet following his father's ghost. His eyes were fixed on a spot just to the left of the Fuller Brush man, who stood it until Muggs was about three slow, creeping paces from him. Then he shouted. Muggs wavered on past him into the hallway grumbling to himself but the Fuller man went on shouting. I think mother had to throw a pan of cold water on him before he stopped. That was the way she used to stop us boys when we got into fights.

Muggs died quite suddenly one night. Mother wanted to bury him in the family lot under a marble stone with some such inscription as 'Flights of angels sing thee to thy rest' but we persuaded her it was against the law. In the end we just put up a smooth board above his grave along a lonely road. On the board I wrote with an indelible pencil 'Cave Canem'. Mother was quite pleased with the simple classic dignity of the old Latin epitaph.

THE BABY BULLET

by

STUART CLOETE

THE OLD man walked into town every Saturday with a flour
sack to buy his groceries – coffee, sugar, Boer meal, salt, cooking fat and a little bag of Boer tobacco.

He called it town, but it wasn't really. It was a dorp, and a
small one at that. Forty-odd houses, a store; a hotel rather
larger than one would expect, because people came to Stru-
mans Baai from Cape Town in the summer for the fishing, and
apart from the bar trade, which was fair all the year round,
commercial travellers on their rounds through the countryside
used the place a lot. It was cheap, clean, and the food was better
than it is at most country hotels.

That was how Dick Winters had heard of the place. Quiet
and cheap, a good place for a rest. Away from it all. And that was
true enough. It was; and fed by a road that even in South
Africa was considered second class. To hell and gone, the city
slickers called it. In the wilds. Quiet, the others called it.
Private, lonely – the adjectives depended on the guy. Anyway,
there was a good beach of yellow sand bordered with old melk-
bos trees, where you could bathe with nothing on. That sort of
defines it. It's been opened up since then. Developed. Now only
the girls can bathe there nude, or nearly so, and a lot of the
bush has been cut. But it was just the place to pick something
up. He had a nose for things.

Dick Winters used to write a column for the old *New York
Express*. The paper'd given him a kind of roving commission –
trip round the world 'and pick up what stories you can in out-
of-the-way places'. He'd done Australia and India. He was in
Africa now, on his way back. He was wondering if he'd been
right about a story, when he saw an old chap coming down the
road with a big red bull mastiff at his heels. When he stopped,

the dog stopped, and they both stopped every few yards to greet someone, to take a look around or maybe just to rest, because the man was old – seventy-odd anyway – and the dog wasn't young any more.

'If you want a story, there's one there,' a commercial travel-ler he'd got into conversation with said. 'There's a story in old Jack and Baby.'

'Baby?' Winters said.

'Sure,' the man said, 'the dog. Got him as a tiny pup and raised him. They were going to knock him off. His mother had too big a litter, and old Jack took him and raised him on con-densed milk. That's why he called him Baby. Least, that's the story they tell here. Quite a character, old Jack. Lives in the wilds back there.' He pointed to where a shoulder of the mountains ran down to the sea. 'In a cave on the cliff, they say. Like to have seen it, but twice five is ten, and ten miles is too much for me.'

Story. If there was a story he was the man to get it. If there was. But he didn't see it. Not now, at any rate, and he had some other stuff to finish up.

Each week old Jack found the trip a little longer and had to rest more. Specially going home loaded. Funny the way the distance lengthened with age. Five miles – ten miles, that is – had been nothing when first he'd come here twenty years ago. When Mr De Lange had said, 'I've got a farm you can live on' – any piece of land's a farm in Africa. 'Very wild,' he'd said, 'and I'd like someone on the place. Fish, make a little garden,' he'd said.

And he'd taken him up on it. The place had just suited him. Since Gert had died he wanted to be alone. No one else seemed very real to him, with her gone. He'd lost touch with the children too. Little Jack was a mining engineer. She'd seen to it that he had a proper education. He'd gone to the States. And later little Gert had followed him. Little Jack indeed; why, now he'd have grown-up kids and grandchildren maybe. He'd be married all right. Always one for the girls, he'd been. And if

you chased girls, one of them got you in the end. How often
had he said that to Gert? 'One of 'em'll get him, Gert. Poor
chap. Thinks he's hunting 'em just because they run. Wonderful thing, the spoor they leave when they run. Never heard of a
chap losing a girl. When a woman runs, she always leaves a
good trail.'

Well, if he had a wife he'd have kids, and by now the kids
would have kids, all in the twinkling of an eye, as it were. Why,
it seemed only the day before yesterday they'd been playing
around his legs, only yesterday that little Jack had got his
diploma from the school of mines. That was the time they'd
been recruiting South African engineers for some new gold
fields or other.

Gert had always written to them. Then, at first after she'd
gone, he'd got people to write for him. But it was always someone different. He'd not wanted to bother the same people, and
then he'd stopped altogether because he thought the letters in
different hands might embarrass the boy. Having a dad who
couldn't write might set him back a bit. And that was before
he'd come here, when he'd been drifting. Think I'm dead, I'll
bet, he thought, and not far wrong either. Three score and ten,
and then a few. Reasonable to think me dead.

They'd written for a long time, but sometimes the letters
never found him. So, even if they thought he might be alive,
they'd not know where he was. That was funny to think of. All
the long string of days, all the events of begetting them and
having 'em born, the anxiety and the raising of 'em, and then
nothing. Just a house that was more cave than house, and the
cats and hens and Baby. Well, that was the end of it. The end
of the long story of his life, of his love.

He sat down to rest again. The old dog came and put his
head on his knee and stared into his face with golden eyes.

He patted his head. 'Gets a bit longer each time, Baby,' he
said. 'Longer and longer, don't it?' The dog thumped the
sand of the track with his tail. A fine dust went up, and there
was a flat piece with ridges on each side behind him where he'd
wagged it.

'And what'll we do when we can't make it any more?' The dog wagged his tail again.

Jack got up and picked the sack off the ground. Road longer, bag heavier each time, he thought. He thought back to the time when he could lift a two-hundred-pound sack of mealies on to his shoulder, to when he could walk thirty miles over the veld and not feel it.

The present was much less to him than the past. They merged, but they were sort of muddled in his mind, as if the whole affair of life was turned over someway, with today way at the bottom, and the days and nights with Gert on top. What a girl she'd been! He saw her with her long black hair, flashing brown eyes, her quick step. He saw her as she'd been when he courted her, not as she'd been when she died. Under fifty, but tired, worn with the hardships of life, with sacrifice. But Gert was never old and worn to him – always lovely, like a flower, like a March lily growing on the hillside. That was Gert.

Only two miles more. But what would happen when the money was done? He'd put enough aside to live to seventy-five. Then, when he'd seen he was going to live longer, he'd scrimped on it. But scrimp as you like, you can't spend the same money twice. There was his small pension, of course, but that wasn't enough, even for him. And the time would come when he couldn't fish or hunt any more. As it was, he couldn't afford lines and hooks. But folks were good to him. They said, 'Here's some old hooks, Jack. Points gone, but maybe you can sharpen 'em up a bit.' When he got home and opened the envelope, not wanting to do it in front of them, he'd find the hooks were brand-new. Took them back, of course. 'Must have made a mistake,' he'd say; 'them's new hooks,' and the man'd say, 'I've got plenty of hooks. You better keep 'em.' Lines were the same; so were lots of other things.

More than twenty years he'd been here. More than twenty since he found the cave in the cliff and put a door on to it and built the chimney. Plenty of driftwood in the cove below him and lots of fish too. Now he couldn't land the big ones, but Baby did it. He'd taught him. Work 'em round till they were near the little beach, and then Baby'd go into the sea and close his big jaws on 'em and bring 'em in. His bulldog jaws that never let go of anything they closed on. Fish was what he'd raised old Baby on – condensed milk, fish, bread and potatoes, with very little meat – and a fine dog he'd grown to be. Twelve for a dog must be near seventy in a man.

He thought of his cave. Of how welcome the cool shade of it would be. He thought of its convenience. There was a trickling spring at the back of it for water. An old cave it was. Bushmen and *strandloopers* had lived there once. He'd cleaned out a big midden of shells from it – clams and black mussels and the remains of a big kind of abalone shell. There'd been bones too – buck bones and tortoise – and he'd found bits of pottery, and a bone needle, and a digging stone with a hole in it. Often as he dozed he thought of the strange wild people who'd lived in it long before the white man came. Thought of them making love, of them cooking over a smoky fire. Why, when he'd cleaned the place up, you could smell that old smoke in the ashes. But Gert wouldn't have liked it. No place for a woman, a cave wasn't. But Gert would have made a plan. Nothing went wrong when Gert was alive.

It had been a mistake to drink when she'd gone, but somehow when he was drunk he was near her. Sometimes he heard her voice and even saw her. That was how he'd lost the farm. And only then, after the sale, had he pulled himself together and figured out how to live. There was enough, if he was careful and drew it out a bit at a time, to last till he was seventy-five. That was long enough. No need to figure further than that. At fifty, seventy-five was a long way off – nearer than at thirty, but still a long way. Time didn't work right, according to arithmetic. Oh, yes, he could figure a bit; it was just writing that he couldn't do. When you were old, time went so fast. Sunday seemed to come two or three times a week. Same when you were happy. Then the days flew. The lovely days. The days with Gert – the years that seemed just days, with the kids sprouting up like corn.

You put the seed in one day, and before you knew where you

were, you were reaping the crop. What was the crop of a man's life, he thought. What did he sow? What did he reap? Happiness. By heaven, he'd had plenty with Gert. And the last few years had been happy too. Happy in a different way. Happy in the stillness with Baby and Tom and Ginger, and the chickens that ate out of his hand, and the wild birds and the buck and the animals around his home.

What did a man reap? What was the harvest of his life? An old man reaped the days of his life. The thousands of days. The thousand or more months if he lived to over eighty. He reaped the memories that he'd garnered – the great book of memories, of beauties, that even a man who couldn't read could thumb over in the darkness of night. Maybe a man who couldn't read could read this sort of book better than one who could. There was no cluttering up of his mind. And what a harvest he'd had. Him alive, an' most of those he knew dead and gone. Plenty of 'em gone even before he came here.

He put down the bag and sank on to the bed. It was made of balks of wood, part of some bulkhead that had been carried away by the wicked sea. Over it he'd nailed chicken wire, and on top of that were sacks of wild white everlastings that rustled when he turned. When they got squashed down, all he had to do was put 'em out in the sun and they came back into shape.

Above the bed was his rifle, an old military gun. There was an arrangement of boxes – all flotsam, and some from foreign lands – that held his stores, his Sunday suit and a few tools. Hardwood pegs driven into the walls held his other clothes, and a spare pair of shoes tied together by their laces. A couple of bushbuck skins lay on the floor, and crates upturned acted as seats and tables. There was also a chair that someone had given him. By the fireplace he had his cook pots, a five-gallon drum with water in it and a tin dipper. He looked at it all with content. It was his. His. He made it. He had very little money left, but owed no man. He owed no one anything. And he had his harvest of memories of gone days, spent days that no one could take from him.

He tried to get up, and managed only with difficulty. *So now I can't get up*, he thought. But he did get up and feed his hens. Six Rhode Islands and a rooster. They'd been given to him as chicks. He fed them from a tin of scraps mixed with a few mealies he'd brought back from the store. But just in case, he thought – just in case he had more trouble, he'd fix a rope to a peg in the wall, so that he could haul himself up, and leave the door open, so that if he couldn't get up, the animals could get in to him – the chickens and the cats. Old Baby always slept beside him, but he'd want to get out. He moved the water and the dipper near the bed. He wouldn't cook tonight. He was too tired.

The next day he could pull himself up in bed, but his legs had given way. The damn things, he thought. Sick of it, that's what they were. They'd struck. That was what happened with the body. Bits of it gave up. Well, he'd be all right with just water and bread and raw potatoes for a day or two. In a day or two he'd be all right. Just give those damn legs a rest. And next Saturday he wouldn't strain 'em. Only go one way. Camp the night in the bush outside the dorp. It would be good to sleep out again with Baby beside him under the stars. Of course, he'd have to take a blanket, but he could put his groceries in the blanket. That was the thing to do. It was a fine plan.

The cats came and went. They sat on his bed, drank some water, and then went out to hunt. The cats could look after themselves if they had to – plenty of birds and mice and rats for them. The chickens perched all round him. They could manage with very little too. They could scratch up a lot.

But Baby was very thin by Saturday. There was nothing left for Baby, and he couldn't get up to cook.

'If I could cook you some potatoes, old Baby,' he said. Baby wagged his tail. He had hardly moved from beside the bed. He just lay there, his head on his paws, staring up at his face. 'Well, Baby, what shall we do now, old Baby?' he said. He talked to all the animals, to the cats and the hens, to the wild birds that were tame about him. Red-winged starlings, wagtails; the swallows that nested above his head in the cave, coming in and out through the little window that had no glass.

They all understood him too. No doubt about that. 'Know every word, don't you, old Baby?' – and Baby wagged his tail.

Well, the Saturday plan didn't work. He couldn't get to the door, much less to the dorp. This was the end, all right, but something had to be done before he lay down to die. The cats were all right. The chickens would live and be safe enough sleeping in the house for a bit anyway. But old Baby –

'Yes,' he said, 'Baby, you're the trouble.'

Baby wagged his tail.

A plan, he thought. The last plan he would make. That was funny, in a way, to think of. The last plan. The last decision. To turn around and lie with his face to the wall and die was not a decision. That would be easy. But this – was going to be the hardest thing he'd ever done. And there was only one way to do it.

When he'd conquered the devil in the bottle, he'd bought a quart of brandy – just to prove to himself that the devil was conquered. It was under the bed, where it had been for twenty years. Mature, he thought, that's what it would be.

'Well, devil,' he said, 'you bin a big bother ter me in your time, so now I'm going to make you do something for me. It's a hard job, devil. A devil's job. But we got ter do it.'

He reached for the bottle and laid it beside him. Then he stretched up for the rifle. He opened the bolt and a long brass shell slid up into the breech from the magazine.

'You're the only one, old Baby,' he said. 'The others I can leave, but you can't just stay here and watch my body till you starve, can you, old Baby? An' that's what you'd do. An' God help anyone that comes near to see what's become of me. So now, devil,' he said, 'we'll do a last job together, and then I'm off up above with a fine pair of wings like a gull to find old Gert, and you can get back to hell, and for once you'll have done something good in your life.'

He had no corkscrew. So, holding the bottle, he knocked off the neck against the ledge above his bed. 'Not forgotten that trick, have I, devil?' he said. 'You ought ter be pleased, because it's one you taught me long years ago.'

Some brandy spilled on the bed, and the long-remembered smell came back to him. 'You still smell the same, devil,' he said. 'You smell different to all men, but that's the way you came to me. Out of a bottle. To some men you come with the perfume of women, of harlots. But I had my woman an' she died. An' in the end she beat you to it, devil, when she stayed my lifting hand. But you were clever, devil, because you showed her to me. You made me hear her voice in the bottle, like a kid hears the sea in the shell at his ear. To some men, devil, you come in the clink of gold, and to some you come in the sound of galloping hoofs. But horses have always been good ter me, an' I don't gamble on my friends.'

He got the tin dipper that was hanging on the edge of the water drum and half filled it with brandy. He lifted it to his mouth and drank it in one gulp. Then he pushed down the safety catch of the rifle and said, 'Baby, Baby, old Baby, come here. This is where we say goodbye. . . . Now, devil,' he said, 'you got ter help me. One shot, devil. No misses. Then I'll forgive you, devil, and that'll be the first time a man born of woman has done that.'

The dog stood up, gaunt-ribbed, with golden eyes that stared into his own. He put down the rifle. Then he raised it again. Between the eyes in the middle of the high-domed forehead. There'd be one shot. The hens would scream and flutter. The cats would bolt out of the door, and he could lie down in peace and die. No more worries. *I'll just lie an' wait for Gert to come and get me*, he thought.

He had the foresight between the dog's eyes, a little above them. The dog just stared into his face. The barrel wavered a little. He held it still with an effort. He brought up the back sight. He took the first squeeze on the trigger. *Now, devil*, he thought, *now*.

And the dog leaped past him. Past him and out of the open door.

'Well, I'm damned,' he said. 'He knows. Gert told him. He's gone to get help, and she's fooled the devil again.'

He reached to the floor for the bottle standing beside him

and threw it in the devil's face. Right between the eyes. It hit a little above them just below his horns.

The bottle crashed against the wall and splintered. A red hen rose screaming from behind the devil's seat, and old Jack fell on the bed.

'What a girl,' he said. 'Same as ever. Nothing can go wrong with you around.' He wiped the sweat from his face and lay down with his back to the wall. *Sure*, he thought, *that's the way to lie. You only lie facing it when you're dying. An' I'm not going to die. I'm just going ter sleep for a bit.*

Winters had just come in from swimming when Baby galloped into the dorp.

There was a shout, 'It's Baby! He's gone mad!'

He saw a man come out of a cottage with a gun. But by the time he'd come out, Baby had gone into the store. He reached the store in time to see him grip its owner, Jan Hoekstra, by the trouser leg. He only held it, then he let go and sat back on his haunches and began to howl. Then he looked round the room as if for help and howled again.

Hoekstra said, 'He's mad. He tried to bite me.'

The man with a gun came in and raised it. Winters knocked the barrel up and the shot went into the ceiling.

'Mad be damned!' he said. 'Something's wrong with the old man!' He went up to the dog and held out his hand, palm up. The dog grasped it in his mastiff jaws. He made no attempt to close them, but tried to lead him to the door.

Story, Winters thought. There was a story here all right.

'Come on,' he said to Hoekstra. 'Come with me and see what's up. Chuck some stuff in a bag. Food, brandy, bandages, iodine. How the hell do we know what's gone wrong? And phone the doctor and police.'

'Wrong?' Hoekstra said. 'The dog's mad.'

'I'll come,' the man with the gun said. 'I want to see.'

'Who'll pay for the stuff?' Hoekstra said.

'I will,' Winters said. 'But hurry.'

'I've got no licence. I can't sell brandy.'

'You drink it, don't you?' Winters said. 'Give me some of yours and I'll repay you in kind.'

'Okay, okay,' Hoekstra said. 'Don't get excited.'

'Who's excited?' Winters said. 'There's a story here and I'm going after it. Fill up a sack. Hold the dog while I get the car.' He had an old one that he'd hired; it'd get most places, and when it stopped going they'd walk.

The dog was nervous. Never been in a car before. He sat in the front seat beside Winters, barking and nearly sending them off the track as he dragged at his sleeve.

'Here it is,' the man who had the gun said; 'just here.' His name was Smit.

'Right,' Winters said. The dog was out before the car stopped. Winters ran after him through the trees and down the path that led to the cliff face. Smit came after them with the bag.

When they reached the cave, old Jack was sitting up, with Baby on the bed beside him. The dog was licking his face. Winters went up to him. He didn't move. Winters took his hand and let it fall.

'He's dead,' Smit said. 'Old Jack's dead.'

'Well, that's that,' Winters said. 'Too late. Looks as if the old boy starved. Too late, that's what we were.'

'Yes,' Smit said, 'too late.'

'We'll go back,' Winters said. 'Nothing to do here now. The police'll be along, I expect.'

'They'll come,' Smit said. 'Jan Hoekstra called them.' He still had his gun with him. He was holding it in the crook of his arm.

Winters went out through the door. A queer way to live, he thought, and a queer way to die. An odd idea struck him. Men were all born one way, but there was a lot of variety in death, in the manner of its coming. He stared out to sea. Looking for a ship. Funny how you always looked for a ship when you looked at the sea. Then he climbed up the path to the car.

As he opened the car door he heard a shot. What did Smit shoot, he wondered.

When Smit came, he asked him, 'What did you shoot?'

'Shoot?' he said. 'I shot the dog.' He broke open his gun, ejected a shell and blew down the barrel. 'Dangerous dog, that,' he said. 'Wouldn't have let anyone in to old Jack, once he realized he was dead.'

'I guess you're right,' Winters said. Yes, he was right. But it was a pity there'd been no story in it. No human interest. He hated to be wrong.

THE LANGUAGE OF ANIMALS

by

KONRAD Z. LORENZ

(from *King Solomon's Ring*)

Learned of every bird its language,
Learned their names and all their secrets,
Talked with them whene'er he met them.

LONGFELLOW

ANIMALS DO not possess a language in the true sense of the word. In the higher vertebrates, as also in insects, particularly in the socially living species of both great groups, every individual has a certain number of innate movements and sounds for expressing feelings. It has also innate ways of re-acting to these signals whenever it sees or hears them in a fellow-member of the species. The highly social species of birds, such as the jackdaw or the greylag goose, have a compli-cated code of such signals which are uttered and understood by every bird without any previous experience. The per-fect coordination of social behaviour which is brought about by these actions and reactions conveys to the human observer the impression that the birds are talking and understanding a language of their own. Of course, this purely innate signal code of an animal species differs fundamentally from human lan-guage, every word of which must be learned laboriously by the human child. Moreover, being a genetically fixed character of the species – just as much as any bodily character – this so-called language is, for every individual animal species, ubiqui-tous in its distribution. Obvious though this fact may seem, it was, nevertheless, with something akin to naïve surprise that I heard the jackdaws in northern Russia 'talk' exactly the same familiar 'dialect' as my birds at home in Altenberg. The superficial similarity between these animal utterances and human languages diminishes further as it becomes gradually clear to the observer that the animal, in all these sounds and movements expressing its emotions, has in no way the conscious intention of influencing a fellow-member of its species. This is proved by the fact that even geese or jackdaws reared and kept singly make all these signals as soon as the corresponding mood overtakes them. Under these circumstances the automatic and even mechanical character of these signals becomes strikingly apparent and reveals them as entirely different from human words.

In human behaviour, too, there are mimetic signs which automatically transmit a certain mood and which escape one, without or even contrary to one's intention of thereby influencing anybody else: the commonest example of this is yawning. Now the mimetic sign by which the yawning mood manifests itself is an easily perceived optical and acoustical stimulus whose effect is, therefore, not particularly surprising. But, in general, such crude and patent signals are not always necessary in order to transmit a mood. On the contrary, it is characteristic of this particular effect that it is often brought about by diminutive sign stimuli which are hardly perceptible by conscious observation. The mysterious apparatus for transmitting and receiving the sign stimuli which convey moods is age-old, far older than mankind itself. In our own case, it has doubtless degenerated as our word-language developed. Man has no need of minute intention-displaying movements to announce his momentary mood: he can say it in words. But jackdaws or dogs are obliged to 'read in each other's eyes' what they are about to do in the next moment. For this reason, in higher and social animals, the transmitting as well as the receiving apparatus of 'mood-convection' is much better developed and more highly specialized than in us humans. All expressions of animal emotions – for instance, the 'Kia' and 'Kiaw' note of the jackdaw – are therefore not comparable to our spoken language, but only to those expressions such as yawning, wrinkling the brow and smiling, which are expressed unconsciously as innate actions and also understood by a corresponding inborn mechanism. The 'words' of the various animal 'languages' are merely interjections.

Though man may also have numerous gradations of unconscious mimicry, no George Robey or Emil Jannings would be able, in this sense, to convey by mere miming, as the greylag goose can, whether he was going to walk or fly, or to indicate whether he wanted to go home or to venture farther afield, as a jackdaw can do quite easily. Just as the transmitting apparatus of animals is considerably more efficient than that of man, so also is their receiving apparatus. This is not only capable of distinguishing a large number of signals, but, to preserve the above simile, it responds to much slighter transmissions than does our own. It is incredible what minimal signs, completely imperceptible to man, animals will receive and interpret rightly. Should one member of a jackdaw flock that is seeking for food on the ground fly upwards merely to seat itself on the nearest apple-tree and preen its feathers, then none of the others will cast so much as a glance in its direction; but, if the bird takes to wing with intent to cover a longer distance, then it will be joined, according to its authority as a member of the flock, by its spouse or also a larger group of jackdaws, in spite of the fact that it did not emit a single 'Kia'.

In this case, a man well versed in the ways and manners of jackdaws might also, by observing the minutest intention-displaying movements of the bird, be able to predict – if with less accuracy than a fellow-jackdaw – how far that particular bird was going to fly. There are instances in which a good observer can equal and even surpass an animal in its faculty of 'understanding' and anticipating the intentions of its fellow, but in other cases he cannot hope to emulate it. The dog's 'receiving set' far surpasses our own analogous apparatus. Everybody who understands dogs knows with what almost uncanny certitude a faithful dog recognizes in its master whether the latter is leaving the room for some reason uninteresting to his pet, or whether the longed-for daily walk is pending. Many dogs achieve even more in this respect. My Alsatian Tito, the great-great-great-great-great-grandmother of the dog I now possess, knew, by 'telepathy', exactly which people got on my nerves, and when. Nothing could prevent her from biting, gently but surely, all such people on their posteriors. It was particularly dangerous for authoritative old gentlemen to adopt towards me, in discussion, the well-known 'you are, of course, too young' attitude. No sooner had the stranger thus expostulated than his hand felt anxiously for the place in which Tito had punctiliously chastised him. I could never understand how it was that this reaction functioned just as reliably when the dog was lying under the table and was therefore precluded from seeing the faces and gestures of the people round it: how did she know who I was speaking to or arguing with?

This fine canine understanding of the prevailing mood of a master is not really telepathy. Many animals are capable of perceiving the smallest movements, withheld from the human eye. And a dog, whose whole powers of concentration are bent on serving his master and who literally 'hangs on his every word', makes use of this faculty to the utmost. Horses too have achieved considerable feats in this field. So it will not be out of place to speak here of the tricks which have brought some measure of renown to certain animals. There have been 'thinking' horses which could work out square roots, and a wonder-dog Rolf, an Airedale terrier, which went so far as to dictate its last will and testament to its mistress. All these 'counting', 'talking' and 'thinking' animals 'speak' by knocking or barking sounds, whose meaning is laid down after the fashion of a morse code. At first sight their performances are really astounding. You are invited to set the examination yourself and you are put opposite the horse, terrier or whatever animal it is. You ask, how much is twice two; the terrier scrutinizes you intently and barks four times. In a horse, the feat seems still more prodigious for he does not even look at you. In dogs, who watch the examiner closely, it is obvious that their attention is concentrated upon the latter and not by any means on the problem itself. But the horse has no need to turn his eyes towards the examiner since, even in a direction in which the animal is not directly focusing, it can see, by indirect vision, the minutest movement. And it is you yourself who betray, involuntarily to the 'thinking' animal, the right solution. Should one not know the right answer oneself, the poor animal would knock or bark on desperately, waiting in vain for the sign which would tell him to stop. As a rule, this sign is forthcoming, since few people are capable, even with the utmost self-control, of withholding an unconscious and involuntary signal. That it is the human being who finds the solution and communicates it was once proved by one of my colleagues in the case of a dachshund which had become quite famous and which belonged to an elderly spinster. The method was perfidious: it consisted in suggesting a wrong solution of all the problems not to the 'counting' dog but to his mistress. To this end, my friend made cards on one side of which a simple problem was printed in fat letters. The cards, however, unknown to the dog's owner, were constructed of several layers of transparent paper on the last of which another problem was inscribed in such a manner as to be visible from behind, when the front side was presented to the animal. The unsuspecting lady, seeing, in looking-glass writing, what she imagined to be the problem to be solved, transmitted involuntarily to the dog a solution which did not correspond to that of the problem on the front of the card, and was intensely surprised when, for the first time in her experience, her pet continued to give wrong answers. Before ending the séance, my friend adopted different tactics and presented mistress and dog with a problem which, for a change, the dog could answer and the lady could not: he put before the animal a rag impregnated with the smell of a bitch in season. The dog grew excited, wagged his tail and whined – he knew what he was smelling and a really knowledgeable dog-owner might have known, too, from observing his behaviour. Not so the old lady. When the dog was asked what the rag smelled of, he promptly morsed *her* answer: 'Cheese'!

The enormous sensitivity of many animals to certain minute movements of expression, as, for example, the above-described capacity of the dog to perceive the friendly or hostile feelings which his master harbours for another person, is a wonderful thing. It is therefore not surprising that the naïve observer, seeking to assign to the animal human qualities, may believe that a being which can guess even such inward unspoken thoughts must, still more, understand every word that the beloved master utters; now an intelligent dog does understand a considerable number of words, but, on the other hand, it must not be forgotten that the ability to understand the minutest expressional movements is thus acute in animals for the very reason that they lack true speech.

As I have already explained, all the innate expressions of emotion, such as the whole complicated 'signal code' of the jackdaw, are far removed from human language. When your dog nuzzles you, whines, runs to the door and scratches it, or puts his paws on the wash-basin under the tap, and looks at you imploringly, he does something that comes far nearer to human speech than anything that a jackdaw or goose can ever 'say', no matter how clearly 'intelligible' and appropriate to the occasion the finely differentiated expressional sounds of these birds may appear. The dog wants to make you open the door or turn on the tap, and what he does has the specific and purposeful motive of influencing you in a certain direction. He would never perform these movements if you were not present. But the jackdaw or goose merely gives unconscious expression to its inward mood, and the 'Kia' or 'Kiaw' or the warning sound escapes the bird involuntarily; when in a certain mood, it must utter the corresponding sound, whether or not there is anybody there to hear it.

The intelligible actions of the dog described above are not innate but are individually learned and governed by true insight. Every individual dog has different methods of making himself understood by his master and will adapt his behaviour according to the situation. My bitch Stasie, the great-grandmother of the dog I now possess, having once eaten something which disagreed with her wanted to go out during the night. I was at that time overworked, and slept very soundly, so that she did not succeed in waking me and indicating her requirements by her usual signs; to her whining and nosing I had evidently only responded by burying myself still deeper in my pillows. This desperate situation finally induced her to forget her normal obedience and to do a thing which was strictly forbidden her: she jumped on my bed and then proceeded literally to dig me out of the blankets and roll me on the floor. Such an adaptability to present needs is totally lacking in the 'vocabulary' of birds: they never roll you out of bed.

Parrots and large corvines are endowed with 'speech' in still another sense: they can imitate human words. Here, an association of thought between the sounds and certain experiences is sometimes possible. This imitating is nothing other than the so-called mocking found in many song-birds. Willow warblers, red-backed shrikes and many others are masters of this art. Mocking consists of sounds, learned by imitation, which are not innate and are uttered only while the bird is singing; they have no 'meaning' and bear no relation whatsoever to the inborn 'vocabulary' of the species. This also applies to starlings, magpies and jackdaws, who not only 'mock' birds' voices but also successfully imitate human words. However, the talking of big corvines and parrots is a somewhat different matter. It still bears that character of playfulness and lack of purpose which is also inherent in the mocking of smaller birds and which is loosely akin to the play of more intelligent animals. But a corvine or a parrot will utter its human words independently of song, and it is undeniable that these sounds may occasionally have a definite thought association.

Many grey parrots, as well as others, will say 'Good morning' only once a day and at the appropriate time. My friend Professor Otto Koehler possessed an ancient grey parrot which, being addicted to the vice of feather-plucking, was nearly bald. This bird answered to the name of 'Geier', which in German means vulture. Geier was certainly no beauty but he redeemed himself by his speaking talents. He said 'Good morning' and 'Good evening' quite aptly, and when a visitor stood up to depart he said, in a benevolent bass voice, '*Na, auf Wiedersehen*'.

But he only said this if the guest really departed. Like a 'thinking' dog, he was tuned in to the finest, involuntarily given signs; what these signs were, we never could find out, and we never once succeeded in provoking the retort by staging a departure. But when the visitor really left, no matter how inconspicuously he took his leave, promptly and mockingly came the words '*Na, auf Wiedersehen*'!

The well-known Berlin ornithologist, Colonel von Lukanus, also possessed a grey parrot which became famous through a feat of memory. Von Lukanus kept, among other birds, a tame hoopoe named 'Höpfchen'. The parrot, which could talk well, soon mastered this word. Hoopoes unfortunately do not live long in captivity, though grey parrots do; so, after a time, 'Höpfchen' went the way of all flesh and the parrot appeared to have forgotten his name – at any rate, he did not say it any more. Nine years later, Colonel von Lukanus acquired another hoopoe, and as the parrot set eyes on him for the first time, he said at once, and then repeatedly, 'Höpfchen' . . . 'Höpfchen'. . . .

In general, these birds are just as slow in learning something new as they are tenacious in remembering what they have once learned. Everyone who has tried to drum a new word into the brain of a starling or a parrot knows with what patience one must apply oneself to this end, and how untiringly one must again and again repeat the word. Nevertheless, such birds can, in exceptional cases, learn to imitate a word which they have heard seldom, perhaps only once. However, this apparently only succeeds when a bird is in an exceptional state of excitement; I myself have seen only two such cases. My brother had, for years, a delightfully tame and lively blue-fronted Amazon parrot named Papagallo, which had an extraordinary talent for speech. As long as he lived with us in Altenberg, Papagallo flew just as freely around as most of my other birds. A talking parrot that flies from tree to tree and at the same time says human words, gives a much more comical effect than one that sits in a cage and does the same thing. When Papagallo, with loud cries of 'Where's the Doc?', flew about the district,

L

sometimes in a genuine search for his master, it was positively irresistible.

Still funnier, but also remarkable from a scientific point of view, was the following performance of the bird; Papagallo feared nothing and nobody, with the exception of the chimney-sweep. Birds are very apt to fear things which are up above. And this tendency is associated with the innate dread of the bird of prey swooping down from the heights. So everything that appears against the sky has for them something of the meaning of 'bird of prey'. As the black man, already sinister in his darkness, stood up on the chimney-stack and became out-lined against the sky, Papagallo fell into a panic of fear and flew, loudly screaming, so far away that we feared he might not come back. Months later, when the chimney-sweep came again, Papagallo was sitting on the weathercock, squabbling with the jackdaws who wanted to sit there too. All at once, I saw him grow long and thin and peer down anxiously into the village street; then he flew up and away, shrieking in raucous tones, again and again, 'The chimney-sweep is coming, the chimney-sweep is coming'. The next moment, the black man walked through the doorway of the yard!

Unfortunately, I was unable to find out how often Papagallo had seen the chimney-sweep before and how often he had heard the excited cry of our cook which heralded his approach. It was, without a doubt, the voice and intonation of this lady which the bird reproduced. But he had certainly not heard it more than three times at the most and, each time, only once and at an interval of months.

The second case known to me in which a talking bird learned human words after hearing them only once or very few times, concerns a hooded crow. Again it was a whole sentence which thus impressed itself on the bird's memory. 'Hansl', as the bird was called, could compete in speaking talent with the most gifted parrot. The crow had been reared by a railwayman in the next village, and it flew about freely and had grown into a well-proportioned, healthy fellow, a good advertisement for the rearing ability of its foster-father. Contrary to popular opinion, crows are not easy to rear and, under the inadequate care which they usually receive, mostly develop into those stunted, half-crippled specimens which are so often seen in captivity. One day some village boys brought me a dirt-encrusted hooded crow whose wings and tail were clipped to small stumps. I was hardly able to recognize, in this pathetic being, the once beautiful Hansl. I bought the bird, as, on principle, I buy all unfortunate animals that the village boys bring me, and this I do partly out of pity and partly because amongst these stray animals there might be one of real interest. And this one certainly was! I rang up Hansl's master who told me that the bird had actually been missing some days and begged me to adopt him till the next moult. So, accordingly, I put the crow in the pheasant pen and gave it concentrated food, so that, in the imminent new moult, it would grow good new wing and tail feathers. At this time, when the bird was, of necessity, a prisoner, I found out that Hansl had a surprising gift of the gab and he gave me the opportunity of hearing plenty! He had, of course, picked up just what you would expect a tame crow to hear that sits on a tree, in the village street, and listens to the 'language' of the inhabitants.

I later had the pleasure of seeing this bird recover his full plumage and I freed him as soon as he was fully capable of flight. He returned forthwith to his former master, in Wordern, but continued, a welcome guest, to visit us from time to time. Once he was missing for several weeks, and when he returned I noticed that he had, on one foot, a broken digit which had healed crooked. And this is the whole point of the history of Hansl, the hooded crow. For we know just how he came by this little defect. And from whom do we know it? Believe it or not, Hansl told us himself! When he suddenly reappeared, after his long absence, he knew a new sentence. With the accent of a true street urchin, he said, in lower Austrian dialect, a short sentence which, translated into broad Lancashire, would sound like 'Got 'im in t'bloomin' trap!' There was no doubt about the truth of this statement. Just as in the case of Papagallo, a sentence which he had certainly not heard often had stuck in

Hansl's memory because he had heard it in a moment of great apprehension, that is immediately after he had been caught. How he got away again Hansl unfortunately did not tell us.

In such cases, the sentimental animal-lover, crediting the creature with human intelligence, will take an oath on it that the bird understands what he says. This, of course, is quite incorrect. Not even the cleverest 'talking' birds, which, as we have seen, are certainly capable of connecting their sound-expressions with particular occurrences, learn to make practical use of their powers, to achieve purposefully even the simplest object. Professor Koehler, who can boast of the greatest successes in the science of training animals, and who succeeded in teaching pigeons to count up to six, tried to teach the above-mentioned, talented grey parrot 'Geier' to say 'Food' when he was hungry and 'Water' when he was dry. This attempt did not succeed, nor, so far, has it been achieved by anybody else. The failure in itself is remarkable. Since, as we have seen, the bird is able to connect his sound-utterances with certain occurrences, we should expect him, first of all, to connect them with a purpose; but this, surprisingly, he is unable to do. In all other cases, where an animal learns a new type of behaviour, it does so to achieve some purpose. The most curious types of behaviour may be thus acquired, especially with the object of influencing the human keeper. A most grotesque habit of this kind was learned by a Blumenau's parakeet which belonged to Professor Karl von Frisch. The scientist only let the bird fly freely when he had just watched it have an evacuation of the bowels, so that, for the next ten minutes, his well-kept furniture was not endangered. The parakeet learned very quickly to associate these facts and, as he was passionately fond of leaving his cage, he would force out a minute dropping with all his might, every time Professor von Frisch came near the cage. He even squeezed desperately when it was impossible to produce anything, and really threatened to do himself an injury by the violence of his straining. You just had to let the poor thing out every time you saw him!

Yet the clever 'Geier', much cleverer than that little parakeet, could not even learn to say 'Food' when he was hungry. The whole complicated apparatus of the bird's syrinx and brain that makes imitation and association of thought possible, appears to have no function in connexion with the survival of the species. We ask ourselves vainly what it is there for!

I only know one bird that learned to use a human word when he wanted a particular thing and who thus connected a sound-expression with a purpose, and it is certainly no co-incidence that it was a bird of that species which I consider to have the highest mental development of all, namely the raven. Ravens have a certain innate call-note which corresponds to the 'Kia' of the jackdaw and has the same meaning – that is, the invitation to others to fly with the bird that utters it. In the raven, this note is a sonorous, deep-throated, and, at the same time, sharply metallic 'krackrackrack'. Should the bird wish to persuade another of the same species which is sitting on the ground to fly with it, he executes the same kind of movements as described in the chapter on jackdaws: he flies, from behind, close above the other bird and, in passing it, wobbles with his closely folded tail, at the same time emitting a particularly sharp 'Krackrackrackrack' which sounds almost like a volley of small explosions.

My raven Roah, so named after the call-note of the young raven, was, even as a mature bird, a close friend of mine and accompanied me, when he had nothing better to do, on long walks and even on skiiing tours, or on motor-boat excursions on the Danube. Particularly in his later years he was not only shy of strange people, but also had a strong aversion to places where he had once been frightened or had had any other un-pleasant experience. Not only did he hesitate to come down from the air to join me in such places, but he could not bear to see me linger in what he considered to be a dangerous spot. And, just as my old jackdaws tried to make their truant children leave the ground and fly after them, so Roah bore down upon me from behind, and, flying close over my head, he wobbled with his tail and then swept upwards again, at the same time looking backwards over his shoulder to see if I was following. In accompaniment to this sequence of movements – which, to stress the fact again, is entirely innate – Roah, instead of uttering the above-described call-note, said his own name, with human intonation. The most peculiar thing about this was that Roah used the human word for me only. When addressing one of his own species, he employed the normal innate call-note. To suspect that I had unconsciously trained him would obviously be wrong; for this could only have taken place if, by pure chance, I had walked up to Roah at the very moment when he happened to be calling his name, and, at the same time, to be wanting my company. Only if this rather un-likely coincidence of three factors had repeated itself on several occasions could a corresponding association of thought have been formed by the bird, and that certainly was not the case. The raven must, then, have possessed a sort of insight that 'Roah' was my call-note! Solomon was not the only man who could speak to animals, but Roah is, so far as I know, the only animal that has ever spoken a human word to a man, in its right context – even if it was only a very ordinary call-note.

THE BEAVERS

by

GREY OWL

(from *Pilgrims of the Wild*, Peter Davies Ltd.)

THE HUNTING ground we were working had been previously trapped over by a noted hunter the winter before, and between that and the low prices we only took fur to the value of about six hundred dollars: not a great sum in comparison to what I had been in the habit of making during those boom years. There would be little left over after the debt was settled and a summer's provisions purchased, not enough to start out in pursuit of that will-o'-the-wisp, the virgin, untapped hunting ground that every trapper sees visions of, gets reports about, sees on maps, but never quite catches up to. So I decided on a Spring hunt to replenish the exchequer, something that went a little against even my principles, as a hunt at that time of the year was looked on as both destructive and cruel by the better class of trapper. But there was a family of beaver remaining over from the organized slaughter of the year before, and like too many of my kind, I salved my conscience by saying that I may as well clean them out before someone else stepped in and took them.

Delayed over a week at the post by the late arrival of a buyer, and more time consumed by the journey in, we did not arrive back at our ground until the last of May. The hunt should have been over by now, and I was a little disturbed over the hardship I could not now avoid inflicting, as the young beaver were most certainly born by now, and would perish after the old ones were removed. This proved to be the case. Whilst making a set at an old, renovated beaver house where I knew the female to be, I heard faintly the thin piping voices of kitten beavers. In apparent clumsiness, I allowed my paddle to drop with a rattle on

the canoe gunwale with the intention of hiding the sound, but
Anahareo had heard it and begged me to lift the trap, and allow
the baby beaver to have their mother and live. I felt a momentary pang myself, as I had never before killed a beaver at this
time on that account, but continued with my work. We needed
the money.

The next morning I lifted the bodies of three drowned
beaver. The mother was missing, however, one trap being
unaccounted for. I found where the chain had been broken,
and dragged for the body unsuccessfully, later breaking the
dam and partly draining the pond, but without avail. She would
be the largest and most valuable, so I bemoaned my loss and
forgot the life that had been destroyed for nothing, and the
helpless kittens left to starve. After a whole day spent in a fruitless search, I removed all traps and equipment and proceeded
to camp, having no intention whatever of returning; but the
next day, after skinning and stretching the catch, for no reason
at all I changed my mind. So inauspiciously do important
events intrude themselves into our lives. I portaged back to
the ruined pond that would never again be good for anything,
and we paddled over to the old beaver house in an effort to discover if the female had succeeded in getting back there, but
could find no indication either by sight or sound of her
presence.

So we turned to go, finally and for good. As we were leaving,
I heard behind me a light splash, and looking back saw what
appeared to be a muskrat lying on top of the water alongside of
the house. Determined to make this wasted day pay, I threw up
my gun, and standing up in the canoe to get a better aim, prepared to shoot. At that distance a man could never miss, and
my finger was about to press the trigger when the creature
gave a low cry, and at the same instant I saw, right in my line of
fire another, who gave out the same peculiar call. They could
both be gotten with the one charge of shot. They gave voice
again, and this time the sound was unmistakable – they were
young beaver! I lowered my gun and said:

'There are your kittens.'

The instinct of a woman spoke out at once.

'Let us save them,' cried Anahareo excitedly, and then in a lower voice, 'It is up to us, after what we've done.'

And truly what had been done here looked now to be an act of brutal savagery. And with some confused thought of giving back what I had taken, some dim idea of atonement, I answered:

'Yes; we do have to. Let's take them home.' It seemed the only fitting thing to do.

This was not such an easy matter as the kittens were well able to take care of themselves in the water, being older than I had thought. By the exercise of considerable patience and ingenuity we eventually caught them, and dropped them aboard, two funny-looking furry creatures with little scaly tails and exaggerated hind feet, that weighed less than half a pound apiece, and that tramped sedately up and down the bottom of the canoe with that steady, persistent, purposeful walk that we were later to know so well. We looked at them in a kind of dumbfounded bewilderment, feeling much as if we had caught a pair of white elephants, hardly knowing what to do with them. And certainly we had not the faintest inkling of the far-reaching effects their unceremonious entry into our affairs was to have.

Had my finger pressed but lightly on the trigger that fateful morning, these two tiny creatures, whose coming saved from slaughter so many of their kin who followed them and materially changed the lives of several people, would have passed like two wisps from some wandering breeze, back into the Great Unknown from which they had so short a time before set out.

It is only fair to say that at the time we did not know what we were letting ourselves in for. From the very commencement it was plain that this experiment was to be no picnic. Any preconceived ideas either of us had on the raising and handling of pets had to be radically changed. These were no cringing terror-stricken wild things with feral eyes that cowered fearfully in dark corners, but a pair of very wide-awake, aggressive personalities, who fastened themselves on us as their protectors. They gave themselves completely into our hands, and proceeded to levy unceasing demands on our attention. They allowed us at no time to forget the responsibilities that we had incurred, and before long they had us trained to sleep with one eye open and one hand on the milk can. Feeding them was a problem. They would not drink the diluted milk out of a dish, and having no feeding bottle we conceived the idea of loading a slim twig with the sweet milk out of the can, closing the beaver's mouth over it with our fingers, and pulling out the stick. Masticating this sticky mass kept them interested for long periods at a time, and they did not need much of it, so this scheme simplified matters considerably. They were very gentle, and they had a kind of naïve disarming friendliness of disposition that took it quite for granted that they belonged, and that we were well disposed towards them and would see them through.

After feeding times they desired to be picked up and fondled and it was not long before they made this a regular habit, falling asleep in odd places such as the inside of an open shirt, half-way up a sleeve, or draped around a person's neck. Should they be removed from these places they would immediately awaken and return in the most determined manner, and if placed in their box they awoke at once, and with piercing outcries demanded to be again taken up, grasping our hands and lifting themselves up by means of them. If their cries were disregarded they would eventually lapse into unconsciousness, but the passage near the box of either one of us restored them to immediate and vociferous wakefulness. They soon got to know our voices and would answer concertedly with loud exclamations when spoken to. We allowed them to roam around the tent at will, and occasionally on their rambles they would become lost and parted. Their bold self-confidence would then quickly desert them, and they became lonely and would call frantically for help, and on being placed together they would throw themselves on their backs with wiggles and squeals of joy, and lie down together holding tightly on to each other's fur. Often as they lay sleeping we would speak to them for the fun of having them awaken and answer us, which they invariably did, in their shrill childish treble. Should this, however, occur too often they would become very impatient and express their annoyance in no uncertain terms. Their voices were really the most remarkable thing about them, much resembling the cries of a human infant, without the volume but with a greater variety of expression, and at all hours of the day and night there was liable to be some kind of new sound issuing from the interior of the box. The best known and easiest to recognize of these was the loud, long and very insistent call for lunch, which chorus broke out about every two hours.

These whimsical little creatures early showed evidence of qualities and capabilities that at once arrested our attention, and it was not long before our diminutive charges became attached to us, and I am free to confess, we to them. Each had a special liking for one of us, and continued faithful to his choice. They lavished this affection on us in a number of curious ways, such as upsetting the box, as soon as they were big enough to do so, and rushing out at us as we passed, or creeping into our blankets at night and cuddling up to us. They would generally lie on our bodies, one on each of us, the favoured position being a rather inconvenient one across the throat. If alarmed whilst out and around, they would come gliding along belly to the ground, each to his chosen friend, and sit quietly as two mice until the supposed danger had passed.

They were continually escaping, and the first few times this happened we hunted for them high and low, feeling ourselves pretty smart to ferret out two such small objects from the underbrush. But our anxiety and subsequent gratification were both quite unnecessary, as we discovered that on hearing us in the brush they would run towards us of their own accord. On this account we became overconfident, and one morning, having failed to close the box before retiring, we awoke to find their chamber empty, and no sign of a beaver any place in the tent. A prolonged and wide search failed to locate the wanderers. We hunted all that day both by canoe and on land, and remained out all night, going back to the tent every so often in the somewhat vain expectation that they might have returned in the meantime. It seemed hard to believe that they would desert us like that, attached to us as they seemed to be, but after all they were wild animals, they were well able to travel and feed themselves, and could now probably get along without us. We felt a little hurt about it. Maybe, too, they could not return; there were plenty of hawks and owls, and an otter would make short work of them. Realizing at last that they had been gone over thirty hours, and that, if living, they would now be far beyond our reach, we gave up the search and went home to get some sleep, not a little sad – and there in the tent, all unconscious of the excitement of which they were the cause, sat two deserters on the bed, soaking wet, and squeezing the water out of their coats on to the blankets.

After this experience we simply pitched our camp near any old lake, and with due regard for predatory birds and beasts, we let them come and go as they pleased. They would walk down to the lake with that methodical step of theirs, bathe, swim and play in the reeds awhile and return, plodding solemnly up and down the water trail together, like two little old men out for a constitutional. They were good housekeepers too. By this time they were beyond the milk stage, and to supplement their natural diet we fed them once a day on porridge and each had his dish, which when empty was pushed over to the side of the tent, and the instinct for stacking used material as far out of the way as possible caused them to try and rear the plates against the wall. This was not easy to do, but they persisted at it and very often succeeded.

At three months of age they ceased to be of any further trouble to us save for the daily feed of porridge, an insatiable and very active curiosity regarding the contents of provision bags and boxes, the frequent desire for petting that seemed to fill some great want in their lives, and the habit they had of coming into our beds, soaking wet, at all hours of the night.

They were scrupulously clean, were gentle and good-natured, they gave out no odour whatever, and were altogether the best conducted pair of little people one could wish to live with. They were very self-effacing, and a good deal of the time were neither to be seen nor heard; but always there came moments, generally about sundown, when they seemed to feel the need of some attention, and getting to know of this we made a point of giving it to them. And they would give little bleats and play with our hands, nibble our finger tips and climb on us, so far as climbing was possible to them, with many absurd but genuine evidences of real affection.

Their little hands – one can call them nothing else – were nearly as effective as our own more perfect members would be, in the uses they were put to. They could pick up very small objects with them, manipulate sticks and stones, strike, push, and heave with them, and they had a very firm grasp which it was difficult to disengage. When peeling a stick they used them both to twist the stem with supple wrist movements, while the teeth rapidly whittled off the succulent bark as it went by, much after the fashion of a lathe.

They were greedy little fellows and were constantly trying to steal from one another. These attempts, however, were never very serious, and seldom were successful, as the owner of the stick was always well prepared, and on the approach of his companion, welcome enough at all other times, he would set up a vigorous vocal protest which continued long after the object of them had given up all thought of plunder. They would none the less allow us to approach and handle them freely whilst eating, without any complaint, but if we attempted to lay hold of their wooden sandwich they would let out a sharp ejaculation or two, and promptly turn their backs on us.

Should we be away up the lake for any length of time, we would, on our return, call them whilst yet some distance away, and they would come to meet the canoe, answering the call with long high-pitched cries, and on close approach would reach up to us with outstretched hands in eager expectancy, grasping our fingers and looking up at us and making the most uncommon sounds. For we always made it a practice to bring along little bits of sweet things we made for them, and they would lie in the water eating them with loud enjoyment and a very audible smacking of lips. This usage gave us nearly as much pleasure as it gave to them, the more especially when we found that whether satisfied or not they did not leave us, but would try to get aboard the canoe, and on being lifted in, the tail providing a very convenient handle for the purpose, they would clamber over our persons with every sign of pleasure.

To beings of our kind, cessation of travelling, the denial of that unappeasable urge to see what lies beyond the hills, meant stagnation, almost a cessation of living, and worse, long hours of idleness with their dark attendant introspection.

The beavers were our salvation. By now they had grown considerably, weighing in the neighbourhood of fifteen pounds apiece, and their fur had come in full, rich, and lustrous. Although they were growing up, they were as much attached to us as ever, and still cuddled up to us in bed. We could, of course, have put them in their place as animals, but their perception of what went on around them was so extraordinarily clear that we felt that we would not be allowed to get away with it. And, moreover, their manner of expressing their desires was so explicit, and they were so sensitive to the least rebuff, that it seemed hardly the thing to do. That they were very responsive to our moods and extremely sensitive could be plainly seen. A bustle of preparation on our part induced them to like activity; as for instance when we were making our bed on the floor, they would run around us pulling at the blankets, and sometimes make off with the pillows. When we laughed a great deal, or held a more animated conversation than usual, they also became very animated. And I found a little self-reproach, and learned to better guard my tongue and temper, when I found that they kept out of sight, when I complained loudly and not too well concerning some pet grievance I might entertain.

These versatile guests of ours accepted camp life as a matter of course in spite of conditions that were so unnatural to their kind. They had no tank but lived precisely as any land animal would have done, getting along quite contentedly with only a wash dish nailed to the floor for drinking purposes. They were quite well satisfied with this arrangement, for though the door was open frequently during soft weather, they made no attempt to go down to the lake. Once we took them to the water hole but they refused to enter or drink out of it, but got off the ice as quickly as possible and scrambled up the snow path back to camp.

Their efforts to carry out their numerous plans resulted in the interior arrangements of the cabin being sometimes grotesque, and often exceedingly messy. The most notable of these was an attempt to build themselves a house. They had taken full possession of the space beneath the bunk with a proprietary air that was very droll to see in creatures so small. This spot they undertook to turn into a kind of private chamber, to which end they one night removed the entire contents of the wood box, and constructed with it a barricade all down the outside, between the bunk and the floor, leaving the end open as a means of egress. Inside the enclosure thus formed they next cut a hole in the flooring, and dug out a tunnel under the rear wall, which when large enough served as a bedroom, though its present purpose was to provide material for plastering the skeleton rampart already erected.

We were not aware of the addition of this mud mine to the domestic arrangements until one day we saw something coming up and over this rampart, to fall with a heavy 'plunk' on the floor – a lump of mud. A stone followed, of fair size; a little later more dobs of mud, large dobs about the full of a quart measure apiece. Inspection revealed the tunnel, and also the fact that the inside of their partition was well and smoothly plastered. The odd consignments that had appeared on the floor were merely a little excess material that had slopped over. When they came out later they collected this and tamped the outside with it. They were really very economical. Moreover they were well organized, as the tunnel being as yet only big enough for one to pass at a time, they sometimes worked in shifts. When they both were on the job together one brought out the material, and the other took it and did the decorating.

All this explained the mysterious thumps and scrapings, and the sound of grunts and loud breathing that had been heard for some nights past issuing from under the bed. This barricade was eventually plastered completely, both inside and out, except at one end where a small aperture was left open, apparently for observation purposes. . . . When soft weather occurred, the burrow being under the low side of the cabin, all the drippings poured off the roof down on to it and soaked through, transforming the stiff mud into a thin batter. At such times they would come out in the cabin so plastered with this gooey mess as to be almost unrecognizable, and would disport themselves all over the floor, or try to clamber on to our knees whilst in this condition.

We read a book dealing with the building of the Union Pacific Railroad in early days, and this construction work of theirs, with its wooden framework and earthen fill, reminded us a good deal of the description given, and the resolution and industry of the Irish workers engaged on it was well emulated by our own ambitious pioneers under the bed. So we now gave them Irish names, McGinnis and McGinty, to be as near alike as possible. These names suited them very well indeed, as they were as energetic and at times as peppery as any two gentlemen from Cork could well have been. . . . The male (now McGinnis) had a little game he used to play. Every day at noon when he arose, he would lie watchfully hiding behind the corner of his entrenchment until one of us passed, when he would charge violently out and engaged whoever it was in mock combat. This tournament took place each morning without fail, and was his one big moment of the day; so we made it a point to be sure of passing the appointed spot when we espied him. Then, soon after the assault, which was always made in silence and apparently deadly earnest, out would come McGinty to speak her morning monologue, declaiming in a loud voice with many different tones in it. And sometimes the two of them would sit there in the morning line-up, as though for inspection and parade, and solemnly wag their heads in the way they have, and make the strangest sounds.

After the morning exercises we fed them titbits which they retired into their house to eat, sitting as far apart as possible, and scolding under their breath to ward off possible attempts at piracy. The very audible smacking of lips as they ate often made us wish they could be induced to take some soup, to see just what effect would be produced. They were very choosy too and had individual tastes, being satisfied with no odds and ends or leavings, and if several pieces were offered them from the same bannock, they spent some time in their selection, like the hero in a novel who, in moments of stress, selects so carefully one cigarette out of a dozen, all identical in appearance. The lunch disposed of, they would emerge for the day's doings in great fettle, coming on deck all cleared for action, forging around the camp very alert and bustling in manner, as if to say 'Well, here we are; what to do?' And almost always, it was not long before everyone was doing, ourselves included.

The fidelity with which their voices and actions registered their emotions was a constant source of interest to us, and they even seemed gifted with some kind of sense of humour. I have seen one of them torment the other until the victim emitted a squawk of complaint, and then, having apparently accomplished his purpose, the aggressor would shake his head back and forth and twist his body as though in convulsions of mirth and then repeat the performance – so that an onlooker once said that he fully expected to hear the creature laugh.

There is no doubt that they possessed, in common with all their kind, capabilities not usually found in animals, though I much doubt that these could be any further developed in so self-willed and independent a nature; but, prepared as we constantly were for the unexpected, I think neither of us will quite forget the first time we saw them engaged in what is, to a beaver, his national pastime. I had seen dogs, wolves, and foxes tussle and had watched most of the other beasts, from cougars to squirrels, tumble around and paw at one another like the animals they were. But these extraordinary creatures, not satisfied with the amusements that other beasts were contented with, stood up on their hind legs, put their short arms around each other as far as they would reach, and wrestled like men! Back and forth, round and round – but never sideways – forcing, shoving, and stamping, grunting with the efforts put forth, using all the footwork they knew how, they would contest mightily for the supremacy. When one was, perhaps after some minutes, finally vanquished, with loud squeals, the bout was immediately terminated and they would make a few hops and turn their attention to their more sober occupations.

These strictly legal pursuits did not, however, supply the capricious and enterprising McGinty with quite all the excitement she craved. She developed a mild criminality complex, one of those 'kinks' we hear so much about. Although she had free access to the few potatoes we had saved, and had helped herself to them at will quite openly, she suddenly seemed to get the idea that stealing them would be more fun. She took to going behind the bag and extracting them stealthily through a hole, and could be seen creeping along close to the wall with her booty, no doubt thoroughly enjoying the thrill. We allowed her to do this of course, and enjoyed watching her. Now opposition is the breath of life to a beaver; their whole life training is associated with the overcoming of obstacles, and the great incentive not being forthcoming in this instance, the pastime soon palled.

She next commenced purloining tobacco. We were apprised of this during the night by some very mournful wailing which we had come to recognize as meaning real trouble, and we discovered the bold buccaneer laid out in the middle of the floor not far from the stolen goods, which had been partly consumed. The poor little beast was evidently suffering and tried to crawl over to us but was unable to get her hind legs under her, as though paralysed. We picked her up carefully and laid her on the bunk. She was Anahareo's pet and clung to her, clutching at her clothes with paws, so like hands, that had lost their strength. She made no further utterance, but the look of dumb appeal, the weak attempts to get as close as possible to this well-loved haven of refuge, spoke more eloquently than any

sound she could have made. A beaver in serious trouble will
sometimes grip you tightly, and look at you and seem to beg. I
had not seen this before, and it moved me profoundly to search
some past experience for a cure. I prepared an emetic, but she
would not, or could not, swallow it. She fell asleep or into a
coma and her heart action nearly ceased, and I suddenly remembered a case of opium poisoning I had seen, or heard of, or
read about somewhere. I told Anahareo to rub her, rub her
hard over the whole body, to massage the hands and feet, to
keep her awake at all costs. It seemed cruel, but it was a case of
kill or cure. Meanwhile under Anahareo's direction I prepared
a hot mustard bath. We put the beaver in it and her head fell
forward into the mixture: we held it up. She was unconscious.
The liquor did not penetrate the fur right away, but the feet
and broad expanse of tail were exposed to it, and it had an
almost immediate, though slight, effect. With her hand under
the breast Anahareo announced an increasing heart action.
The unconscious animal became alive enough to moan and hold
up her head, but drooped again soon after being taken out, and
soon the heart weakened so that its beat was almost imperceptible. Anahareo rubbed hard and continuously, and kept her
awake while I prepared another bath. Placed in it she came to
her senses again. We went at the thing systematically, and the
camp soon had the appearance of a hospital ward, as we bathed
the helpless little creature and tried to rub the life into her
with towels. She was slipping away from under our hands, eyes
closed, motionless, sinking. There seemed little hope. We
worked over her for ten hours. We kept her heart going, but
during that time she had three convulsions. Yet she still lived,
and the time of dawn, so often fatal, was nearly past. I had seen
more than one life go out on its grey receding tide. At daylight
she had seemed to pass the crisis. She began to show signs of
returning vigour. Her heart beat strongly; she stood up on her
four legs. Then she took one last convulsion and straightened
out. I dropped my towel; this must be the end.

'Well, Pony,' I commenced, and then turned to put wood in
the stove, and found other business in that direction. I didn't

want to see. There would be a heartbreak in the death of this small dumb beast. Then I heard a cry behind me, not a wailing, not a lamentation as I had expected, but a declaiming, a discoursing with strange half-human sounds in it, a long loud monologue as of one laying down the law. And then I turned to see McGinty sitting bolt upright and making some attempt to comb her wet bedraggled coat. Truly, at the eleventh hour. And then I heard another sound from Anahareo.

It was the first time I had ever heard her cry.

Meanwhile McGinnis, either having become lonesome, or sensing in that undefinable way peculiar to animals that something was wrong, had been for some time trying to climb into the bunk, so we restored his partner to him and gave him some attention. For once he would have none of us, but flew to McGinty and smelled her carefully as though to be sure of her identity after so long an absence, and plucked at her and made small sounds, short mumbling little whimpers that we had never heard before, and ran beside her nose to nose, while she exclaimed in that strident voice of hers, as was her fashion. And from under the bunk the whimpering sounds continued for quite some time; and later when we looked in to see if our patient was quite recovered, the two of them lay with their hands firmly embedded in each other's fur, as they had done so often when they were very, very small.

This dramatic episode put a period on McGinty's debut into the underworld, and for some time after she was quite exemplary. Any real misfortune seemed to have quite a chastening effect on them.

They had contradictory, if not complex characters, with strongly marked individual traits. McGinnis, if reprimanded, obeyed immediately and busied himself elsewhere, only to return to the forbidden act at a later date with an air of the most disarming innocence, to again retire when requested. McGinty had to be practically forced into compliance, and would seize the first opportunity to continue whatever depredation she had been engaged in. As soon as she saw that she had again attracted unwelcome attention, she would start to squeal in advance protest against the inevitable interference, meanwhile addressing herself to the matter in the most determined manner, sticking at it until the last possible moment.

On one point, however, they were strongly in accord, and that was in a determination to find out, by hook or by crook, what lay concealed beyond their reach up on the table. This table and its inaccessible contents had had an irresistible fascination for them from the time it was first set up. They seemed to think that they were missing something here. They were especially clamorous at meal times, and although we often gave them all the food they could dispose of, it did not assuage their burning desire to explore this piece of forbidden territory. They tried by every means possible to them to accomplish this object, and they once succeeded in pulling down the oilcloth cover. The resulting crash of tin dishes must have been very edifying, but this, apparently, was not enough. I had an idea they would eventually do something about it, but was not prepared for what actually did happen. We had never left them alone more than a few hours at a time on account of the cold, but one day, it being quite soft, we both took a trip to a lumber camp some miles away, and being invited to stay the night felt safe to do so. The cook, who had heard about the beaver, was very interested and expressed a desire to see them, so we suggested that he come over. As we were leaving he gave us a good-sized parcel of treats for the beaver and said that he would be along to see us that day. As this was to be our first visitor here we wanted to give him a welcome, and hurried home to prepare it.

We found the door hard to open. That was because the blankets were piled against it. This, however, was the least of our troubles. Beaver can, under good direction, do a lot in a short space of time; in this instance the supervision had been adequate and the results sweeping.

The place was a wreck.

The beaver had at last got the table where they wanted it, having brought it down to their level by the simple expedient of cutting off the legs. We hadn't thought of that; there was always something you didn't think of with these hooligans. The long-coveted contents of this piece of furniture must have been disappointing, consisting mostly of utensils, but these had been removed and most of them we found in the den later; some of them were never recovered and probably had been deposited in the far end of the tunnel. Our other fixtures were lying scattered over the floor in various stages of demolition. The washstand also was down and the soap had disappeared. A five-gallon can containing coal oil had fallen to the floor and had landed, luckily, right side up. The floor itself had escaped serious damage but was covered with chips, and slivers, and the dismembered trunks of our butchered belongings. The scene must have been very animated whilst in progress.

Since that time I have been subjected to similar and even more devastating visitations, but as an introduction to what might lay in store at a future date this was a little staggering, and certainly we were in no shape to receive a guest.

Meanwhile these whimsical playmates of ours, interrupted in their setting-up exercises by our arrival, were cautiously inspecting us through the loophole in their fortification, and identifying us now came out, two little capering gnomes that hopped over the piles of debris to welcome us home.

It was no use to punish them, as they would not have known what it was all about, being no longer in the act. We had thwarted their natural instincts and must pay for it.

So we fed them the dainties that the cook had sent while they sat amongst the wreckage and ate them – enjoying the finishing touch to what probably had been the most perfect day of their lives.

Personally I had always been too busy hunting to celebrate the festive season, beyond submitting to a kind of hypocritical sentimentality that prevented me from taking life on that day; but never being quite sure which day it was, even this observance had fallen into disuse. But I was now a family man, and being, besides, sure of the date, we would now keep it in style.

I whittled out some boards of dry cedar, painted them with Indian designs and attached them to the sides and tops of the windows where they looked, if not too closely inspected, like plaques of beadwork. We painted hanging ornaments with tribal emblems and hung them in places where the light fell on them. We laid two rugs of deerskin; these were immediately seized as play-toys by the two Macs, and had to be nailed down, when the beaver compromised by pulling handfuls of hair out of them; a pleasing pastime. Having killed a large eagle in my travels, I made a war-bonnet, a brave affair of paint and eagle feathers and imitation beadwork, that sat on a wooden block carved in the semblance of a warrior's face, and painted with the Friendship Sign in case we had a guest. It had quite an imposing effect as it stood on the table, at one end. We distributed coloured candles from the rafter. Viewed from the outside, through a window, the interior exhibited a very pleasing appearance though a little like the abode of some goblin whose tastes were torn between the pious and the savage.

On Christmas Eve all was ready. But there was one thing missing; Anahareo decided that the beavers were to have a Christmas tree. So while I lit the lantern and arranged the candles so their light fell on the decorations to the best advantage, and put apples and oranges and nuts in dishes on the table, and tended the saddle of deer meat that sizzled alongside of the factory-made Christmas pudding that was boiling on top of the little stove, Anahareo took axe and snowshoes and went out into the starry Christmas night.

She was gone a little longer than I expected, and on looking out I saw her standing in rapt attention, listening. I asked her what she heard.

'Listen.' She spoke softly. 'Hear the Christmas Bells,' and pointed upwards.

I listened. A light breeze had sprung up and was flowing, humming in the pine tops far above; whispering at first, then swelling louder in low undulating waves of sound, and sinking to a murmur; ascending to a deep strong wavering note, fading again to a whisper. The Carillons of the Pine Trees; our Christmas Bells.

Anahareo had got a fine balsam fir, a very picture of a Christmas tree, which she wedged upright in a crevice in the floor poles. On top of it she put a lighted candle, and on the limbs tied candies, and pieces of apple and small delicacies from the table, so they hung there by strings and could be reached.

The beaver viewed these preparations with no particular enthusiasm but before long, attracted by the odour of the tree, they found the hanging titbits and sampled them, and soon were busy cutting the strings and pulling them down and eating them with great gusto. And we set our own feast on the table, and as we ate we watched them. They soon consumed all there was on the tree, and as these were replaced the now thoroughly aroused little creatures stood up on their hind legs and grabbed and pulled at their presents, and stole choice morsels from one another, pushing and shoving so that one would sometimes fall and scramble to his feet again as hastily as possible, for fear everything would be gone before he got up, while they screeched and chattered and squealed in their excitement. And we forgot our supper, and laughed and called out at them, and they would run to us excitedly and back to the tree with little squawks as if to say 'Looky! what we found!' And when they could eat no more they commenced to carry away provision against the morrow, sometimes between their teeth, on all fours, or staggering along erect with some prized titbit clutched tightly in their arms, each apparently bent on getting all that could be got while it lasted. And when we thought they had enough and no longer made replacements, McGinty, the wise and thrifty, pulled down the tree and started away with it, as though she figured on another crop appearing later and had decided to corner the source of supply.

It was the best fun of the evening, and instead of us making a festival for them, they made one for us, and provided us with a Christmas entertainment such as had never before been seen in any other home, I'm pretty sure. And Anahareo was so happy

to see her tree well appreciated, and the beaver were so happy
to patronize it, and everybody seemed to be so thoroughly
enjoying themselves, that I perforce must be happy too just to
see them so.

Stuffed to the ears, and having a goodly supply cached beyond the barricade, the revellers, tired now, or perhaps overcome by a pleasant fullness, soon went behind it too. Heavy
sighs and mumbles of contentment came up from the hidden
chamber beneath the bunk and soon, surrounded by all the
Christmas Cheer they had collected, they fell asleep.

And after they were gone a silence fell upon us and all was
quiet. And the stove began to be cold; and the place was suddenly so lonely, and the painted brave looked out so soberly at
us from under his feathered bonnet, that I put on a rousing,
crackling fire, and drew out from its hiding-place a bottle
of very good red wine that was to have been kept for New
Year.

And we drank a toast to the beaver in their silent house across
the lake, and to the friendly muskrats in their little mud hut,
and all our birds and beasts, and to McGinnis and McGinty,
who now lay snoring in the midst of plenty; and another to the
solemn wooden Indian, and yet another to the good Frenchman
who had supplied the wine.

And as we pledged each other with a last one, we declared
that never was there such a Christmas anywhere in all the
Province of Quebec. And certainly there never had been on this
lake before.

At this time there came to live with us an old man who had
for many years trapped muskrats on these lakes. This hunt was
his by right and he depended on it. On account of the danger to
the beaver his coming meant only one thing – we must move.
So . . . Anahareo and I collected the beaver, loaded them into
the barrel and catching a passing team moved everything to a
little lake that lay beside the road, near to the town. Here, under
some big elms, we made camp, while McGinnis and McGinty
disported themselves around an old beaver house and dam that

stood at the foot of the little pond. There was plenty of feed and water and these old works besides, and they would be well fixed here until I could locate another colony in which to introduce them. When our work was finished, we went down to the lake and called them. They came racing over and tumbled their black dumpy bodies all about our feet, labouring under some great excitement, doubtless on account of the old beaver works. They calmed down a little to eat some sticks of candy, still jabbering away in concert, telling us, no doubt, about their discoveries, and the new estate that had fallen to them with all its ready-made castle and appurtenances. They were hardly able to contain themselves, and after a few moments of gambolling with us, they hurried off to their small properties like a pair of kids to a circus, two absurd but happy little creatures enjoying their new freedom to the utmost, and who from now on would live as they were intended to.

It was almost a year since we had found them, two tiny helpless orphans at the point of death, and this celebration seemed a fitting anniversary. And my heart warmed the more towards them as I reflected that in their new-found self-sufficiency and independence, they still retained that child-like attachment to ourselves that we had feared to lose.

Once during the evening they came bustling up to camp, and coming inside combed themselves and talked loudly and long, and roamed around the tent as of yore, evidently recognizing it, which was not remarkable as it had been their only home for half their lives. They smelled at the stove in which they had so many adventures, and McGinnis burnt his nose on it, while McGinty upset the grub-box, disclosing the bannock, of which they ate a goodly portion, and altogether seemed very much at home in these familiar surroundings. They had their usual petting party and even slept a while, and it was all so like those eventful days on the Birch Lake trail that seemed now so far away, that we were glad to be back in the old tent again with the little stove going and our two small friends beside us in its glow. Soon they headed for their lake, two gnome-like capering little figures down the water trail, and we followed them to the landing as we always did, and somehow wished that they were small again.

We watched the two V's forging ahead towards the ancient beaver lodge until they disappeared into the dusk. And in the starlight, the wake of their passing made pale rippling bands of silver that spread wide behind them, and touched the shore at last, and so were lost. Once, in answer to a call, a long clear note came back to us, followed by another in a different key. And the two voices blended and intermingled like a part-song in the stillness of the little lonesome pond, and echoed back and forth in the surrounding hills and faded to a whisper, and died.

And that long wailing cry from out the darkness was the last sound we ever heard them make.

We never saw them any more.

THESE ARE PAN BOOKS –

David Attenborough
QUEST IN PARADISE

The sensational land-divers of Pentecost, the incredible cargo cult of Tanna. Fire-walking and the 'calling' of turtles in Fiji. A strange and rarely-seen ceremony on Tonga. The fabled dance of the wonderful birds of paradise in New Guinea. These are all told in David Attenborough's exciting account of his voyages of discovery to the South Seas. *Illustrated.*   (3/6)

David Attenborough
ZOO QUEST FOR A DRAGON

TV's famous zoologist recalls an enchanted journey through the islands of Indonesia – Bali, Java, Borneo, and finally Komodo, the remote island where he at last caged the awesome dragon, the largest lizard in the world. This exciting account is David Attenborough at his liveliest. *Illustrated.*
(2/6)

Gavin Maxwell
RING OF BRIGHT WATER

The bewitching best selling account of life with two otter pets. 'Surely one of the most appealing accounts of animal-human relationships ever written. I read it with sheer delight' – Rachel Carson, author of *The Sea Around Us*. *Illustrated.*   (5/–)

Garry Hogg
THE OVERLANDERS

The true story of the indomitable explorers who braved unknown horrors to open up the awesome continent of Australia. 'A record of truly heroic endeavour in the face of tremendous odds'. – *John O'London's*. *Illustrated.*   (3/6)

PICK OF THE PAPERBACKS

Katherine Tottenham
THE PAN BOOK OF HOME PETS

PAN ORIGINAL. How to choose, house, feed, handle, breed and keep healthy every kind of pet ... cage birds, rabbits, hamsters, snakes, mongooses, ponies and scores more. *Illustrated*. (3/6)

John S. Vinden, FZS
THE PAN BOOK OF THE HOME AQUARIUM

A Pan Original. A new ABC of fishkeeping specially written for PAN by a Fellow of the Zoological Society. For the beginner and for the enthusiast – a comprehensive guide to one of today's simplest, most fascinating hobbies. (2/6)

Catherine Fisher
THE PAN BOOK OF DOGS

This book, specially written for PAN, gives you the *facts* – down-to-earth information – on buying a dog, training, health and welfare, etc. And there are full details of over 90 breeds. Fully indexed. *Illustrated*. (3/6)

Rose Tenent
THE PAN BOOK OF CATS

Free-lance journalist Rose Tenent is well known on both sides of the Atlantic as a cat expert. In this comprehensive handbook she discusses types and breeds, care of cats in sickness and health, breeding, etc. Specially written for PAN, this is a mine of information on the most popular of pets. Fully indexed. *Illustrated*. (3/6)

THESE ARE PAN BOOKS –

Herbert van Thal
MASTER STORIES OF THE 20TH CENTURY

Bennett, Forester, Hemingway, Huxley, Lawrence, Maugham, Steinbeck and Wodehouse are among the authors in this superb collection – in choosing which a rattling good read rather than a great name has been the deciding factor.

(3/6)

Lady Cynthia Asquith
THE SECOND GHOST BOOK

L. A. G. Strong, Nancy Spain, L. P. Hartley, Elizabeth Bowen, Walter de la Mare . . . in all 20 distinguished British authors have contributed stories to this new collection. 'Each story defies your hair not to rise, your flesh not to creep' – *Time and Tide*.

(2/6)

Lady Cynthia Asquith
THE THIRD GHOST BOOK

Stories that will take you in a cold embrace – 27 startling tales of the tormented and the damned. Here are ghosts of every kind and in every mood; ghosts human; ghosts animal; ghosts tender; ghosts vindictive. Superbly written and deliciously hair-raising.

(2/6)

George Mikes
THE BEST OF MIKES

A Pan Original. George Mikes' own selection for PAN from *How To Be An Alien* and his many other brilliant best-sellers. 'Mikes is both funny and wise' – *John O'London's*. With many drawings by Nicolas Bentley and David Langdon.

(3/6)

PICK OF THE PAPERBACKS

Jane Grant
COME HITHER, NURSE

This is the account, partly serious but mostly gay, of the three-year training up to the State Exam, of Jane and her friends, in a London teaching Hospital. If anyone wants to know what it is really like to be a nurse, this book will tell them.   (2/6)

Jane Grant
COME AGAIN, NURSE

The hectic and hilarious sequel to *Come Hither, Nurse*. 'As entertaining as its predecessor' – *Birmingham Post*. 'Rich vein of humour, tragedy and romance' – *Vanity Fair*. (2/6)

Lee Gibb
THE JONESES
HOW TO KEEP UP WITH THEM

You know Jones – he has a bigger house, a newer car than you. Bankrupt, he drives out of Carey Street in his wife's Jaguar. Divorced, he turns up with an heiress not mentioned in the case. Can you, Robinson, keep up with him? Yes – this indispensable guide tells you how. *Illustrated*.   (2/6)

Lee Gibb
THE HIGHER JONES

The biting, outrageously funny follow-on to *The Joneses*. A wickedly accurate guide to Jonesmanship in the Britain of the Sixties. 'Witty and observant' – *Daily Telegraph*. 'Satirically disturbing' – *Books of the Month. Illustrated*. (2/6)

THESE ARE PAN BOOKS

Jean Kerr
PLEASE DON'T EAT THE DAISIES

Compulsory reading for anyone who possesses a husband, a wife, a child, a dog, a house or a sense of humour. 'Jean Kerr cooks with laughing gas' – *Time*. Recently filmed by MGM starring Doris Day and David Niven.   (2/6)

Jean Kerr
THE SNAKE HAS ALL THE LINES

A crisp collection of devastating commentaries on marriage, children, suburbia – not to say LOLITA. A hilarious new look at life.   (2/6)

TO OUR READERS

A very wide range of PAN best-sellers – the pick of the paperbacks – is readily available from your bookseller or newsagent, and in the coming months many exciting new titles will appear. Full details are given in our illustrated four-monthly list, a copy of which will be sent to you on request. Please write to:

PAN LIST, PAN BOOKS LTD.,
8 HEADFORT PLACE, LONDON, S.W.1,

PICK OF THE PAPERBACKS